PSYCHIATRY THE ULTIMATE BETRAYAL

PSYCHIATRY
THE
ULTIMATE
BETRAYAL

BY BRUCE WISEMAN

FREEDOM PUBLISHING
LOS ANGELES

Freedom Publishing, Los Angeles, CA 90028

First Edition

Printed in the United States of America

Wiseman, Bruce
    Psychiatry—the Ultimate Betrayal

    Exposé
    Includes Index

    1. Exposé   2. Psychiatry
    3. Human Rights   4. Mental Health

ISBN #0-9648909-0-9

COVER ART: Peter Green and Carrie Cook.

PHOTO CREDITS (as they appear in the book): Bettmann Archives, 1-3; UPI/Bettmann, 5 and 7-11; FPG International, 12; Reuters/Bettmann, 14.

Manufactured in the USA by the Courier Companies, Inc.

*This publication was made possible
by a grant from the United States
INTERNATIONAL ASSOCIATION OF
SCIENTOLOGISTS Members' Trust.*

CONTENTS

While a shocking statement, one which many in the psychiatric community would certainly regard as ill-considered if not radical, this was no uninformed judgment—coming as it did in a 1993 interview from no less an authority than Dr. Thomas Szasz, Professor of Psychiatry Emeritus at the State University of New York at Syracuse and Lifetime Fellow of the American Psychiatric Association.

The Hungarian-born doctor is the author of 23 books, including the 1960 classic *The Myth of Mental Illness*—described as "bold and often brilliant" by *Science* magazine[4] and still selling well today. Szasz, now in his seventies, remains a man of laser-like perceptions and razor wit, one who presents his views with clarity and intellectual depth. Nor has his integrity ever been at issue.

It's no secret that Dr. Szasz has been an outspoken critic of his profession. He has unflinchingly lambasted his fellow psychiatrists for such matters as abuse of power, their support of involuntary commitment procedures, and their willingness to carelessly utilize such high-impact treatments as heavy tranquilizers and electroshock.

However, Thomas Szasz was not limiting his comments above to the confines of the psychiatric hospital and couch. He was talking about the decline of our entire social structure. "Psychiatry is a part of the general liberal ethos," he added. "You know, everybody is a victim, everybody has special rights, no responsibilities. This psychiatric view has so completely infiltrated American thinking, people don't even think of it as psychiatry."[5]

Could he be right? This *change* that humanity has undergone: is it the result of psychiatry—and its cousin, psychology—seeping into our lives like some conscience-numbing drug, preaching a doctrine of short-term pleasure and tomorrow be damned?

It's an important question, given that our future lies in the balance. And on the surface, Szasz's argument has a ring of truth. Who among us hasn't heard ludicrous "psychobabble" used to explain away or justify the most abhorrent human behavior?

Why would a man of Szasz's intellect and near-legendary repute—a man with almost a half-century of front line psychiatric experience, who could just as easily point the finger of blame at the scourge of drug abuse, the breakup of the family, the drowning tide of immorality—why would he single out *psychiatry* as the "most destructive force that's affected the

American society within the last fifty years"?

His reasoning is clear enough. He claims that while most of us have paid little attention, the psychiatric profession has slithered into our schools, our courtrooms, our legislatures, our workplaces, and—bit by bit—into our homes. He says it has been slowly replacing the staunch foundations of our culture—individual responsibility, virtue, standards of achievement—with attractive but cheap substitutes such as the lowering of standards to avoid stress or the explaining away of individual responsibility because of "psychological trauma".

Could he be right?

WHAT IS PSYCHIATRY?

The word *psychiatry* seems to have slipped into the language in Germany in the early 1800s. One psychiatric historian tells us, it "literally means mind healing." And, as you shall see, it is significant that he adds with a figurative sigh that this definition "remained in the realm of wishful thinking."[6]

A more common term for psychiatrists in the nineteenth century, and perhaps more accurate, was "alienist," taken from the French *aliéné* which means "mad." The term was apt, for during this period, these doctors carved their niche in European and American society by taking on the care and treatment of the insane.

It was a dirty job few wanted, and it offered a ray of hope for unfortunate asylum occupants.

Consider their conditions as recounted by an anonymous reporter in 1795: "A humanitarian is bound to shudder when he discovers the plight of the unfortunate victims of this dreadful affliction; many of them grovel in their own filth on unclean straw that is seldom changed, often stark naked and in chains, in dark, damp dungeons where no breath of fresh air can enter. Under such terrifying conditions, it would be easier for the most rational person to become insane than for a madman to regain his sanity."[7]

Significantly, the 1700s and 1800s also marked the advent of the philosophy of materialism—a philosophy that molded a new view of man. One historian, J. R. Kantor, tells us, "No factor in the evolution of scientific psychology stands out more prominently than the doctrines of French Materialism in the eighteenth century and German Materialism in the nineteenth century…. Materialism is essentially a non-scientific move-ment, a phenomenon of social transformation and change. In the religious domain a materialist is simply an atheist."[8]

Materialism is merely an idea that says nothing exists but matter—the physical. There is no God, no soul, no validity to religion and its accom-panying moral stance. One can readily see the consequences of such a belief riding in on the coattails of a rapidly-advancing Science and even being passed off as scientific fact—as indeed it has been.

Through intellectual sleight-of-hand, scientific materialism boldly claims that since spiritual matters or the mind or the will can't be measured with physical instruments, they therefore don't exist and have no place in scientific theory.

Prior to materialist philosophy, the general trend in thought was to con-sider mind and body as separate entities. In religion, mind was commonly considered synonymous with soul or man's spiritual aspect. Thus, each man and woman was regarded as a composite of mind and matter.

The ramifications of the differences between these two views are vast. Nor, considering our plight today, can we afford to ignore them. In mate-rialism, a human life is simply matter animated by electrochemical processes—"97 cents worth of chemicals," to borrow an Army expression from World War II.

If, however, one views man as having a spiritual nature or if one views the mind as distinct from mere brain chemistry, the human mind and life itself take on significantly more meaning. One is not just genetic matter. One is an individual, self-willed and responsible for one's destiny.

Even though, as noted above, materialism is philosophic—and not sci-entific—in nature, it usurped the mantle of science through the fields of psychiatry and psychology in the late nineteenth century. The permanent roots of this movement took hold in 1879 at the University of Leipzig in Germany, where the first experimental psychology laboratory was set up by the "Father of Psychology," Wilhelm Wundt.

WUNDT PAVES THE WAY

To Wundt the mind was simply the brain. One text tells us, "His scholastic record had been only mediocre, so he did not qualify for state aid. One of his maternal uncles, however, convinced him to study cerebral

9

anatomy, and the mysteries of the brain soon captivated him completely."[9]

Wundt's view was clear. "It truly appears to be a useless waste of energy," he remarked, "to keep returning to such aimless discussions about the nature of the psyche, which were in vogue for a while, and practically still are, instead, rather, of applying one's energies where they will produce real results."[10]

And one of the results, perhaps the prime one, was a departure from the traditional view of man—a *radical* departure.

Man's character suddenly became regarded as the product of genetics or the result of his upbringing. And what was truly drastic about this change was that man went from being held accountable for his behavior to having his conduct assigned to causes beyond his control. The concept of "free will," long a civilizing and inspiring influence, was relegated to the dustbin of superstition, along with religion. This was a gigantic shift in man's view of himself, and one with enormous consequences.

It is no surprise then, to find that religion and philosophy—the forces which had lifted mankind from the pit of barbarism—were derided by this new and modern view. They had no place in this intellectual construct.

One of Wundt's students, William James—who went on to become the "Father of American Psychology"—viewed religion as not true or genuine, but deemed it therapeutic because it made the believer feel better. A James' biographer, Clarence J. Karier, tells us, "By the time James published *The Varieties of Religious Experience* in 1902, Friedrich Nietzsche, in *Gay Science* (1882), had already declared, 'God is dead. God remains dead. And we have killed him.' With both Nietzsche and James we pass from a culture with God at its center to a culture with man at its center. This fundamental shift in Western thought initiated a corresponding shift in the ideological structure of the social system....Western society underwent a transformation of the basis for personal and collective values....Salvation was now a matter of survival, sin became a sickness, and such religious rituals as confession, designed to alleviate guilt and atone for sin, were replaced by individual and group psychotherapeutic interventions, designed to alleviate the guilt of anxiety neurosis.

"These, then, were the signs of an emerging therapeutic society, a society born in the closing decade of the nineteenth century and nourished in the secular world of the twentieth century....William James, as one of the first secular theologians of this new therapeutic society, conceptualized the fundamental ideas that came to underpin that society."[11]

Another of Wundt's students was Emil Kraepelin, the German psychiatrist who bequeathed to the world the term "paranoia" and went on to become the "Father of Psychiatry." Like his mentor, Kraepelin was a pure materialist, seeing mental traits as hereditary and even supporting the sterilization of certain psychopaths so the defective genes would not be passed on.

But few of Wundt's pupils carried the "Man-is-an-animal" theme as far into the spotlight as Russian physiologist and psychiatrist Ivan Pavlov did in the early twentieth century. His story is found in nearly every beginning psychology textbook. Pavlov and his countryman Vladimir Bekhterev—who also studied under Wundt—developed conditioned response theories through experiments on dogs. This laid the groundwork for a fundamental materialistic psychiatric concept which remains to this day: that, like dogs, men are basically stimulus-response mechanisms. Furthermore, Bekhterev's and Pavlov's experiments in conditioning established the foundation for much of the inhuman brainwashing and mind-manipulation techniques used by the Soviet Union and China in the mid-twentieth century, as well as experiments along the same lines in the United States.

While this is a necessarily brief review of one of the most momentous periods in the history of man's philosophical strivings, the facts are inescapable, as is the legacy that evolved from them.

ENTER SIGMUND FREUD

Sigmund Freud arrived on the world scene around the beginning of the twentieth century and added further materialist fodder to this new view of mankind by proposing that man was the sum of his past experiences. Thus, again we have man being the effect, the product, of his environment. Here's where we discover past "psychological abuse" being used to justify current criminal or immoral behavior. And we also find sexual promiscuity being overtly promoted under the guise of getting rid of one's "inhibitions."

Freud wrote without reserve that, "Free sexual intercourse between young males and respectable girls" was urgently necessary or society was "doomed to fall a victim to incurable neuroses which reduce the enjoyment of life to a minimum, destroy the marriage relation and bring hereditary ruin on the whole coming generation."[12]

While much of Freud's research has since been proven of dubious validity, and the value of his psychoanalytic theories are argued endlessly among psychiatrists and academics, certain aspects of his legacy are undeniable.

Religion, for example, with its shrinking congregations and declining influence. Make no mistake—Freud called religion the "enemy."[13] In *The Future of an Illusion*, he—almost with pleasure, it seems—predicted religion's demise: "The scientific spirit generates a certain posture toward matters of this world; before matters of religion it stops for a while, hesitates, at last there too crosses the threshold. In this process there is no stopping; the more the treasures of our knowledge become accessible to people, the more the defection from religious belief will spread, at first only from its obsolete, offensive vestments, but then from its fundamental presuppositions as well."[14]

Along with religion's demise came certain casualties of course. Dr. Al Parides, Professor of Psychiatry at UCLA in Los Angeles, California, said recently that psychiatric values had been "very influenced especially by the Freudian influence in regard to sex and in regard to morality generally." He added, "If you look at the personal lives of all Freud's followers—his initial disciples—these people certainly have an unbelievable amount of particular problems in the sexual area.... The amount of deviancy as far as their sexual behavior and so forth is enormous. If you are saying that psychiatry promotes a certain form of morality that is a deviant morality in regard to many areas including sexual behavior—yes, I would agree."[15]

It has been argued that organized Western religion contributed to its own demise by not fulfilling men's deepest needs. That ritual replaced the sacred and that institutionalization distanced the churches from their members. Perhaps or not, but that is not our subject. Regardless of the "enemy's" weakened state, the inescapable fact is that if the defection from religious belief is truly a valid criteria, we can declare Freud victorious.

THEN AND NOW

It is easy to look back on a man's life and criticize him for his blunders now that we have the fruits of his labors and the hindsight he was not privy to. When we examine the personal and professional histories of

Freud, Wundt, Kraepelin, and their like, we see men trying to bring what was then the cutting edge of science to the study of man. In search of scientific truth, they attempted to shed the "religious superstitions" of their forefathers and bring the rigors of science to the investigation of human behavior. A noble idea, this, but when the dust had settled, the materialist view proved to offer less enlightenment than hoped.

"The magnitude of the efforts to be expended on our task," wrote Emil Kraepelin in his classic essay *One Hundred Years of Psychiatry*, "the impenetrable darkness that hides the innermost workings of the brain and their relation to psychic manifestations, and finally the inadequacy of our instruments for dealing with extremely complicated issues, must cause even the most confident investigator to doubt whether it is possible to make any appreciable progress toward psychiatric knowledge and understanding."[16]

Yet while this progress has indeed remained minimal, psychiatry's materialist and anti-religious slant has survived and even prospered. In a 1976 survey of members of the American Psychological Association, 95 percent reportedly admitted to being atheists or agnostics.[17] So did a majority of psychiatrists in an American Psychiatric Association Task Force report.[18] Dr. Al Parides—a former California state chairman for the American Psychiatric Association—confirmed this, saying psychiatrists are "more likely to be atheists."[19]

To put this in perspective, *Webster's* defines an atheist as one who "rejects all religious belief and denies the existence of God."[20] *Statistical Abstracts of the United States* shows that less than a half percent of the population of North America is atheist. Even if one includes persons "professing no religion, nonbelievers, agnostics, free thinkers, and dereligionized secularists indifferent to all religion," they still amount to only 7 percent of the population.[21]

It is an odd situation. Obviously the beliefs of psychiatrists are utterly out of synchronization with what the rest of the continent is thinking. Yet in their attempts to enlighten society, mental practitioners have gone to great lengths to convince the rest of us that we should come around to their way of viewing things.

The problem with this atheist and materialist perspective is not merely that they are taking a stance against the beliefs of devout churchgoers. They are, in fact—intentionally or not—striking against the very roots of

13

our culture. Probably the majority of Americans and, indeed, other citizens of the world, may not consider themselves deeply religious, but they do believe strongly in the religious ethic. It *is* the civilizing influence that separates man from the beasts—and most people inherently understand this. They see the essential wisdom in the moral codes of our spiritual heritage and generally respect and admire those who practice them.

High school principle Mike O'Sullivan expressed this sentiment in a 1994 *Los Angeles Times* article when commenting on religious clubs formed at his school. "I put out the red carpet for the positive things they are thinking about," he said. "Who could be against them leading their lives in a socially acceptable way?"[22]

And closer to the formative years of our nation, George Washington remarked, "Of all the dispositions and habits which lead to political prosperity, religion and morality are indispensable supports."[23]

Benjamin Franklin, the venerable American statesman of the 1700s, wrote a personal moral code for himself—a standard of conduct and rules for living that most will find familiar, as they are gleaned from the tested and timeless moral inheritance of our race:

1. Temperance: Eat not to dullness; drink not to elevation.

2. Silence: Speak not but what may benefit others or yourself; avoid trifling conversation.

3. Order: Let all your things have their places; let each part of your business have its time.

4. Resolution: Resolve to perform what you ought; perform without fail what you resolve.

5. Frugality: Make no expense but to do good to others or yourself; i.e., waste nothing.

6. Industry: Lose no time; be always employed in something useful; cut off all unnecessary actions.

7. Use no hurtful deceit; think innocently and justly, and, if you speak, speak accordingly.

8. Justice: Wrong none by doing injuries, or omitting the benefits that are your duty.

9. Moderation: Avoid extremes; forbear resenting injuries so much as you think they deserve.

10. Cleanliness: Tolerate no uncleanliness in body, cloaths, or habitation.

11. Tranquility: Be not disturbed at trifles, or at accidents common or unavoidable.

12. Chastity: Rarely use venery but for health or offspring, never to dullness, weakness, or the injury of your own or another's peace or reputation.

13. Humility: Imitate Jesus and Socrates.[24]

That this moral code conflicts with psychiatry's agenda can be seen when comparing Dr. Franklin's words with those of psychiatrist G. Brock Chisholm, a highly influential past president of a leading psychiatric body, the World Federation for Mental Health. In 1945, Chisholm said: "The re-interpretation and eventually eradication of the concept of right and wrong which has been the basis of child training, the substitution of intelligent and rational thinking for faith in the certainties of the old people, these are the belated objectives of practically all effective psychotherapy."

He added: "The fact is, that most psychiatrists and psychologists and other respectable people have escaped from these moral chains and are able to observe and think freely."[25]

Chisholm went quite a distance further: "We have swallowed all manner of poisonous certainties fed us by our parents, our Sunday and day school teachers, our politicians, our priests, our newspapers and others with a vested interest in controlling us. 'Thou shalt become as gods, knowing good and evil,' good and evil with which to keep children under control, with which to prevent free thinking, with which to impose local and familial and national loyalties and with which to blind children to their glorious intellectual heritage."

Chisholm also laid out the agenda for his peers. "If the race is to be freed from its crippling burden of good and evil," he said, "it must be psychiatrists who take the original responsibility."[26]

One wonders what Ben Franklin would have thought of Chisholm's remarks. And how the good Dr. Franklin would respond, seeing Chisholm's fantasy as it has actually played out in a present where the once-definable line between good and evil has become decidedly gray—an age when drugs, murder and promiscuity are daily fare.

In light of what we see in our streets today, it is almost macabre to read Chisholm's refutation of his anticipated critics a half century ago: "The pretense is made, as it has been made in relation to the finding of any extension of truth, that to do away with right and wrong would produce

15

uncivilized people, immorality, lawlessness and social chaos."[27]

...INTO OUR SCHOOLS

It has become an inescapable and oft-repeated fact of life that our schools are not the halls of learning they once were. Academic achievement has fallen. Drug and alcohol abuse, permissive sex, and violence, which once used to be the sole province of the more degraded sectors of society, have now entered our classrooms.

Why are our kids—once shielded from corruption—now bombarded daily by iniquities that were unheard of in the school rooms of yesterday? And as we can see from the continuous decline in social mores, why are they graduating—or dropping out—instilled with poorer and poorer values?

As far back as the late 1960s, Mrs. Joseph Bean, the wife of a Glendale, California, school district trustee attacked these questions head-on in a scathing speech before her husband's school board. "The traditional philosophy of education," she said, "recognizes that there are absolute truths, eternal truths, immutable truths, and that the school is vitally interested in transmitting these absolutes to our young.

"Without official recognition and without official adoption," she said, "a new philosophy has largely replaced the official one in this country's schools. This philosophy is behaviorism and holds that man is not responsible for his actions, that he is a victim of his environment and not accountable for his acts. Behaviorism is the predominant scientific and social philosophy of our age."[28]

Strong words, but in no way exaggerated. There appears to have been a concerted effort by the psychiatric community to introduce materialistic philosophies such as behaviorism and other psychiatric theories into the society at large. As early as 1949, William Menninger, president of the American Psychiatric Association, told the membership it needed to heed the words of G. Brock Chisholm, the man who wanted to rid children of the "poisonous certainties fed us by our parents, Sunday and day school teachers...."

Menninger remarked, "Two years ago G. Brock Chisholm urged us to participate in community affairs in order to apply our psychiatric knowledge to civic problems. Our Committee on Preventive Psychiatry is recommending that we assume citizenship responsibilities for policy forming at whatever level we can—in the Board of Education, City Council, civic clubs, welfare groups, legislative committees, Congressional hearings....We can exert an effective influence on the betterment of mental health...."[29]

It is very clear that an influence has indeed been exerted in our schools —by people who seem to think they know better how to raise the "citizens of tomorrow." And it has definitely permeated.

But—Dr. Menninger's good intentions notwithstanding—there are those who would argue that our children, and our world, are not the healthier for it.

...INTO OUR COURT ROOMS

We have become almost deadened to it.

A savage murderer is found innocent by reason of insanity.

Or maybe he wasn't insane. Maybe he just had "diminished capacity." Perhaps it was "battered wife syndrome" or an "irresistible impulse." Whatever. Makes no difference. He/she has a good chance of acquittal.

We shrug. It doesn't make sense somehow. If you commit the crime, you are supposed to pay the price. Is that not why we have laws and penalties? Or did we somehow misunderstand the basic concepts of law, order, and justice in our civics classes? Perhaps we are behind the times, and this is just some archaic notion of yesteryear that has no place in modern society.

Nevertheless, many of us feel impotent as we watch powers apparently higher than ourselves, members of some intelligentsia we know little of, decree these exceptions and loopholes to our laws. And helplessly we watch legal accountability erode as the tide of crime rises.

In 1994, a bemused world watched two California juries become hope-lessly deadlocked in the trials of Erik and Lyle Menendez, adult brothers who had brutally killed their parents with a shotgun at close range as mother and father sat on a sofa eating berries. The brothers had claimed self-defense because of a history of sexual abuse.

One of the Lyle Menendez jurors remarked, "I don't think the general public thinks the jury is any more than a bunch of idiots."[30]

But stupidity is not what crippled the two sets of twelve men and women. It was the psychiatric notion that some criminality is excusable. Once someone—either in the courtroom or in his private life—has bought the idea that being a "victim of abuse" gives one an alibi for any and all shortcomings in life, it is hard to bring him back to the fold of those who believe in personal accountability.

This is seen in the comments of one juror in the Lyle Menendez case, who instead of calling for a sentence (the jury had to choose between manslaughter and murder—there was no "not guilty" option), offered that both brothers "need a lot of help, no doubt...."[31]

The *Los Angeles Times* reported exactly how the psychiatric concept of "abuse" and "victimization" so confused the issues, how even with a clear-cut case of killing before them, it was impossible for a dozen people to think with the law and enforce it: "The testimony had taken five months, but two of the men on the Erik Menendez jury were sure they would have a verdict in an hour.

"What was there to argue about? The younger Menendez brother was obviously guilty of first-degree murder. He was a baldfaced liar, making up that stuff about being molested by his father.

"So after their jury went behind closed doors in the late afternoon of Dec. 15, both men thought they would be done in no time. Pick a foreman. Vote. Go home.

"They couldn't have been more wrong.

"Soon they were listening to another juror, a woman passionately telling of her personal experience in an abusive relationship. She knew a victim of abuse when she saw one—and Erik Menendez, to her, fit the bill."[32]

What frustration for one juror who simply wanted to implement the law. "There's a possibility [of abuse]," he said, "but I don't think that would rectify the fact that they did take the law into their hands to kill their parents."[33]

In a 1994 article for *Esquire*, author John Taylor tracked this river of legal chaos to its source. "...Psychiatrists themselves were responsible for legitimizing the irresistible-impulse concept in the first place. An insanity defense of one sort or another has been around since the thirteenth century, when the medieval jurist Bracton wrote, 'For a crime is not committed unless the will to harm be present.' But not until the Fifties—that dewily innocent age when psychiatrists believed they could find a cause for all deviant behavior—did the profession argue that criminal defendants would be able to ask for acquittal on the grounds that, while they knew what they were doing was wrong, they just couldn't help themselves. And in 1958, in Section 4.01 of the Model Penal Code, it became writ."

Taylor points out that there may be some truth to the notion that "evil" is a medieval superstition and "free will" an Enlightenment myth. It could also be true, he notes, that all wrongdoers suffer either from a chemical imbalance or from a bad upbringing. The problem with such ideas is that they represent a view of human nature that can't coexist with the one embodied in the legal system. "English common law, after all, was developed," he wrote, "not to explain human nature but to control it. At its core is the idea of individual responsibility, the belief that holding people accountable for what they do is the one thing that will make them behave properly.

"Without this belief...people lose the motivation to control their worst impulses."[34]

Taylor's last remark is not too dissimilar to Mrs. Bean's comment earlier. She—in talking about the educational system—used the phrase "not accountable for his acts."

It would seem both these people are upset about the same thing, an ideology that calls for a lowering of standards, one that, under the banner of helping people, appears to have a net result of excusing and even bringing out their worst.

...INTO OUR WORK PLACES

Our legislatures and parliaments have always been a source of occasional odd laws, but in recent decades we have seen a new current of thought that views sectors of the citizenry as victims of their environment and so pushes for special rights for all manner of "victims of society."

While few recognize this as a psychiatric influence, Howard Rome, president of the American Psychiatric Association, pointed out in 1966 that it is nothing else: "The seeds of present social change were sown in the eighteenth century. They flowered in the nineteenth century's age of psychological man. The ideas of those times begot psychiatry as a social action movement. In this sense psychiatry was a spin-off from political philosophy. For better or for worse psychiatry chose to espouse the rights of the least of men. In our time its canons have become the metaphysic of the age of secular science. They are the *raison d'etre* of modern humanism."[35]

The psychiatric idea that poverty causes crime—a theory popularized by the Mental Hygiene movement of the early 1900s—has spawned a

19

spate of welfare programs to solve criminality. Yet despite this theoretically good idea and the generosity of taxpayers, the lawlessness continues to mount. So deep did psychiatric thought run by the 1960s, that United States President Lyndon Johnson referred to his country not as a nation torn, but as a "sick society." Today this current runs so deep that, as Szasz said, "people don't even think of it as psychiatry."

To choose just one example among many, in 1993 the new California Sexual Harassment Law went into effect, as passed by the state legislature. The initial writing of the law was fought by the business community because it would have required all employers in the state to take a course on sexual harassment—presumably some sort of psychological "sensitivity training."

As the law is now written, sexual harassment is broadly defined as not only obviously offensive behavior, but "sexually explicit jokes, comments about an employee's anatomy and/or dress, sexually oriented noises or remarks, questions about a person's sexual practices, use of patronizing terms or remarks,...displaying sexual pictures, writings, or objects...."[36]

What businesses fear are not employee claims of actual, real unwanted sexual advances in the work place. These are remediable. The worst nightmare for employers are those workers who fondly believe that life has dealt them a bad hand, who are going to claim they have been "victimized" by some remark, gesture, etc. and then seek legal recourse to compensate them for their psychological damages.

The way the law is written, it promotes the psychiatric notion that employees are so weak, so incapable of dealing with others and sexual matters, and so easily offended and prone to psychological harm, that they need protection under the law.

We end up with business management—those who have presumably worked the hardest—on guard, catering to and in fear of the weakest and most malicious members in their employ.

Flanking this intrusion from the legislative front, almost yearly a new wave of hobby horses gallop through corporate America and other countries, touting new cures for work place ailments. They stay until the newness wears off and the discovery is made that perhaps they are not the panacea they claimed to be.

Executive burnout. "Sensitivity" classes. Relationship training. Human resources management. Seminars on getting "motivated" and "focused." They come and go, particularly in large corporations. Couched in the authoritative dress of the latest pseudoscientific buzz words, they offer odd solutions based on "what's new" in the understanding of human behavior. When they are effective at all, it is usually found they are based on common-sense principles that have been around for ages, such as "communication is important" or "maintain an orderly work place" or "utilize time wisely."

Stress, too, has become a major point of discussion in the work place. Businesses have been hit with a soaring number of workers' compensation insurance claims for *stress*. Workers' comp was originally created so that people physically injured on the job would not suffer financially from medical bills and loss of income. But this well-intended concept has become a windfall for many lawyers and, yes, psychiatrists who have encouraged employees to file claims that their jobs have driven them into depression, anxiety, or any number of non-optimum mental states which the mind doctors then, of course, treat. In short, this is the same "victim of the environment" notion we find in the legal system—that the employee is not responsible for the condition he is in.

Naturally, the results have been to drive up insurance premiums for management and those who remain on the job, despite whatever mental pressures *they* have to endure. Adding salt to the wound, psychiatrists have managed to make money at both ends of this employer's conundrum by offering "stress management" classes to businesses, inferring they will reduce the likelihood of stress claims.

Most employers hit by such claims feel a common sense of frustration. Many must wonder why it is that the employee isn't being held answerable for his own mental condition? Isn't this the door to social anarchy, when anyone can blame another—and make him pay—for whatever mental turmoil one feels?

The employers feel in their gut that something is wrong with the thinking surrounding these stress claims, but most can't quite see what it is. Few realize that behind this trend is a psychiatrist telling the insurance company and the employee that the worker is not responsible for his mental condition. It is the same "victim" theory that was sold to the courts, schools and legislatures. In this situation, however, it has been repackaged for insurance companies and business.

Doubtless there are numerous psychiatrists who feel they are doing the right thing, as Howard Rome said, espousing "the rights of the least of men."

However, here we see again how this philosophy seems to reward the weak or litigious and punish those who carry the load.

...AND, BIT BY BIT, INTO OUR HOMES

In centuries past, a person came home to solace and safety. The atmosphere was one he or she created for his family, nurturing the values he or she deemed fit. There was limited outside influence to corrupt the sanctity of the home.

But things are no longer so simple.

Most homes have a television. A VCR. A radio. A telephone. Many now have computers. And the wonders of our electronic age have brought us not only the world but also its dirty laundry.

The TV set that once showed awed viewers live coverage of man's first steps on the moon now flashes nude flesh, bloodied bodies, and perverse messages to grownups and children alike. In discussing the quality of television programming, the word "wholesome" has vanished from our vocabularies. In fact, those who use it are ridiculed.

A 1995 Columbia University survey showed that 67 percent of the adults surveyed agreed that popular culture encourages drug use. Yet of the 12-to-17-year-olds questioned, 76 percent said pop culture—TV, movies, magazines and music—encouraged the illegal use of drugs. Our kids may be in trouble, but they are not stupid.[37]

As this book was being written, we took a sampling of subject matter from the week's television schedule:

Beverly Hills 90210: "Donna and Kelly scour the campus for men to pose for their calendar; Steve learns the fraternity president is gay."

Babylon 5: "A Centauri slave seduces Londo for information that could destroy him."

In the Heat of the Night: "Bubba races to Atlanta to care for his nephew, who has overdosed on drugs."

Melrose Place: "Sydney takes over jailed Lauren's escort business...."[38]

These were all listed on the same night on network and local TV at 8:00 and 9:00 PM.

If you want some idea of how hardened we have become, take another look at Ben Franklin's moral code earlier in this chapter and consider briefly how often you see these precepts violated on today's television screen.

In the face of this assault, we react in different ways. We try to shield the children or be discriminating or perhaps we have accepted some concept that all this "life experience" is good for us and our young, that they will see it all anyway, or that when it comes to morality, perhaps we need to be more open-minded.

Particularly about sex. It is an incessant topic. Premarital sex. Extramarital sex. Masturbation. Homosexuality. And sexual relations between unmarried couples—once frowned upon to protect the sanctity of the family—has become heavily promoted and commonplace. It is hard to bring a video into your home that doesn't include some sexual reference, language, or scene, irrelevant of story line.

Few would deny that sex is certainly an important and pleasurable part of our lives, but it is only one part of our lives and it is completely out of proportion to have television hammer it into our living rooms, night after night. It is centuries-old common sense that a mind constantly swimming in sexual distraction can find it difficult to pursue life's more productive enterprises.

A definite message is being pushed regarding sex: That we should not be so stuffy about it. That, for the sake of universal brotherhood, we should be more accepting and not so condemnatory of those whose practices we consider immoral. That no sexual behavior is ever really wrong—it just depends on who you are and what you feel like doing.

Even novels are now riddled with what writer William F. Buckley called the "O.S.S."—the obligatory sex scene. A book on writing fiction tells us, "...facing reality, a glance at the best-seller fiction list shows that an inordinate number of titles contain at least one steamy scene.... In the old days, the hero went into the bedroom with a female, the door would close, three asterisks would appear on the page, and nine months later she would have a baby. Today the reader follows them into the bedroom, helps them undress and anything goes."[39]

And where does all this originate? It almost seems that a movement existed to unseat the old and experiment with the new, to get the public to

23

set aside its traditional ideas and make way for bolder thinking. How else could such change happen so rapidly?

There was such a movement.

"Those concerned with the teaching of mental health in the schools may well find themselves attempting to teach in the midst of one of the most hotly contested battlegrounds of our times," said Ewen Cameron, president of the American Psychiatric Association in 1953. "For there, and in the home, is being decided what are to be the prevalent personality structures of our times. Are ideals of passivity, acceptance, and traditionalism to prevail, or the concepts of aggressive competition and self-assurance? Is the prevalent personality to be that of adaptiveness or aggressiveness? Should creative individualism or conventional conformity take the lead? What room or compromises are there for erroneous but, nonetheless, age-old and therefore perhaps supportive beliefs about guilt, sex, and the right to parenthood?"[40]

Cameron died in the next decade amidst the scandal of having performed brutal brainwashing experiments for the CIA, but his message lived on.

G. Brock Chisholm waved his own flag for sexual freedom. "… Loaded down by the weight of guilt and fear…the unfortunate human race, deprived by these incubi of its only defenses and its only reasons for striving, its reasoning power and its natural capacity to enjoy the satisfaction of its natural urges, struggles along under its ghastly self-imposed burden."[41]

These are really just extensions of Freud's call for free love, the first major scientific validation of promiscuity's benefits to humanity. As the Viennese doctor put it, "…no neurasthenia or analogous neurosis can exist without a disturbance of the sexual function."[42]

The result of such thought is what we see on our TV and movie screens.

Another curse that has descended on today's homes is drugs. Entering via both adults and children, this plague started with an alliance between psychiatry and the intelligence community, which then escaped to the streets and brought about the Drug Revolution of the 1960s—a time when drug pioneer Timothy Leary, a psychologist, told the world to "tune in, turn on, and drop out."

For the most part, psychiatrists seem to truly believe in the necessity of using psychotropic drugs. They see no fruitful alternatives. Even Dr.

William Glazer—one of the world's foremost authorities on tardive dysk-inesia, a physically crippling side effect of many psychiatric medications—told us, "Unfortunately, more often than not we have to continue people on these medicines because they really help these people with their symp-toms of psychotic illness."[43] Whether or not they "really help" is discussed later, but the fact is, mental health practitioners *believe* they have no choice.

This leads to a simple fact of life today: No profession on the planet, with the possible exception of illegal drug dealers, promotes and doles out mind-altering drugs to the extent psychiatry does. And not only to patients. Research has shown psychiatrists take more self-prescribed psy-chotropic drugs than any other profession.[44]

Another source of this tide of "new thought" into our homes has been the printed media. Our magazines and newspapers offer up psychiatric advice as counsel from the experts. Standing at the supermarket checkout stand, one can peruse the racks—where most of the periodicals are aimed at a female readership—and find an array of articles on "relationships," pop-psych advice, sex, and more sex. One is given the distinct feeling that courtship, engagement, and marriage have given way to fleeting flings and live-ins with a string of partners, with little thought of the future. Psychi-atric advisors seem to speak less of the concept of matrimony and more about a substitute called "commitment" or another called "relationships."

As a test of Szasz's contention, we compared the first six months' *Reader's Digest* issues from 1960 with those of 1993 and found a detectable change. The 1993 issues ran three advisory-type articles written by psy-chologists or quoting them for their authoritative advice. In 1960 there were *no* such articles. In fact, there were two *against* psychiatric advice. One 1960 piece was entitled "What's the Truth about Psychoanalysis?"—a scathing indictment of Freudian analysis that claimed the therapy was essentially useless.

The author, H.J. Eysenck, a British psychology professor, reached a conclusion similar to Szasz's—that a negative impact on society had resulted: "If orthodox psychoanalysis has thus failed to live up to its promise, what of the widespread attempts of laymen to 'psychoanalyze' themselves and their friends? This amateur doctoring has resulted in end-less confusion and much harm. People talk about their 'inferiority complexes' when they really mean their feelings of inferiority—quite a different matter, of course, because they are aware of their feelings, while complexes are supposed to be unconscious. Others speak of 'avoiding repressions' when they really mean that they want to disregard accepted standards of moral and ethical behavior and indulge in promiscuity and adultery. They bring up their children 'unrepressed'—and are surprised at the terrific growth of juvenile delinquency." [45]

Another 1960 *Reader's Digest* article called "How to Stay Married" also lambasted the psychology experts: "One of the chief factors that contributed to a happy marriage in our household is that neither my bridegroom nor I had ever read any of those paralyzing tracts on marriage before we exchanged vows. If in 1929 there was a Spock [46] on Spousery, we were happily unaware of it." [47]

It would appear that over the years—like some dinosaur in a tar pit—we have stepped from the solid ground of inherited cultural wisdom to become mired in a new religion of plummeting mores and standards. And now we struggle, so anxious about our survival that we have forgotten exactly how we got there.

The fact is, the modern-day home is under constant barrage from the purveyors of materialism, telling us to lower our standards, relax our values, and join in the party. And common sense would tell us that this is taking a heavy toll.

The question is: where is this sales pitch really coming from—this continuous harping on our "erroneous beliefs about guilt and sex," as psychiatrist Ewen Cameron put it?

When we look closely at these messages from our schools, our televisions, our literature, and our courts—these advices to ease up on our values to "avoid unnecessary stress," to consider our "self-esteem" over the good of others—these clearly have their genesis in recommendations by the psychiatric community. Even when they *appear* to be coming from somewhere else, that "somewhere else" ultimately adopted it from psychiatrists or psychologists.

When the TV writers and executives, the teachers, the attorneys and the magazine editors have been sold on this "better way of living" or these psychiatric explanations for human behavior and, in turn, feed it to their audiences, we can perceive a false *apparency* then that these secondhand sources are the hawkers of this new ideology—as though this "better understanding of life" came from nowhere and is simply the latest in mature and evolved thought. The reality is that they simply accepted it without intellectual inspection from the self-proclaimed "authoritative" voices of psychiatry.

In light of all this, that ring of truth in Szasz's original statement grows louder.

But then that brings not only psychiatric theories into question, but the very practice itself. If these ideas are harming society, what are they doing to actual psychiatric patients?

CHAPTER II

A Look Behind the Wizard's Smoke:

Does Psychiatry Actually Work?

THERE IS AN OLD STORY ABOUT A MOTORCYCLIST WHO IS BARRELING down the highway with his jacket collar flapping in his face. To remedy the constant battering he pulls over, removes his jacket and puts it on backwards. Then he blasts back onto the road at full throttle. It isn't long before he collides violently with another vehicle.

Ambulances come. Paramedics work the victims. Shortly a doctor arrives on the scene and steps over to several attendants who are tending to the mangled motorcyclist. "How's he doing?" asks the physician.

One of the paramedics looks up with a grimace. "Not so good," he says, shaking his head. "He was breathing when we got here, but by the time we got his head turned around straight, he was dead."

Society has commonly viewed psychiatrists as being much like the bewildered paramedics—by the time these mental healers get a man's head on straight, they have lost the patient. He is so muddled by their actions—drugs, shock treatments, or confusing psychotherapy—that he is of little use anymore. And he is not the person he once was.

Possibly this belief has been fostered, in part, by the fact that we can often tell when someone has been "seeing a shrink." The person seems dull, or drugged. Or he appears unduly sensitive, overly involved with his own thoughts and feelings or maybe even artificially euphoric. A common assessment is that he simply isn't himself.

For this and many other reasons, the public has often viewed "head-shrinkers" as being ineffectual and somewhat oddball in their practices. And this is not a new attitude. When the so-called father of psychiatry, Emil Kraepelin, reviewed the previous century of psychiatric practice in 1917, he remarked, "Then as now, psychiatric treatment was held in low repute."[1]

THE MEDIA MESSAGE VERSUS THE REALITY

The media message we receive about psychiatry is entirely at odds with the general public's view.

Utilizing advertising, popular magazines, talk shows, and a gamut of multifaceted promotional campaigns, psychiatry has tried over the past fifty years to create a more acceptable public image for itself. And a gullible media, one that considers itself simply a messenger with no responsibility for the prevailing theories it parrots, has largely fallen right in line.

Steps towards this goal of acceptance occurred in a significant way during World War II when a number of psychiatrists gained prominent medical positions in the military of the U.S. and other countries. Here, they arranged to implement psychiatric services to screen recruits and treat newly-named war illnesses such as "shell shock" and "battle fatigue." In doing so, they began to popularize the notion that psychiatry was the cure for any and all mental problems. Additionally, by screening out large numbers of potential inductees (as high as 16 percent) as mentally unfit, they created the impression the country was sicker than anyone suspected, a fact only the psychiatrists could apparently detect and, presumably, a problem only they could resolve.

"At the moment," cautioned the president of the American Psychiatric Association somewhat prematurely in 1946, "we have popular acceptance of psychiatry and keen interest in it; in fact, one might almost say that psychiatry is oversold, and is in the embarrassing position of being called upon to perform miracles which unfortunately can occur only in some of the absurd formulations in popular moving pictures and novels. It is perhaps well to call public attention to the fact that we have not yet solved the problem of mental disease...."[2]

Two years later, however, public acceptance began to wane and psychiatry was again fighting to be accepted as a bona fide scientific practice. The APA president tells us its "Council took constructive action to alter the status of psychiatry which had provoked the repeated and sincere criticism that we were isolated, inarticulate, and incoordinated."[3] The public face of psychiatry thus became a public relations matter and was targeted for change. Like any business organization, the APA saw that its poor image was not good for commerce.

And change happened. Today, though psychiatry may still be suspect among the public it has won over both government and the media. The profession and its treatments inundate talk shows, magazines and the front pages of our newspapers. We are told constantly about new cures for depression and anxiety, and we are simultaneously informed of hosts of heretofore unknown mental illnesses that may be affecting millions.

With little fear of overselling its capabilities, psychiatry has successfully positioned itself as *the* solution to emotional problems. For example, the *World Book Encyclopedia* flatly tells us, "Mentally ill people need specialized treatment from mental health professionals, such as psychiatrists and psychologists."[4]

The acceptance of this zealous sales pitch by the media and government—the gradual belief that psychiatry has all the answers—may mark the entry point where the profession went from being "crackpots" and the butt of jokes to becoming "the most destructive force in American society" that Szasz speaks of. For today, through mass media and government-funded courts, schools, and social programs, it has spread its gospel into virtually every facet of society. Even now, psychiatry's current monopoly on mental health is due in good measure to its sustained modern-day marketing—as demonstrated within the "Campaign Kits" issued by the APA's Public Affairs Network to its members.

The glossy-covered 1989 package claims the campaign is "on behalf of the millions of Americans who suffer mental illness."[5] But the contents reveal a more pragmatic purpose—to, as it bluntly says, "work together to fix psychiatry and psychiatrists in the public's mind as a positive healing force at work constantly across the country."[6]

The kit is centered around the APA's major public relations push and one of its primary tools: Mental Illness Awareness Week. The name communicates the intent. The objective: "create interest in mental illnesses and the treatments that are available."[7] A recent slogan was "Mental Illness: It's more than what you think."[8] This motto was splashed across one poster against a backdrop of a catalogue of disorders now in the proclaimed province of psychiatry—anxiety, withdrawal symptoms, Parkinson's disease, school phobia, hyperactivity, dream anxiety, and more than a hundred others.

The campaign package tells how to bring in business through other doctors. "Psychiatrists have a bad rep among non-psychiatric physicians," it admits. "An increase of psychiatry's profile among non-psychiatric physicians can do nothing but good. And, for those who are bottom-line oriented, the efforts you spend on building this profile have the potential to yield dividends through increased referrals."[9]

It advises how to maximize "opportunities" in a community. "Tell someone that millions of teens need some sort of help with a mental illness and they'll yawn and scratch absently. But lead a bewildered community, gathered after a teen cluster suicide, to an understanding that the problems their kids face are *real*, and they will listen. You will seldom have such dramatic opportunities to reach your audience, but there will be other opportunities to hit them—literally—where they live, if you keep a sharp lookout."[10]

And to help "hit" their audience, a sample flyer for public consumption starts out like this: "No one is immune to mental illness. In fact, you probably know someone who suffers from a diagnosable and treatable disorder. The U.S. National Institute of Mental Health recently learned that one in five Americans has some form of mental illness in any given six months. That means between 30 million and 45 million people—possibly your friends, family members and co-workers—suffer from symptoms that can be effectively treated."

After throwing out the "recently learned" one in five, or 20 percent, figure, the net is cast even wider: "You may have heard someone comment, 'Harry just isn't the same these days.' Perhaps you said it yourself about an 'average' person. Harry is overly sensitive or irritable or he's drinking too much.... All these behavior changes suggest a possible mental disorder which, with appropriate diagnosis and treatment, can be cured or controlled."[11]

We are given the distinct impression that mental illness is being *promoted*, i.e. there seems to be a beckoning finger to those with life problems to abandon responsibility for their difficulties and place them on the shelf of mental illness. As psychiatrist Walter Afield told us, "I think what's happened is we have a tendency to identify more illness or define illness which never used to be defined as illness." He recalled a recent conference "where Russian psychiatrists were talking about [how] in America you talk about treating marital maladjustment reactions and in Russia we just call that bad luck."[12]

The campaign kit continues with information about how to handle the media. This is the design behind the occasional blitz on mental health issues that appear in the papers or on television talk shows. These are planned campaigns. The package gives an array of helpful tips on how to get the APA's message out. On "Becoming a Media Source," it tells how to become the person reporters will call when they want expert psychiatric opinion. "What are the advantages or payoffs for your hard work?" it asks. "Your reputation with reporters, editors, and producers can often shape or limit a story."[13] Of course, there is also the obvious fact that it could increase the psychiatrist's prestige and bring him customers.

Another section instructs how to get legislatures to make proclamations on behalf of Mental Health Awareness Week. The Campaign Kit closes with a copy of the annual resolution mental health lobbyists get proclaimed at the U.S. Senate and House of Representatives. It rolls off the somber news about the nation's mental health:

"Whereas mental illness is a problem of grave concern and consequence in American society, widely but unnecessarily feared and misunderstood;

"Whereas thirty-one to forty-one million Americans annually suffer from clearly diagnosable mental disorders involving significant disability with respect to employment, attendance at school, or independent living;

"Whereas more than ten million Americans are disabled for long periods of time by schizophrenia, manic depressive disorder, and major depression;

"Whereas between 30 and 50 percent of the homeless suffer serious, chronic forms of mental illness;

"Whereas alcohol, drug, and mental disorders affect almost 19 percent of American adults in any six-month period;

"Whereas mental illness in at least twelve million children interferes with vital developmental and maturational processes;

"Whereas mental disorder-related deaths are estimated to be thirty-three thousand, with suicide accounting for at least twenty-nine thousand, although the real number is thought to be at least three times higher...."

And so it goes. But we are told there is a light at the end of the tunnel:

"Whereas research in recent decades has led to a wide array of new and more effective modalities of treatment (both somatic and psychosocial) for some of the most incapacitating forms of mental illness...."

"Whereas appropriate treatment of mental illness has been demonstrated to be cost effective in terms of restored productivity, reduced utilization of other health services, and lessened social dependence...."[14]

As is common with lobbied legislation, the American Psychiatric Association is not mentioned anywhere in this proclamation as its source. By appearances, it comes from the hearts of the nation's legislators and represents the concerns of all Americans. In truth, however, the public's view of the situation is quite different. A 1986 poll in *Science* magazine showed only 1 percent of Americans think mental illness is a major health problem and 55 percent don't even think it exists.[15]

We would do well to remember, then, the source of articles or statements on the network news about "the tragedy of mental illness." As can happen in marketing, the general public is rarely, if ever, informed that, while these are presented as vital societal issues, they are simply orchestrated PR actions by the APA, with the sole purpose of driving in business.

There is, of course, nothing wrong with a business organization promoting its services. It's a necessary part of any commercial enterprise. However, in psychiatry's case, we have to ask if it is ethical to be selling our society a plethora of new mental illnesses for the purpose of bringing in new business? It is one thing for advertisers to try to sway the public on the social necessity of dandruff shampoo and quite another to convince people they cannot deal with their lives and need professional help because they are ill. Quite apart from the concern, confusion and even fear that spreads in the wake of alarming pronouncements like these inflated claims of widespread societal mental breakdown, they also foster a society in which, as Thomas Szasz said, "everybody is a victim, everybody has special rights, no responsibilities."

And the crucial question must be asked: Is psychiatry even capable of performing the cures it is laying claim to?

PUT TO THE TEST

A study reported in *American Psychologist* in 1978 not only sheds some light on this question but, together with other data, indicates we may be dealing with nothing less than fraud of gigantic and destructive proportions.

The report covered a 1939 project which had the goal of reducing delinquency in underprivileged children. More than 600 children between the ages of five and thirteen were randomly divided into two groups. Half received individual psychiatric counseling for about five years while the other half received no therapy. The therapists reported that about two-thirds of the boys receiving treatment "substantially benefitted" from it. More than 35 years later, almost 80 percent of the original 600 were located and follow-up studies were done. The results? "Almost without exception, therapy appeared to have had a negative, or at least a non-positive, effect on the youngsters in later life," the study said.

The treated boys were *more* likely to have committed more than one serious crime. And when evaluated for alcoholism, mental illness, stress-related diseases, and job satisfaction, the treated group was worse off than the control group.

The author of the follow-up, Joan McCord, concluded, "The objective evidence presents a disturbing picture. The program seems not only to have failed to prevent its clients from committing crimes—thus corroborating studies of other projects—but also to have produced negative side effects."[16]

In an interview with *Science News*, McCord was asked her opinion of the study's outcome. "I've got some hunches," she remarked. "It's possible that people become too dependent on counselors, and therefore they do not acquire the skills of those who do not have therapy," she said. "They come to see themselves as 'needing help.'"[17]

McCord's work, as she mentioned, was by no means the only study to reveal the damaging effects of psychiatric therapy.

After reviewing research on how therapists relate to their patients, two leading researchers concluded, in a *psychotherapy handbook*, that the majority either do not help at all or actually do harm: "The odds are two out of three that [the therapist] is spending his energy, commitment, and care for mankind wastefully; he is either ineffective or harmful. Two out of three of his colleagues, he can be quite certain, are ineffective or harmful."[18]

Even Nicholas Cummings, former president of the American Psychological Association pointed out, "It may be that the mental health movement has promised the American people a freedom from anxiety that is neither possible nor realistic, resulting in an expectation that we have a right to feel good. We may never know to what extent we ourselves have contributed to the steep rise in alcohol consumption and the almost universal reliance by physicians on the tranquilizer."[19]

Studies of former mental patients have shown consistently that before 1950 they committed fewer violent crimes than the average citizen.[20] But since the advent of widespread drug, shock and psychosurgical treatments in the 1940s and '50s, these patients are now committing more violence than the general population. A California study showed an ex-patient arrest rate for violent crime in the early '70s that was nine times that of the populace at large.[21]

Another revealing research project was conducted by psychologist H. J. Eysenck. After World War II, he investigated several thousand cases of mentally disturbed servicemen and women in British hospitals. Among those given psychoanalysis, he found an overall improvement rate of 44 percent. The betterment rate of those given any other form of psychotherapy was about 64 percent. However, several hundred patients had received no therapy at all, except treatment for physical ailments. The improvement rate among these untreated patients was about 72 percent.

Summarizing Eysenck's findings, one psychology text concludes, "These data led some scientists to compare psychoanalysis with 'witch doctoring' and to suggest that psychoanalysis might actually *retard* the patient's progress."[22]

Indeed, the Eysenck study showed a spontaneous recovery rate for untreated neurotics of 45 percent within a year of the onset of their troubles and 70 percent after two years. Within five years, about 90 percent were dramatically improved or cured.[23]

Given the fact that psychotherapy commonly continues for years, compare Eysenck's findings on improvement without treatment to a comprehensive review of psychotherapy results done by author Thomas Kiernan in his consumer's guide to psychotherapies. "The results of over forty studies on neurosis reported in psychotherapeutic literature during the past twenty years (covering over 14,000 cases and dealing with both psychoanalytic and eclectic therapies) indicate that the aggregate percentage of positive effect in such therapies is just a hair's breadth above 50 percent."[24]

Elsewhere he remarks, "Psychotherapy in general is at best no more than 50 percent effective...and in fact is probably much less effective than that."[25]

Kiernan notes that regarding the Eysenck study "most ordinary physicians are aware of these rather startling statistics, which perhaps explains why doctors hesitate to refer many of their emotionally troubled patients to psychiatrists after determining that there is nothing organically wrong with them. They know that episodes of neurosis and demoralization are likely to be temporary in nature and are more inclined to let time work its wonders. Indeed, many experienced nonpsychiatric physicians I have discussed these points with seem to believe that there is an inverse correlation between recovery from neurosis and psychotherapy—that is, the more psychotherapy, the smaller the recovery rate."[26]

We can see now why psychiatrists may have a "bad rep among non-psychiatric physicians," as the campaign kit noted.

Psychologist Bernie Zilbergeld, in his book *The Shrinking of America*, points out that much of psychiatry's claims of success may be due to its own wishful thinking. "It was not until the last ten or fifteen years," he remarks, "that therapists, and not all of them, have been willing to consider the possibility that change can be for the worse, that therapy can fail not only by not producing change but also by producing the wrong kind of change. Then he adds, perhaps generously, "The findings...do indeed indicate that counseling makes some people worse, but this has been hard to see and admit because of the positive thinking of those who do the counseling."[27]

An extraordinary story from World War II also validates the notion that psychiatric intervention may be useless or unnecessary in a large percentage of cases. A French mental hospital lay in the path of an oncoming German army. All patients were returned home to relatives except 153 who were considered too ill to leave. The Germans arrived faster than the French anticipated and the patients were left to fend for themselves.

After the war, a commission was formed to determine the fate of these people. Of those traced, 37 percent of these abandoned, untreated, and "hopeless" patients were found to have adjusted to the community.[28]

A similar conclusion was reached in a similar follow-up of 118 schizophrenics who had been discharged from Vermont State Hospital 20 to 25 years earlier. Schizophrenia is the diagnosis for the common man's idea of the classic lunatic: hearing voices, bizarre behavior, delusions, etc. The study showed that through apparently spontaneous recovery, coming for the most part well after treatment, fully 68 percent had lost all symptoms of schizophrenia.[29]

Psychologist Stanley Peele, reporting on this study, noted, "The results corroborated similar results from three European studies and another American study over the past decade indicating that half or more of the schizophrenics eventually recovered or significantly improved."[30]

The implications of these findings become shocking when we discover that schizophrenics under psychiatric care, are virtually never expected to recover.

According to the "bible" of psychiatry, the *DSM-IIIR* (*Diagnostic and Statistical Manual—Third Edition Revised*), "A return to full premorbid functioning in this disorder is not common."[31] The previous edition of *DSM-III* was even more adamant. "A complete return to premorbid functioning is unusual—so rare, in fact, that some clinicians would question the [original] diagnosis."[32]

What makes matters sadly worse is that it is standard practice for psychiatrists laboring under this belief to put all schizophrenics on mind-altering medication and maintain them on it thereafter. If left in the hospital, the discomforting reality is that these 118 Vermont patients would have most likely spent a lifetime on drugs and undergone the obviously debilitating effects that entails.

It seems clear, particularly from the Vermont and Eysenck studies that the mind has a remarkable capacity to heal itself. What then happens to the mind's self-restorative mechanisms when they are overwhelmed with drugs, shocks, or even confusing in-depth counseling?

The inescapable possibility—in fact, probability—is that such psychiatric treatments have the potential to alter the mind's normal functioning, thus deranging some of its natural recuperative powers. The tragic outcome is a patient who unnecessarily deteriorates in his insanity for extended periods of time or even for life. Is this what psychiatrists mean when they claim the ability to "control" mental illness?

PATIENT SUICIDE

Psychiatric patients have higher suicide rates than the general population—as much as fifteen times higher.[33] While on the surface this may appear self-explanatory or justified, a glib acceptance would not be in order. We are talking about human lives and a 1500 percent difference warrants closer inspection to discover whether or not psychiatric interventions and treatments are actually exacerbating the situation.

• One study of children in psychiatric hospitals found that 75 percent had suicidal ideas, threats, and/or attempts.[34]

• An investigation of self-inflicted deaths at Atascadero State Hospital in California showed that nearly 69 percent occurred within the first year of incarceration.[35]

• A research project in 1975, looking into suicides among those who at some time had received psychiatric treatment, showed that 51 percent of these cases had psychiatric contact within thirty days of their death.[36]

• A 1968 study found "most [two thirds] of the subjects...had seen a doctor shortly before they died and [80 percent] were taking psychotropic drugs."[37]

• Research by British psychiatrist Martin Weller, reported in 1986, found that recently discharged patients had a suicide rate more than seventeen times higher than the rest of the population.[38]

When we consider, in light of these studies, that a great many of these patients may have recovered without psychiatric intervention, we are left to ponder how many of these suicides could have been prevented by *avoiding* psychiatric care.

When we asked Dr. Szasz if psychiatric treatment bore some responsibility for the high rate of suicide, his answer was unequivocal. "Absolutely...due to stigma and the so-called treatment.... By making it even more difficult for the person to come back to normal life, because whatever problems he had are compounded."[39]

UNWORKABLE TREATMENTS

Some in the psychiatric community may protest that not all their treatments are harmful. But others point out that even ineffective treatment can be harmful if it falsely raises hope or wastes the time and money of expectant recipients.

Psychologist Zilbergeld claims, "Some clients pay heavily for believing in the permanence of therapy-made changes. When problems recur, they often feel confused and guilty. They wonder how this could happen and what they have done wrong."[40]

Worse, when problems recur, since patients are told they are ill and not responsible for their condition, they are left to believe their difficulties are unsolvable.

However, being ineffective may be the lesser of two evils in the minds of some psychiatrists. One traditional psychotherapist, quoted in Thomas Kiernan's book *Shrinks, etc.*, commented, "People have always claimed the kind of work I do does little good, that nobody really gets better as a result of analysis. That used to worry me, but not any more. Because at least my kind of therapy doesn't do any harm. It takes sick people and tries to make them well. If it doesn't always succeed, well, O.K. But these new so-called therapies—why they're just as likely to take healthy people and make them sick."[41]

Psychologist J. Hillman says it more succinctly in the title of his book: *We've Had 100 Years of Psychotherapy and The World's Getting Worse.*[42] And Dr. Walter Fisher put it even more pointedly, if less delicately, in the title of his book when, as the assistant superintendent for an Illinois state mental hospital, he co-authored *Power, Greed, and Stupidity in the Mental Health Racket.*[43]

In a Vanderbilt University study, young male clients were divided into two groups. One group was assigned to receive individual counseling by professional therapists. These were veteran counselors, with an average length of experience of twenty-three years. The second group was assigned to receive counseling from college professors with no experience or training in therapy. Results: "Patients undergoing psychotherapy with college professors showed, on the average, quantitatively as much improvement as patients treated by experienced professional therapists."[44]

A damning 1979 review of forty-two studies comparing the effectiveness of professional therapists with those of little training, found the trained counselors were significantly more effective in only one of the studies. In the majority, the professionals and paraprofessionals were equally effective, and in twelve of the reports, the lesser trained counselors came out ahead. Psychologist Joseph Durlak, who did the review, commented, "...It is frustrating to admit that we do not know exactly why paraprofessionals with relatively little clinical experience and training can achieve results equal to or better than those obtained by professionals." He later adds, "These data suggest that professionals do not necessarily possess demonstrably superior clinical skills, in terms of measurable outcome, when compared with paraprofessionals. Moreover, professional mental health education, training, and experience are not necessarily prerequisites for an effective helping person."[45]

As to psychiatric efforts to treat addictions, the failures of methadone are well known. Methadone, developed by Nazi chemists in World War II, was given freely to heroin addicts to break their habit and found to be more addictive than the drug it replaced. In 1987, 527 New York citizens entered rehabilitation programs because they had become addicted to illegally purchased methadone. Sixty percent of the 31,000 methadone patients in New York were still active drug abusers as of 1989, and the percentage was on the rise.[46]

Dr. Jerome Jaffe, former President's Director for Drug Abuse, and a supporter of the methadone program, was quoted on a newscast to the effect that religion has helped more addicts than methadone.[47]

Alcoholism fares no better. Zilbergeld writes, "Alcoholics Anonymous seems to be about as useful as professional therapy for drinking problems, but when drop-outs and relapses are considered, it is clear that far less than 50 percent of people are helped by either."[48]

Regarding the effectiveness of drug therapy (which will be covered in greater detail in a later chapter) early [1986] results of a massive study carried out by the National Institute of Mental Health found that drug treatment did not help severely depressed patients any more than ordinary psychotherapy—and we have seen how poorly psychotherapy fares. It also concluded that, for those with milder depression, drug therapy and psychotherapy were not significantly more effective than placebo treatment.[49]

In his book, *Diseasing of America*, Dr. Stanley Peele says that the neurosciences have made remarkable progress in recent years, from the invention of new ways to scan cerebral activity to the discovery of brain-activating chemicals to the creation of drugs that mimic the effects of chemicals found in the brain. As a result, he points out, antipsychotic drugs and antidepressants are today's primary tool for dealing with mental illness.

"Yet it has remained surprisingly difficult," Peele adds, "to translate these advances into improved prognoses for mental disorders such as depression and schizophrenia."

Cutting to the chase, he adds, "Not only have we failed to eliminate depression and schizophrenia, but they have actually increased in the latter part of this century. Moreover, despite the feeling that mental patients are being much better managed through the use of drugs, systematic evaluations of drug therapy effectiveness have not been overly impressive."

Peele points out that while the majority of physicians may endorse the use of psychotropic drugs for these conditions, "*Hardly any* regard them as a cure and nearly all recognize that they work only irregularly and produce serious side effects and few benefits for at least some patients suffering from the conditions under attack. What is more, there is a residual uneasiness about making patients depend on drugs (and the medical approach requires them to do so for the rest of their lives) when their benefits are so variable and when some people do as well without them."[50]

ANTI-PSYCHIATRY ORGANIZATIONS

Another unique aspect of psychiatry, unlike any other branch of medicine, is that it has ex-patient organizations which oppose its practices. Groups such as the Network Against Psychiatric Assault, the Mental Patients Liberation Project, and the Mental Patients' Association have assembled since the 1970s to protest psychiatric treatments and intervention.

Leonard Frank, a prominent leader in the ex-patient movement—whose writings in opposition to electroshock treatments are well respected in academic circles—finds this significant. His stance against psychiatry came from personal experience. In 1962-63 he was involuntarily committed to several California mental institutions. "I was forcibly administered 85 shock treatments—50 insulin and 35 electric shock treatments," he explained. "And as a result of those treatments, I suffered a memory loss of about two years, the period immediately preceding shock treatment, when I had virtually no memory at all....I came to the conclusion, very early on, that I was reduced to about the level of an eighth grader in terms of my education, and my college education was virtually blotted out....I was very, very reduced education-wise, to say nothing of the reduction in my overall humanity as a human being. I was less a person."

The main social organization *supportive* of psychiatry's activities is the National Alliance for the Mentally Ill (NAMI). Yet it is significant to note that this association is primarily composed of patients' *families*, not the patients themselves. As Frank pointed out, NAMI members "have a vested interest in the commitment laws because that is the way that they have in dealing with their children or family members who they don't get along with."[51]

Furthermore, since psychiatry serves to lift a considerable burden off the hands of many families by incarcerating or medicating unmanageable or intolerable family members, it has, naturally, gained family support from some. But backing from those who actually receive treatment at the hands of psychiatrists is rare indeed.

Lucille Barry, a former New York state member of NAMI, told us the group is composed of local subgroups referred to as grass roots affiliates. "We at the grass roots are thoroughly disillusioned with the National Alliance," she said. "It seems very significant to me," she went on, "that their newsletters...seem to be filled with recording these major grants from the drug companies who are purportedly working on new and better models of treatment for mental illness."

At one point Barry went to Jamestown, New York to speak before a disaffected Alliance affiliate. The group's reason for cutting the NAMI umbilical cord? "The same reason I had," Barry remarked. "We feel that NAMI was bought by the big drug companies. It's no secret. Not only is it true in the psychiatric world but even in the ordinary medical doctor world. It's no secret that doctors, and especially psychiatrists, are given 'incentives.' And I think the incentives had been extraordinarily generous to NAMI."[52]

PROMISES OF GOOD THINGS TO COME

As noted, a common characteristic in psychiatric literature throughout its history consists of remarks to the effect that, though they do not have effective treatments now, the future is bright. Someday they will. This is frequently cited as justification for the often less-than-desirable practices psychiatry does have—such as drugs and electroshock. These are held out as acceptable holding actions until the *real* solutions come along.

As psychiatrist Jonas Robitscher put it, "Psychiatry has always had this in abundance: enthusiasm harnessed to a belief, often without rational basis, in the possibility and imminence of change."[53]

One book, *Freud and the Americans*, tells of psychiatric hopes in the early 1900s. "Magazines eagerly printed almost any hopeful medical news: the speculation that insanity might be caused by a toxin and cured by an anti-toxin, that insanity was not a 'disease' but an inability to adapt to environment. Some physicians urged that the old words 'chronic and incurable' be abandoned. Psychiatry, they insisted, despite lack of improvement in recovery rates, was on the threshold of a golden age."[54]

Decades later, by 1988, the message hadn't changed. Psychiatrist Paul Appelbaum said: "The real advances will come from the laboratory in Bethesda or San Diego or New York. Someone in a lab somewhere will find a receptor that when properly stimulated clears thought disorders and stops auditory hallucinations, or they'll find a virus.... It's that solution that can solve the public policy problems.... If you've got a good treatment, society, given the magnitude of the disorder, is going to let you use it. And the rest of us are just trying to hold the fort until those on the science side of things come up with something."[55]

Yet modern psychiatry is neglecting to inform the public that it is still waiting for the "science side of things to come up with something." In fact, it is presenting a very different picture. Remember the previously mentioned proclamation the APA had read before Congress? It paints an image of mental illness as a vanquished beast. With considerable fanfare the proclamation heralds "recent and unparalleled growth in scientific knowledge about mental illness," "a new threshold of opportunity for future research advances," and "a wide array of new and more effective modalities of treatment."

Something is wrong with this picture. In fact, the situation would seem to be a recipe for chaos.

The figures vary considerably according to source, but according to mental health champion and promoter Tipper Gore, wife of the U.S. Vice President, as much as 28 percent of the populace is mentally ill, i.e. is having difficulties it is not responsible for (it is, after all, ill) and cannot handle on its own.[56] This leaves us with more than a quarter of our population that is not held accountable for its aberrant behavior. The 28 percent are then being told to seek professional help which, as we have seen, is of dubious value and possibly harmful. And sadly, PR and marketing rhetoric will not mend the broken minds and souls that come to them for help.

"What do you do when you don't know what to do?" wrote British psychiatrist R. D. Laing in 1985. "No wonder there are more suicides among psychiatrists than in any other profession."[57]

PHYSICIAN, HEAL THYSELF

Taking Laing's question to heart, if psychiatric treatment is as beneficial as claimed, it stands to reason that those most knowledgeable in these treatments and theories—the psychiatrists and psychologists themselves—should be the sanest, wisest, most successful people of all in the art of living.

However, we find, as Dr. Laing said, the well-documented fact that psychiatrists commit suicide twice as often as doctors in general.[58] And this is *five times* the rate of the population at large. During their residencies, psychiatrists commit suicide nearly *nine times* the rate of the general populace, a rate that is again higher than any other medical specialty.[59]

Additionally, researchers reporting in the *The Journal of Clinical Psychiatry* found, "The occurrence of suicides by psychiatrists is constant year-to-year, indicating a relatively stable over-supply of depressed psychiatrists from which the suicides are produced."[60]

According to an article in *American Journal of Psychiatry*, one possible explanation is "that his production had fallen so far short of his ideal that he could not endure the anticipation of criticism by the reviewers."[61]

A joint study on physician suicide performed by the American Medical Association and American Psychiatric Association in 1987, once again noted psychiatrists as having the highest rate. Researchers interviewing the surviving families found that by far the most common reason given for the death—in 94 percent of the cases—was to "escape from mental pain," which, of course, is the very thing psychiatrists claim they can alleviate. Additionally, "more than half (56 percent) of those in the suicide group had prescribed a psychoactive drug for themselves."

Forty-two percent had been seeing a mental health professional at the time of their death.[62]

The book *The Impaired Physician* tells us, "A psychiatrist's committing suicide is deeply unsettling. The event is a grim reminder of the recent statistics that suggest a higher risk for members of that specialty. The suicide especially upsets those who fantasize that psychiatrists, by reason of their training, are better equipped to deal with emotional distress."[63]

But a high incidence of suicide is not the only peculiarity in the lives of these doctors. In one survey of psychiatrists, fully 91 percent of them agreed that members of their specialty have "emotional difficulties that are special to them and their work as contrasted with non-psychiatrists."[64] And a fascinating Swiss study compared the military conscription records of inductees who eventually became psychiatrists versus the records of those who became internists and surgeons. It found that significantly more of the eventual psychiatrists were declared unfit for military service due to psychiatric disorders.[65]

Research into an Alcoholics Anonymous population showed that of the physician members, 17 percent were psychiatrists—even though they represent only 8 percent of the medical profession.[66] A similar 1983 study among women physicians revealed that female psychiatrists, while constituting only 9.5 percent of women doctors, made up 22.1 percent of the alcoholic physicians. The study's authors concluded, "The only training specialty that is clearly overrepresented is psychiatry."[67]

Drug abuse is equally problematic. One survey of 500 practicing physicians, reported in *The New England Journal of Medicine* in 1986, stated, "Psychiatrists had much higher rates for all types of use [of psychoactive drugs] at any time (83 percent) and for current self-treatment (48 percent) than did other groups of physicians."[68] This is to say that nearly half of the psychiatrists reviewed were taking self-prescribed drugs.

Marriage is another sore spot. A survey in *Medical Economics*, covering seven branches of medicine, discovered that psychiatrists led in more categories of marital problems—including sexual difficulties—than any other specialty. They had the shortest marriages, were most likely to "carry on and scream" to handle family quarrels, and were most likely to have problems due to extramarital affairs (so were their spouses).[69]

It seems only reasonable to expect that those trained in an understanding of the mind would be better able to causatively deal with their own mental functioning. Yet psychiatrists-in-training may not be as prepared as one might expect.

One has to wonder how many undergo the painful realization that struck psychiatric intern Dr. Stephen Seager—an event he related in his 1991 book, *Psych Ward*: "I realized that despite my credentials and experience, I knew little if anything about medicine and even less about myself. I could recite numbers and compose long lists of diseases. I knew a hundred drugs inside and out, but suddenly that seemed to pale in significance. At that moment, I realized I knew nothing about medicine because I knew nothing about people."[70]

Toward the end of his internship, he tells us, "There is a phrase in psychiatry called the 'Aha moment.' It happens the instant that little light goes on and you get your first glimpse into what's really happening.... I suddenly saw things very clearly. My aha moment was this: *I'd been learning psychiatry for nearly a year and I knew absolutely nothing about it.*"[71]

A 1989 article in *The Atlantic Monthly* gives us an uncomfortably close look at the world of these healers of the mind: "Psychiatrists often say that analysts are crazy. Analysts say that psychiatrists, being unanalyzed, are crazy. Both of them say that social workers and psychologists, whose training is more limited and subject to fewer quality controls, are crazy, and are particularly harmful because a little bit of knowledge is a dangerous thing. Social workers and psychologists accuse psychiatrists and analysts of being pompous asses—pompous *crazy* asses, so puffed up with theoretical abstractions that they are out of touch with the real world."

The writer echoes the words of one training psychoanalyst: "I very rarely have found a healthy, well-integrated, happy person *seeking* this profession."

A clinical psychologist is quoted as saying, "I question your calling it a myth that therapists are crazy because the *fact* is that most of them *are*. If you need any proof, let me tell you that every patient who comes into this office who has had a previous experience with another therapist has some kind of horror story to tell, about some *major* failing on the therapist's part, including, quite often, sexual abuse, verbal abuse, things that cross the boundary of mere bad technique and come pretty damn close to the criminal."[72]

Escape from "These Moral Chains"

The psychiatrist's redefinition or, as proposed, eradication of the concepts of right and wrong—as when mental health leader Chisholm urged his colleagues to escape "from these moral chains"—may go a long way toward explaining the undeniable erosion of personal values that is so evident in our world today.

An examination of "thirty introductory psychological texts turned up no references to the possible reality of spiritual factors," reported psychologist Allen Bergin. "Most did not have the words *God* or *religion* in their indexes."[73]

Psychiatrist Thomas Szasz's research found that "although an entire volume of the *Standard Edition* of Freud's collected works is devoted to an index, there is no entry for *responsibility* in it. True to the faith of the master, his acolytes must have felt that responsibility was so unscientific a concept that it was not worth indexing."[74]

In Jeremy Levens' novel, *Satan*, the Devil complains, "Psychotherapy worries the hell out of me.... It keeps turning evil into neuroses and explaining away people's behavior with drives and complexes.... Modern psychiatry is putting me out of business."[75]

This new psychiatric view of morality may also explain the following:

A 1986 article in the *American Journal of Psychiatry* opens with: "Sexual contact between psychiatrists and patient is explicitly prohibited by the Hippocratic oath and the American Psychiatric Association (APA) code of ethics. Nevertheless, some psychiatrists do become sexually involved with their patients. Professional liability insurance carriers have noted a sharp increase in the number of malpractice claims for sexual misconduct filed in recent years against psychiatrists. Likewise, sexual misconduct complaints to APA ethics committees have multiplied in the past decade."[76]

This claim of multiplying complaints is significant because a 1988 Associated Press release tells us, "Professional societies in the mental health field undertook a major effort about 10 years ago to halt the sexual abuse of patients."[77] In short, after their efforts, reports of sexual misconduct increased substantially.

A Los Angeles survey showed that 10 percent of male psychiatrists engaged in sexual contact with their patients.[78] In a nationwide survey reported in the aforementioned 1986 article, 7.1 percent of the male psychiatrists and 3.1 percent of the female—over 6 percent of the respondents overall—acknowledged having what is euphemistically called "sexual contact" with their patients.[79] Yet 65 percent of psychiatrists questioned said they had treated patients who were sexually involved with previous therapists. Only 8 percent reported the misconduct, which might serve to further illustrate how much responsibility is assumed by the profession's members in policing themselves.[80]

Be that as it may, this casts a suspicious light on that 10 percent figure. In fact, in a 1990 *US News and World Report* article, experts put the sexual shenanigans figure at more like 25 percent, or one out of every four psychiatrists.[81] And a 1973 California study claims the figure is an astronomical 51 percent.[82]

In Minneapolis, a social worker at a center that specifically handles therapist sexual abuse cases reported, "Sometimes medications get mishandled, including overmedicating a client to keep her docile and in the relationship. It all smacks a little of prostitution, except that the therapist is like a pimp and a john all rolled into one."[83]

Another study of psychologists showed that of those who had sexual contact with patients, fully 80 percent were recidivist, and had done so with more than one client.[84]

Nor are patients the only targets of promiscuous activity. A 1979 survey published by Kenneth Pope, former head of the ethics committee for the American Psychological Association, revealed the startling news that one out of every four female psychology students had sexual contact with her professor or supervisor before receiving her doctoral degree.[85]

A disturbing view of this psychiatric sexual permissiveness comes from a group calling itself the Rene Guyon Society. Guyon, a judge on the Supreme Court of Thailand for thirty years, authored books and papers on human sexuality, including that of children.[86] The society says it has 5,000 supporters including "psychiatrists, parents, physicians, singles" and claims to be "A Voice of 20th Century Child (and Adult) Psychiatry."[87]

They claim that Freud suggested in 1897 that "children should have heterosexual experiences at the very early ages of four, five and six." Their motto is: "Sex before eight, or else it's too late."[88]

Clifford Linedecker, author of *Children in Chains*, tells us, "The society is family oriented, and counseling is offered to reluctant wives and mothers who have doubts about their young children becoming sexually active."[89]

The group lobbies for changes in legislation for such areas as kiddie porn and statutory rape, and urges that "laws be altered so that children are encouraged to have sexual relations with each other and with adults as early as possible."[90]

IN THE EYE OF THE BEHOLDER

The public's view of the psychiatric profession has always been a source of anguish to mental health professionals. APA president Karl Bowman commented in 1946, "Unfortunately, the public is obsessed with the idea that large numbers of persons who are not mentally sick are being railroaded to mental hospitals by designing relatives and friends who seek to 'put them away,' and that only a strenuous fight against commitment can save them from unjust imprisonment in a mental institution."[91]

Two years later, APA president Winfred Overholser lamented, "There has been an outpouring of books, with scenes purportedly laid in mental hospitals, some of which have depicted in lurid terms the alleged horrors of such institutions. Several motion pictures, wholly misrepresentative of psychiatric facts, have achieved more or less notoriety. There has been a large amount of sensational material in journals of varying degrees of responsibility."

He later added, "There are great possibilities for psychiatric advance, but there are likewise resistances, fears, and readiness in some quarters to exploit our differences and disagreements, forces which may prove disruptive and which may retard psychiatric progress."[92]

A survey of APA presidential speeches over the past half century shows that the profession is acutely aware of the public disdain it has generated. The subject comes up frequently.

A sampling:

"How can we deny," Dr. Harvey Tomkins asked the membership in 1967, "that there is rampant in our society an element of distrust of our intentions and practices as physicians, reflective of many images that must discomfit us if for no other reason than that they are so widespread?"[93]

In 1975, president John Speigel remarked, "Although it is difficult to define, I have chosen to call it a sense of contempt toward the mental health enterprise, radiating vaguely from a variety of quarters." He spoke of the "harsh questioning of the scientific basis of our professional expertise.... Is not the whole enterprise [psychiatry] more of an illusion—a successful public relations effort, perhaps, but certainly not the practical and effective application of a body of scientifically certifiable findings or theories?"[94]

And in September, 1993, 150 years after the founding of the Association, the problem of public repute remained at psychiatry's doorstep.

"Twelve months ago," said APA head Joseph English, echoing his predecessors, "I promised that we would develop a strategic plan to improve the public image of psychiatry."[95]

The problem of public esteem existed even as far back (and earlier, actually) as the time of Benjamin Rush, the father of American psychiatry at the beginning of the nineteenth century. Along with some American presidents, Rush has the dubious distinction of being one of the few men in history to have a periodical published in his name—with the purpose of speaking out against him and his works. William Cobbett wrote *The Rush-Light*, a publication which achieved considerable popularity in Philadelphia. So intensely did he oppose Rush that even after the doctor sued Cobbett and virtually bankrupted him, the man moved to another state and continued his public writings.

One of Rush's modern-day biographers, Dr. Carl Binger, wrote, "The doubts that Cobbett cast on Rush's claims for his methods were, as matters of fact, justifiable. Indeed, in the long run, they probably helped discredit a system of medicine that time has not sustained. Cobbett claimed to have established mathematically that Rush had killed more patients than he had cured."[96]

Historically, psychiatrists have even had trouble gaining the respect and agreement of their own kind. What APA president Bowman called, a half century ago, "many differences of opinion in psychiatry" and "some fairly fundamental differences among ourselves"[97] are even more evident today. A casual review of any bookstore section on psychology demonstrates what experts have called "a bewildering rat-maze of conflicting schools, theories, rationales, methods and techniques,"[98] "diverse, competing, and often mutually exclusive beliefs and practices,"[99] and "the disconcerting fact that psychiatric theories are nearly as numerous and varied as psychiatric symptoms."[100]

Dr. Walter Fisher was Assistant Superintendent of the Elgin State Hospital in Illinois when he wrote, "The field of mental health is highly subjective, capricious, and dominated by whims, mythologies, and public relations. In many ways it is a pop culture with endless fads but with no real substance."[101]

Psychologist Carl Rogers concurs: "Therapists are not in agreement as to their goals or aims.... They are not in agreement as to what constitutes a successful outcome of their work. They cannot agree as to what constitutes a failure. It seems as though the field is completely chaotic and divided."[102]

Few people know that when the Ralph Nader Group investigated the American community mental health system in the 1970s, they even questioned the validity of psychiatry itself. They asked of the National Institute of Mental Health, "How do they know that what they [psychiatrists] do does anyone any good?". It was, to say the least, a discomfiting question. As the group reported, they raised "issues that have been too long ignored by psychiatry. Furthermore, the very lack of response we have received to these questions indicates that many psychiatric claims to 'expertise' are based on *imputed* knowledge and *assumed* effectiveness rather than on factual evidence."[103]

It is, therefore, not surprising that psychiatrists still feel under critical public scrutiny.

Psychiatrist Brian Doyle bemoaned in a 1987 article in *Psychiatric Annals* that "lay people and medical professionals alike tend to assume that psychiatrists are at high risk for impairment: mental illness, alcoholism, drug abuse, and suicide. People often react with anxiety and hostility when a psychiatrist identifies himself as such in a social gathering. The depiction of psychiatrists is usually unflattering in the media. In movies, for example, more psychiatrists are 'Dr. Dippy,' (ineffectual, crazy, ridiculous) or 'Dr. Evil' (powerful, malignant, destructive) than are 'Dr. Wonderful' (perceptive, empathetic, healing). It is the same in medical circles; today's medical students face the same denigration of psychiatry and its practitioners as was true a generation ago. Ostensibly meaning to compliment an individual psychiatrist, fellow physicians may refer to him or her as 'the only sane psychiatrist I know.'"[104]

Interestingly, the Hippocratic Oath speaks of these matters we have touched upon: damaging treatments, harmful drugs, and other improprieties.

The venerable creed is, as well, quite clear on how a doctor earns—or loses—his public respect:

"I swear... I will use treatment to help the sick according to my ability and judgment, but never with a view to injury and wrongdoing. Neither will I administer a poison to anybody when asked to do so, nor will I suggest such a course.... But I will keep pure and holy both my life and my art.... Into whatsoever houses I enter, I will enter to help the sick, and I will abstain from all intentional wrongdoing and harm, especially from abusing the bodies of man or woman....

"Now if I carry out this oath and break it not, may I gain forever reputation among all men for my life and for my art; but if I transgress it and forswear myself, may the opposite befall me."[105]

BEHIND THE WIZARD'S SMOKE

It would seem that behind the wizard's smoke is very little substance.

Yet the media message and marketing gospel would have us believe the wizard is all-knowing and works wondrous magic with his insight into the mysteries of life.

Undoubtedly a great many mental health professionals are paving this road with good intentions. But how much harm does this do to millions of unsuspecting children and adults who look to these self-proclaimed experts for help?

What is it doing to our justice system, our schools, our homes?

And how many lives have been changed for the worse by people heeding the advice of healers who—though they may mean well—by statistics, are themselves *less capable of dealing with life than the average man in the streets?*

Perhaps the public's gut suspicions about psychiatry are not so far off, after all.

CHAPTER III

FROM LUNATIC ASYLUMS TO LIVING ROOMS

SINCE THE FIRST EYEBROW WAS RAISED AT THE SIGHT OF ERRATIC behavior, society has had to deal with the problem of the madman. And it *is* a problem. Anyone who thinks otherwise has never lived around insane people or had his life disrupted by their actions.

They destroy in the name of some imagined wrong, they refuse to maintain their physical needs and, even if they simply mope, their presence almost inevitably makes life miserable for those around them.

Most families feel considerable relief when they "put away" the son, daughter or relative who has been screaming obscenities day and night or who believes all are poisoning him.

For this reason, mothers, fathers, and others at wit's end have welcomed psychiatric services with open arms over the past two centuries. Why wouldn't they? *Any* offer to remove insanity from one's midst sounds good when one is pressed to the limit of his emotional or financial resources.

This has been the foremost function of psychiatry since its inception—to remove the mentally disturbed from streets and shaken homes so the functioning majority can get on with the business of living.

THE EARLY YEARS

Before psychiatrists came on the scene in the early 1800s, the only public handling of the insane was to put them in an almshouse (the "poor-house"), where they lived in sordid conditions.

In Williamsburg, Virginia, back in 1773, the first American state-supported (colony-supported, actually) institution was established for "Ideots, Lunatics, and other persons of unsound Minds."[1]

This was, of course, not the first insane asylum in the world. The infamous Bedlam of London was created in the thirteenth century, and Europe had its share of such sanitariums long before their appearance in the U.S.

In the early 1800s, the American states gradually began erecting their own institutions, beginning with Kentucky in 1824.

During this era, the pioneering American "expert" on the insane and how to treat them was the aforementioned Dr. Benjamin Rush. His *Medical Inquiries and Observations upon the Diseases of the Mind*, published in 1812, was the first such publication in the United States. In fact, Rush is so well recognized as the father of American psychiatry that today his likeness adorns the seal of the American Psychiatric Association.

The doctor's treatments included spinning patients for extended periods, alternating hot and cold baths, deliberately terrifying the person by dropping him into frigid water, and other methods of threat, deceit, and coercion. "The deception," he said, "would be a justifiable one if it served to cure him of his disease."[2] Only by allowing the doctor full control over the patient, he believed, could madness be cured.[3]

Another treatment forced the patient to remain standing for "four and twenty hours." Why? "The debility thus induced in those muscles would attract morbid excitement from the brain, and thereby relieve the disease."[4]

Rush's primary theory was that mental derangement occurs because the brain is "overcharged" with blood ("the cause of madness is seated primarily in the blood vessels of the brain"); he advocated bleeding the body to the point of debility to relieve the "excessive action" in the patient's brain. An average of twenty to forty ounces of blood was let per treatment.[5]

Bloodletting *was* effective. Needless to say, if one bleeds a patient long enough, his "excessive action" will decline.

Another of the doctor's beliefs was that resentment and mortification could be used to trick patients into letting go of their delusions. He "proved" this theory with a patient who thought of himself as a plant. The man was told that because he was a plant he would not live without being watered. But when he thought he was being treated with water from a teapot, in reality a friend was urinating on his head. When the patient learned the truth, according to Rush's story, his shock and resentment cured him.[6]

But Benjamin Rush's most remarkable hypothesis of all may well be his theory of "negritude"—that black skin was brought about by disease and that the sick Negro should be white. "However well they appear to be satisfied with their color," he remarked, "there are many proofs of their preferring that of the white people."[7]

Perhaps the most amazing fact about Benjamin Rush is that, despite what one medical scholar calls "his consummate ability to fool himself consistently," which "helped to kill an unmeasured plenty of his patients in Philadelphia,"[8]—despite this, he was still regarded by many as *the* authority of his day. A goodly number of well-educated Americans believed him implicitly because he "wrote the book" and presented himself as the authority in the treatment of madness.

Which brings up the question of how many of today's "most modern" psychiatric theories and treatments will find themselves in the dustbin of history alongside bloodletting and negritude?

The experiments of Rush and his cohorts notwithstanding, the primary function of psychiatry in the nineteenth century was to house the insane. And this it did, commonly without any treatment at all.

THE TWENTIETH CENTURY: PSYCHIATRY MUSHROOMS

"To the man who wants to use a hammer badly," wrote Mark Twain, "a lot of things look like nails that need hammering."

Toward the end of the nineteenth century, with the materialist philosophy painting its new view of human behavior, psychiatry began to turn its eye from the maintenance of the insane to the *prevention* and *eradication* of insanity. Several agendas began to take shape, notably the Freudian movement, Eugenics, and the Mental Hygiene movement.

Convinced of the scientific rightness of their views, leading voices of the profession saw a multitude of nails that needed hammering.

Through proper social engineering under their direction, some thought they could rid the world of the nightmare of not only madness but many other maladies they felt needed rectifying.

Yet even though all of these agendas ultimately failed, each drive served to propagate psychiatric theories and numbers around the world, laying the groundwork for a growing psychiatric community.

And each left its own peculiar view of humanity imprinted on an unsuspecting populace.

Today we find our thinking—rightly or wrongly—riddled with many of the principles popularized by these movements.

FREUD

One agendum was Freudian theory which developed in the 1890s and became a movement not long after the turn of the century. A great number of Sigmund Freud's followers took up the banner of aid to humanity and vowed to rid the world of neuroses through the application of Freudian principles. The social implications of the Vienna doctor's theories were not small. Disseminated broadly in their heyday, they called for radical permissiveness in sexual mores and child rearing, and left parents in constant worry of unwittingly perpetrating untold psychological harm upon their children.

To this day, thanks to the large-scale Freudian indoctrination of teachers, doctors, social workers, and others, many a mother and father is filled with dread, fearing irreparable mental damage, whenever some minor or major trauma strikes their child. Even though one former American Psychiatric Association president, Alfred Freedman, echoed the feelings of many when he said, "It is possible that Freudian theory may be proven no more scientific than astrology or phrenology,"[9] the layman has little inkling that his odd notions of sex and raising children are even remotely Freud-related. He simply knows he learned them somewhere.

When lawyers turn to "childhood trauma" as a defense for criminality, it is *assumed* that the jury and the public will understand this: "everybody knows" that psychological damage comes from one's childhood.

And this is only one element of Freud's legacy. There have been many offshoots of his work, due, in part, to the fact that the work itself is open to almost limitless interpretation. Albeit extreme, a sample of Freud's modern-day impact was seen in 1992 when the world—for the first time in a half century—began hearing reports that conjured up specters of Nazi Germany and racial hygiene.

Concentration camps. A thing called "ethnic cleansing." It was all too familiar, except this time it was happening in the former republic of Yugoslavia. Among the three prominent ethnic groups there—Serbs, Moslems, and Croats—the Serbs had embarked on a modern-day campaign of weeding out undesirables. An estimated 110,000 lives were taken and 1.5 million were driven from their homes.

Civilized people across the globe watched in dazed horror. How could this happen in the Europe of today?

What few knew is that there was a specific driving force behind the savagery. In 1990, Serbian psychiatrist Jovan Raskovic published his Freudian-based theories on the races of Yugoslavia in *Luda Zemla* (*A Mad Country*). "I noticed that the majority of the Serbian population…exhibited signs of an oedipal personality, which is to say a moderate dose of aggressivity accompanied by submission. The oedipal personality is made up of two parts: one very devoted, expressive of a complete obedience to authority, that is to say to the father who owns the pleasure and has absolute power, and the other part which, in certain situations, destroys this authority through its means of revolting. In the latter case, all who possess power and pleasure would be simply eliminated. Therefore, Serbs by nature possess the qualities of authority with certain aggressive and open elements."

"I have noticed that Muslims are fixated on the anal phase and this phase is characterized by being received, which is part of their character. Their character tends to appropriate things, dominate like a boss, value people by their possessions, their money, their social position, etc."

Croats, according to Raskovic "are fixated on the castration complex." He explains that "the character of castration is closed and hermetic. It is under perpetual influence of fear of castration, losing something that belongs only to himself. The character of castration is afraid of being abused, of being treated without dignity."[10]

In short, in Raskovic's world, which boasted the authority of medical and psychiatric credentials, Serbs are destined leaders and Croats and Muslims are the lesser races. The doctor pushed his book and psychiatric theories heavily throughout the former Yugoslavia as part of a media campaign in which he was hailed as the greatest psychiatrist and scientist of his era.

This is the same man who created the Serbian Democratic Party, whose members instigated hostilities in the republic of Croatia. Remarkably, or perhaps not, the three most senior officials of that political party were his patients.

The psychiatrist organized numerous meetings at which he addressed the Serbs, inflaming passions against the Croats and Muslims. While the reader who has heard nothing of this aspect of the turmoil in the former Yugoslavia may doubt the importance of the part this man played, he had no such doubts. In a chilling statement on Belgrade television—published in the *Vreme* and *Vjeskik* newspapers on January 24, 1992—Raskovic proclaimed, "I feel responsible because I made the preparations for this war, even if not the military preparations. If I hadn't created this emotional strain in the Serbian people, nothing would have happened.

"My party and I lit the fuse of Serbian nationalism not only in Croatia but everywhere else in Bosnia-Herzegovina.... We have driven this people and we have given it an identity. I have repeated again and again to this people that it comes from heaven, not earth."[11]

Unfortunately, Raskovic's death in 1992 did little to defuse the racial hatred he had fanned with his alleged scientific claims. With Raskovic's help, his student, psychiatrist Radovan Karadzic, attained political power and carried on the genocide.

These psychiatric roots of the "ethnic cleansing" program in the former Yugoslavia have tended to remain hidden from public knowledge. It is perhaps all too easy, in the confusion of war, to simply blame such brutality on man's darker side.

But let's not be naive.

This was not the first time that psychiatric ideology was the driving force behind such acts against humanity.

THE EUGENICS AGENDA

A major psychiatric campaign of the early twentieth century came from the eugenics movement. Given the materialist atmosphere of the time— the view that Man is essentially an animal—it is not surprising that eugenics, the control of human breeding for optimum offspring, would become popular.

Psychologist G. Stanley Hall, a Wundt student, was one early and influential U.S. adherent of eugenic principles. Biographer, David Hothersall, tells us, "Given Hall's theoretical position we should not be surprised that he was interested in eugenics. He was in fact an enthusiastic proponent of eugenic controls and left money in his estate to establish a chair of genetic psychology at Clark University. Hall was a firm believer in 'higher' and 'lower' human races. He believed the Negro race to be at an early stage of human development, and dependent upon the 'higher,' more advanced white race for its development and supervision."[12]

The word *eugenics* was coined in the late 1800s by Francis Galton, an English psychologist, and half-cousin to Charles Darwin, the man who formulated the Theory of Evolution. Clearly, Darwin himself set the stage for the basic tenets of eugenics: "With savages, the weak in body or mind are soon eliminated; and those that survive commonly exhibit a vigorous state of health. We civilized men, on the other hand, do our utmost to check the process of elimination; we build asylums for the imbecile, the maimed, and the sick; we institute poor-laws; and our medical men exert their utmost skill to save the life of every one to the last moment. There is reason to believe that vaccination has preserved thousands, who from a weak constitution would formerly have succumbed to smallpox. Thus the weak members of civilized societies propagate their kind. No one who has attended the breeding of domestic animals will doubt that this must be highly injurious to the race of man. It is surprising how soon a want of care, or care wrongly directed, leads to the degeneration of a domestic race; but excepting in the case of man himself, hardly any one is so ignorant as to allow his worst animals to breed."[13]

One reviewer of Galton notes: "Galton extended Darwin's theory of natural selection into a concept of deliberate social intervention, which he held to be the logical application of evolution to the human race. Galton was by no means satisfied to let evolution take its course freely. Having decided to improve the human race through selective breeding, brought about through social intervention, he developed a subject which he called 'Eugenics,' the principle of which was that by encouraging better human stock to breed and discouraging the reproduction of less desirable stock, the whole race could be improved."[14]

Galton's view of Jews: "The Jews are specialized for a *parasitical* existence upon other nations."[15]

Galton on blacks: "The average intellectual standard of the negro is some two grades below our own."[16]

This psychologist's eugenic concepts sat well with many psychiatrists of the day who were frustrated by a century of failure in the treatment and understanding of insanity. Now hereditary factors could be blamed. And it didn't take a genius to figure out that something could be done about breeding.

Virtually synonymous with similar movements of the time such as Social Darwinism and Racial Hygiene, Eugenics became the leading psychiatric agenda of the day. In 1897, Dr. M. W. Barr, president of the American Association for the Study of Feeblemindedness, strongly advocated sterilization as a eugenics measure.[17]

And, in the early twentieth century, psychiatrist Edwin Katzen-Ellenbogen, who was ultimately convicted of war crimes committed as a doctor at Buchenwald Concentration Camp, "drafted for the governor the law for sterilization of epileptics, criminals and incurably insane for the state of New Jersey."[18] Other states—22 in all—followed suit with similar laws. (It is interesting to note that, at the time of this writing, sterilization is being strenuously promoted in South Africa as *the* solution to population control.)

German authors Drs. Hans Georg Guse and N. Schmake tell us that Emil Kraepelin "had adopted the central thesis of Social Darwinism, whereby a person's social rank is the expression of a natural allotment of qualities and abilities.... Kraepelin began to then consider the mentally handicapped as 'a heavy burden for our nation.' Along with many other academics, he saw the solution to social disorder in a strong leader: 'An unrestricted ruler with the power to intervene in our way of life would bring about the reduction in insanity within a few decades!' Kraepelin supported the idea of sterilization for certain psychopaths, maintaining that the passing on of inferior hereditary traits would thus be avoided."[19]

In 1914, the head of the American Medico-Psychological Association —today known as the American Psychiatric Association—said in his presidential address: "That a radical cure of the evils incident to the dependent mentally defective classes would be effected if every feeble-minded person, every imbecile, every habitual criminal, every manifestly weak-minded person, and every confirmed inebriate were sterilized, is a self-evident proposition. By this means we could practically, if not absolutely, arrest, in a decade or two, the reproduction of mentally defective persons, as surely as we could stamp out smallpox absolutely if every person in the world could be vaccinated."[20]

Although this covered a wide field of people indeed, this was no isolated sentiment. In 1916, Lewis M. Terman, professor of psychology at Stanford University warned, "if we would preserve our state for a class of people worthy to possess it, we must prevent, as far as possible, the propagation of mental degenerates."[21]

Alfred Hoche, a professor of psychiatry, and Karl Binding, a German jurist and retired professor from Wundt's alma mater, the University of Leipzig, published *The Release of the Destruction of Life Devoid of Value* in Leipzig in 1920. It went a step further than the recommendation of mere sterilization. It advocated the outright killing of mental defectives, "euthanasia" as it was called: "For the idiots...the continuation of life for society as well as for the person himself has no value."[22]

By 1922 at a psychiatric congress in Dresden, Germany, a proposal was put forth requesting legalization of euthanasia.

The psychiatric social experiment called Eugenics had embarked on a road from which there was no turning back.

Another up-and-coming man threw his support behind the eugenics movement in 1925. "Those who are physically and mentally unhealthy and unworthy must not perpetuate their suffering in the body of their children," he wrote, advocating the sterilization of defectives.[23] But even this man, Adolf Hitler, did not yet endorse their killing, as did psychiatrists such as Hoche.

In 1933, when Hitler came to power he implemented the Nazi Act for Averting Descendants Afflicted with Hereditary Diseases. It authorized sterilization of the unfit. Within six years, 375,000 forced sterilizations were performed, over 300,000 on so-called mental defectives such as the feeble-minded, schizophrenics, and alcoholics.[24]

The chief architect of this law was not Hitler, but the world-renowned Dr. Ernst Rüdin, Professor of Psychiatry at Munich University. Rüdin, a co-founder of the Society for Racial Hygiene and friend of Emil Kraepelin, was honored on his sixty-fifth birthday by fellow racial hygienist, Dr. Alfred Ploetz, who lauded Rüdin thusly: "Just recently he received the Goethe Medal for the Art and Science from the Fuhrer 'in recognition of his achievements in the development of German Racial Hygiene.' The Reichsminister of the Interior Dr. Frick sent him the following telegram: 'To the indefatigable champion of racial hygiene and meritorious pioneer of the racial hygienic measures of the Third Reich I send my sincerest congratulations on his 65th birthday.'"[25]

Hitler was considered an invaluable ally, and "The magazine of the Eugenic and Racial Hygiene Society welcomed Hitler's accession to power as a major gain for them, as he was so much in accord with their own thinking."[26]

The marriage between psychiatry and Eugenics became all too clear. On July 16, 1933, the German Union for Mental Health changed its name to the German Institute for Mental Health and Racial Hygiene.[27]

In 1938, another player entered the stage. Dr. Werner Catel, Professor of Neurology and Psychiatry at the University of Leipzig, suggested to the father of a deformed child that the man write to the Fuhrer and seek permission to end his child's life. In response, Hitler sent his personal physician, Professor Karl Brandt, to discuss the matter with Catel. As author of the book *Border Situations of Life—Contribution to the Problem of a Limited Euthanasia*, Catel must have had much to say on the subject.

The child, of course, was killed. But it was only the beginning.

"DELIVER THOSE YOU CANNOT HEAL"

Shortly after this meeting, a group of physicians were called to the Reich Chancellory to form a Euthanasia Committee. Dr. Herbert Linden, psychiatrist and ministerial advisor for health in the Reich Ministry, was appointed its director. Of the four other doctors on the committee, two were psychiatrists, including the influential Dr. Catel. Shortly, another seven psychiatrists were added.

In 1939, the following document was signed and released by Hitler: "Reichleader [Philipp] Bouhler and Dr. Brandt, M.D. are charged with the responsibility of enlarging the authority of certain physicians to be designated by name in such a manner that persons who according to human judgment can upon most careful diagnosis of their condition of sickness be accorded a mercy death."[28]

World War II journalist Joseph Harsch gives us further insight into the document in his book, *Pattern for Conquest*. "Those who proposed it (the plan for euthanasia) are understood to have asked Hitler for a written edict, or law which would officially authorize them to proceed with the 'mercy killings.' Hitler is represented as having hesitated for several weeks. Finally, doubting that Hitler would ever sign the official order, the proponents of the project drafted a letter for him to sign which merely expressed his, Hitler's, general approval of the theory of euthanasia as a means of relieving incompetents of the burden of life. While this letter did not have the character of law, it was adequate in Nazi Germany. The Fuhrer had expressed approval of the practice. It went ahead."[29]

According to the 1991 documentary film *Selling Murder*, in October of 1939, a film was made entitled *Dasein ohne Leben* or *Existence Without Life*. The main character was a professor—used "to add spurious scientific respectability" to the film. The documentary explains, "The [film's] script demands that demonically mad faces arise like a specter out of the scene.... Unedited film shows the techniques used such as sharp underneath lighting to make the patients appear grotesque.... His [the professor's] lecture, scripted by psychiatrists... first claims that care for the sick has become indiscriminate and too costly."

The professor closes the movie with a dramatic appeal to all: "We call upon a merciful destiny to liberate these regrettable creatures from their existence without life.... Allow me to close with a few purely human and personal remarks and so to extend the framework of this lecture. If I knew that I—and this could happen to anyone—would be struck down by the disaster of some incurable mental illness and that such an existence without life would lie before me, I would do anything for this not to happen. I would rather die. I am convinced all healthy people think like this. But I am also convinced that every incurable mental patient or idiot if he could recognize his position would prefer an end to such an existence. No sensible human being could deny him the right to die. Is it not the duty of those who care for the incapable—and that means total idiots and the incurable mental patients—to help them exercise their rights? Is that not a sacred demand of charity? Deliver those you cannot heal!"[30]

But truth be known, the mercy killings had already begun.

Earlier that year, Project T4, named after the address of its headquarters on Tiergartenstrasse 4, had been implemented by Third Reich physicians. It was called the Euthanasia Program. *Selling Murder* tells us, "To carry out the killings, enthusiastic and politically reliable psychiatrists, doctors, nurses, and orderlies were recruited."[31]

THE EVER-SMOKING CHIMNEYS

What followed—the murder of 275,000 mental patients from 1939 to 1945, according to data from the Nuremberg Trials—has been documented in graphic detail in numerous texts. Jews and other racial "undesireables" were next. "The systematic 'treatment' of Jews under T4 began in April, 1940, with a proclamation from the Reich Interior Ministry that within three weeks all Jewish patients were to be registered. In June the first gassing of Jews took place: 200 men, women, and children were killed in the Brandenburg facility; they had been transported to the killing center in six buses from the Berlin-Buch mental institution."[32]

Patients sent to killing institutions were told to take showers in specially-built rooms designed with false shower heads. Carbon monoxide was pumped in until all were dead. The bodies were commonly burned in near-by furnaces, a fact that caused some nearby suspicious townspeople to protest about the ever-smoking chimneys.

Some of the murders were carried out through gradual overdosing or slow starvation.

One writer notes: "In the fall of 1939 a group of psychology students were given a tour of the state psychiatric institution Eglfing-Haar in Nazi Germany. Dr. Pfannmüller, a psychiatrist and director of the institution, explained the 'euthanasia' or 'mercy killing' program that was being used on the inmates. In the children's ward twenty-five children were being starved to death. They ranged in age from one to five years. Pfannmüller lifted up one emaciated child who was near death and told the students that food is withdrawn gradually, not all at once. 'With this child,' he said, 'it will take another two or three days.'"[33]

Ludwig Lehner, one of the students and later a prisoner of war, said in a sworn statement at the Nuremberg War Crimes Trials, "I shall never forget the look of that fat, grinning fellow with the whimpering little skeleton in his fleshy hand, surrounded by the other starving children."[34]

Dr. Fredric Wertham wrote in his book, *A Sign for Cain: An Exploration of Human Violence*: "It has been stated that the psychiatrists were merely following a law or were being forced to obey an order. Again and again we read—as if it were historical fact—of Hitler's secret order to exterminate those suffering from severe mental defect or disease.... There was no law and no such order. The tragedy is that the psychiatrists did not have to have an order. They acted on their own. They were not carrying out a death sentence pronounced by somebody else. They were the legislators who laid down the rules for deciding who was to die; they were the administrators who worked out the procedures, provided the patients and places, and decided the methods of killing; they pronounced a sentence of life or death in every individual case; they were the executioners who carried the sentences out or—without being coerced to do so—surrendered their patients to be killed in other institutions; they supervised and often watched the slow deaths."[35]

Wertham, himself a psychiatrist, reiterated how the doctors of T4 quickly expanded the euthanasia program to include others "unworthy of life": "By the middle of 1941, at least four of the death hospitals in Germany and Austria not only killed patients but became regular murder schools.... They gave a comprehensive course in lethal institutional psychiatry. Personnel were trained in the methods of assembly-line killing. They were taught the mass-killing techniques, 'gassing,' cremation, and so on. It was called basic training in 'mercy killing.' The 'material' for all this training was mental hospital patients. On them the methods were tried out and tested before they were applied later to Jewish and other civilian populations of the occupied countries. Technical experience first gained with killing psychiatric patients was utilized later for the destruction of millions."

The now-experienced murderers moved on to new pastures. "Toward the end of 1941 the gas chambers in the death institutions were dismantled, transported to the east, and there freshly erected for their new tasks in concentration camps.... Some of the same psychiatrists who selected patients in hospitals went to concentration camps and selected death candidates there. Himmler had the idea of having the inmates of these camps examined 'to comb out' those to be eliminated. He needed suitable physicians. So the central bureau of the 'euthanasia' program supplied him with 'experienced psychiatrists.'... In 1941 a commission of five went to the concentration camp Dachau to select prisoners to be transferred to Mauthausen to be killed. All five men were psychiatrists, and their chief was a professor of psychiatry of the University of Berlin."[36]

This psychiatric plan for a better world—Eugenics...Racial Hygiene ...the Euthanasia Program...T4—took on a new name.

The future would call it the Holocaust.

Although it is commonly held that Adolf Hitler is responsible for this blood-spattered chapter of human history and the snuffing out of millions of lives, the facts are he did not originate the idea of killing off undesirables nor did he initially order it or plan its execution.

It also was not done by faceless Nazi generals and soldiers with swastikaed sleeves.

It was done, in fact, by psychiatrists, implementing their ideas on how to improve life for all.

THE LEGACY CONTINUES

It seems logical to assume that once the consequences and horror of T4 came to light, it—and its alleged scientific premise —would be universally condemned. But not so.

Shortly after the war, in October 1945, prominent Canadian psychiatrist, G. Brock Chisholm said in a speech, "...it would indeed be good for the race to prevent future wars. It would seem to be true that, whatever the destiny of the race, the killing off of large numbers of its physically fit, intelligent and socially minded younger men can hardly be advantageous. A case might be made for wars if they could be fought by the old men and the mental defectives but that does not seem to be even a remote possibility.... Any country could be paralysed and destroyed at leisure by a well organized attack.... This can hardly possibly be a useful procedure from a racial point of view unless conceivably it could serve to reduce population pressures in some parts of the world. This end could surely be attained, however, in less painful ways and with better selection...."[37]

He also said, "Clear and honest thinking can almost always be expressed in simple words which are understandable by the *people who matter* in a democracy." (Emphasis added.)[38]

The speech was endorsed by the Under Secretary of the Interior of the United States, who referred to Chisholm as "that extraordinary creature: a man of maturity."[39] The evening after the speech, Chisholm met in a panel discussion with the U.S. Secretary of Commerce, the Federal Security Administrator, the Deputy Director of War Mobilization and Reconversion, and psychiatrist Dr. Daniel Blain, the future Medical Director and PR man for the American Psychiatric Association.

Chisholm went on to head up the formation of the World Health Organization (WHO) in 1946 and serve as its director general for five years. One of his assistants at WHO said, "From its inception this agency has borne the impress of this man's personality and skills."[40] Chisholm then served as the president of the World Federation for Mental Health in the 1950s—one of the "non-governmental organizations in official relations with WHO."[41]

As an aside, this is the same man who, while serving as Canada's Deputy Minister of Health and Welfare in 1945, told an Ottawa audience "that any child who believes in Santa Claus has had his ability to think permanently injured."[42]

Chisholm was not the only man to carry the philosophical torch of T4 out of the ashes of the Third Reich. In 1951, Dr. C.P. Blacker, who ultimately became the chairman of the Eugenics Society in England, remarked of the German Euthanasia Program, "These people were mercifully killed. The idea of merciful killing is not unknown in this country; in fact, a society on a voluntary basis…exists to promote it."[43]

1965 saw the publication of *Euthanasia and Destruction of Life Devoid of Value* by a man who became professor of forensic and social psychiatry at the University of Marburg in Germany. The book speaks of the "comparatively few mental patients" killed by T4. It was touted as highly recommended reading by an American psychiatric journal at the time.[44]

In 1982, author Lenny Lapon interviewed American psychiatrist Gisela Ebert Fleischmann, who had been a medical student in Nazi Germany. In a few sentences, Fleischmann reveals how the T4 banner of "hereditary mental illness" is the same flag psychiatry is waving today:

Lapon: "That's what happened. Karl Brandt and Viktor Brack admitted at Nuremberg that they killed 60,000 and they probably killed five times that many."

Fleischmann: "This was all based on inheritance and so on. Inferior genetic material had to be eliminated. So you know the story. That's how they did it."

Lapon: "What do you think of genetics?"

Fleischmann: "Well, of course, now it's popular again. For a while, research was at a minimum because of Nazi Germany. Everybody was afraid to do research...."[45]

As a final note on the Eugenics agenda, on February 20, 1994, the *Los Angeles Times* flashed the following headline on its front page: "Genetics, Not Parenting, Key to Temperament, Studies Say." A century after Galton we find the drum still beating for Eugenics. Couched in the seemingly unimpeachable terms of "scientists," "geneticists," and "mapping the brain wave," we are informed that "exposure to warm and loving parents will not make a shy child less and less shy; nor will exposure to highly active parents make an inactive child more and more active."

On the surface it looks like incontrovertible evidence. It is only in passing that the article tells us, "...none of the researchers has found any direct genetic link to human behavior...."[46]

While geneticists have made great progress in the understanding of hereditary *physical* defects, the truth is that after more than a century of study, human and social experimentation, and millions spent on research, there is no hard evidence that Eugenics and its modern-day counterparts have any scientific merit.

There is, however, abundant proof that they have brought much misery to man.

Yet many in the psychiatric profession continue to disseminate them to the world as though they were proven and foregone conclusions.

THE MENTAL HYGIENE MOVEMENT

Paralleling the Eugenics crusade was another psychiatric vehicle known as the Mental Hygiene movement.

This drive marks the point in history when psychiatry laid its claim as the authority on human behavior in everyday living. Prior to this, members of the profession dealt fairly exclusively with the insane. Their new claim as experts on the common man's mind did not come about, however, because of any discoveries by the psychiatric community. There were no scientific breakthroughs behind it. It was simply agreed upon that someone should teach the world how to live properly and psychiatry—believing it had superior knowledge to that of the layman—elected itself to the task.

Prior to this, the problems of life were solved with common sense or through traditional values—distillations of centuries of wisdom—that had served humanity not perfectly perhaps, but well.

The genesis of the Mental Hygiene movement is usually told as follows: In 1908, Clifford Beers, a former mental patient, wrote the sordid story of his incarceration in a book entitled *A Mind That Found Itself.* The book was so well received that Beers went on to found the National Committee for Mental Hygiene, an organization formed to assist the cause of the mentally disturbed as well as promote the prevention of mental illness.

But there is more to the story. Before Beers published the book, he sent the manuscript to the Father of American Psychology, William James. James endorsed it wholeheartedly. And, "Armed with William James' support, he went to talk to psychiatrists, neurologists, social workers and social-minded laymen." [47]

In September, 1907, he took the manuscript to well-known psychiatrist Adolf Meyer. A member of the Eugenics Society, Meyer had been a student of Alfred Hoche, co-author of *The Release of the Destruction of Life Devoid of Value*, the book promoting the killing of mental defectives. He also studied under Swiss psychiatrist August Forel, "whose influence on the young student was great," according to one biographer. [48] An example of Forel's views: "Even for their own good the blacks must be treated as what they are, an absolutely subordinate, inferior, lower type of men, incapable themselves of culture. That must once and for all be clearly stated." [49]

We are told by psychiatric historian Robin McKown that until Clifford Beers went to Meyer, Beers' plan to help the mentally ill was a "nebulous project."

"On one thing Meyer was heartily in accord with the younger man. There was a desperate need for an organized program to deal with all the problems connected with mental illness, both for the individual patient and for the community. Meyer had for a long time been thinking along similar lines himself. In his own mind it seemed to him this 'sensitized layman,'…was an excellent person to whom to entrust the organization of such a program. Within a few days he had given Clifford a name for his movement—the committee of 'mental hygiene.'

Beers delayed publication [of his book] until Dr. Meyer had time to correct certain errors."[50]

In 1909, the National Committee for Mental Hygiene was formed, with Beers as its head. Adolf Meyer and William James were among the original twelve charter members.

James' role was not small. In a biography by Clarence Karier we are told: "James was not only a theoretical conceptualizer of the therapeutic society but also an active historical actor, helping to shape its development. Late in life (1909), as an executive committee member of the National Committee for Mental Hygiene, he wrote to John D. Rockefeller and 'begged' him for a million dollars to support the efforts of the National Committee for Mental Hygiene. Sending along a copy of Clifford W. Beers' *A Mind that Found Itself*, James tried to interest Rockefeller in broadly supporting the emerging mental health movement. As he put it, 'if I myself, by Heaven's grace, should ever be able to leave any money for public use it should be for "Insanity" exclusively.'

"Shortly thereafter, the foundations under Rockefeller's influence began to pour millions of dollars into the mental hygiene movement, into the development and construction of psychopathic hospitals, and into the training of psychiatrists, psychologists, and mental health workers in a variety of institutions across the country. In this and other ways, James was actively involved in the practical work of creating the institutional framework through which the therapeutic society came into existence."[51]

French psychiatrist Robert Castel co-authored a history covering the early days of the movement: "From the outset, it [the Committee] sponsored studies that looked beyond a narrowly defined notion of insanity. Thus the first such study, carried out in a Baltimore school in 1913, purported to show that 10 percent of the school children were in need of psychiatric assistance. Pilot programs were also begun at Sing Sing prison. The upshot of this research was that psychiatric departments were established in the juvenile courts and the prisons."

Thus psychiatry entered the justice system. Next, Castel explains how it insinuated itself into family life. "The differences between the mental hygiene movement and traditional psychiatry grew more pronounced in the postwar years. The movement took a particular interest in children's problems [Meyer's area of interest] and played a leading role in the child guidance movement, which first flourished in the twenties.... As one official of the movement put it, 'the [children's] clinic treats these problems by treating not only the child through whom they become manifest, but as well the family, schools, recreational and other involved factors and persons which contribute to the problem, and whose disorder the problem may reflect."[52]

We see, then, how the psychiatric community first elected itself as an authority on the art of living and assumed its right to interfere with school and family for the public good. It issued pamphlets such as "Sex Education," "The Job of a Parent," and "The Problem of Bedwetting."[53] This advice coming from a group that, as we noted in the last chapter, statistically survives less well than the average man in the street.

Castel adds: "Increasingly, then, the mental hygiene movement fostered a shift away from the traditional institutions and methods of psychiatry. In every important area of social life, these were replaced by new methods under the auspices of new kinds of specialists. The change marks the transition from a focus on mental *illness* to a focus on mental *health*, which opened the door to manipulative methods inspired by psychological medicine. Once again, we may cite Adolf Meyer as witness; he summed up his considerable ambitions as follows: 'Mental hygiene as a philosophy of prevention is an ideal and a guiding principle working wherever possible with the assets of life before the differentiation into the "normal" and the "pathological."'"[54]

Dr. Charles Dana expressed this concept even more clearly in 1913, saying the ideal psychiatrist "has not only to be the diagnostician and prescriber of drugs and diet, or surgery and mechanical therapeutics, but he has to be the educator and instructor of his patients.... He must join with the teachers showing how children should be educated and taken care of while they study. He should follow them at the period of their youth and maturity, correct mental faults, advise them as to marrying, even marry them at times and tell them about the management of the children. He must help and uplift the religion of those who have any and give a religion or high and positive ideals to those who have not. He must show them how to live happily and to use with scientific efficiency the forces which nature has given them; which two things are often the same.... It is, in other words, necessary that we now proceed to develop a kind of social and economic neurologist as well as one of clinical and laboratory attainments.... He must be a kind of superman, one with higher ideals, more potent inhibitions and wiser in life and wider in outlook than those whom he is trying to guide."[55]

Another target of the Mental Hygiene movement—reached via social workers—was the poor. (Adolf Meyer's wife is considered to be the first social worker.) Again, Castel tells us about "what Kathleen Woodruff has called the 'psychiatric deluge,' the result of the simultaneous triumph of psychoanalysis and social hygiene.... Social work had lacked a methodology of its own. The 'new psychology' was to provide it with one.... Thus 'moral deficiency' became 'psychological maladjustment' or 'emotional instability': in any case, the idea was that psycho-medical techniques could be applied directly to the treatment of moral deficiencies.... The medical director of the Mental Hygiene movement, Dr. Thomas Salmon, declared that attention must be focused exclusively on the individual, 'first, last, and all the time.'... In short, the problem was not to help the unemployed worker to find a job, but rather to explain psychologically why he had lost his old job and why he could not find a new one."

Thus, Castel says, the psychiatric deluge flowed into familiar moralistic channels. "By the time the crisis hit in the thirties [the Depression], the transition was complete; the public welfare system was staffed by professionals who had been trained (whether for good or ill) in an atmosphere permeated by the ideas of mental hygiene and psychoanalysis for fifteen years. The truth of the matter is that welfare in America has never really recovered from this deluge. Bureaucracy and psychology still dominate the welfare system...."[56]

The Mental Hygiene movement expanded rapidly around the globe, setting up groups in the 1920s in Canada, France, Belgium, England, Bulgaria, Denmark, Hungary, Czechoslovakia, Italy, Russia, Germany, Austria, Switzerland, and Australia. Twenty-four countries had Mental Hygiene Associations by 1930.

The movement not only took it upon itself to solve for people the problems of everyday living, it also joined arm in arm with the Eugenics crusade. As German author Bernard Schreiber reports, "Routinely these [mental hygiene] associations had as their medical specialists psychiatrists who espoused eugenic medicine and lay members who were simultaneously active in the Eugenics Societies which had by this time become very numerous.... From the Annual reports of the National Council for Mental Hygiene one can see many names that are also common in the Eugenics Society." [57]

The Mental Hygiene movement, in fact, drew strongly from the Eugenic Movements of whatever country they were in.

Among these "eugenic hygienists" were such major psychiatric players as Adolf Meyer, Emil Kraepelin, and Ernst Rüdin.

The Mental Hygiene movement was the first to popularize the psychiatric notion that poverty causes crime and that criminals are not responsible for what they do. One doctor wrote, "Children's crimes, regarded as a reflection of slum poverty and 'depravity' of parents, were now found to rest on the basis of neglect, ignorance, and the suppression of normal 'instinctive urges.' The sting of criminal prosecution was replaced by a calm, inquiring attitude seeking for the emotional causes of delinquency. ...From this evolved the essential structure of the child guidance movement.... School problems, phobias, compulsive habits, tics, enuresis [bedwetting], and the myriad troubles that parents expected children to 'outgrow' became the material for analysis and treatment. The Commonwealth Fund, uniting with the National Committee [for Mental Hygiene] proposed a five-year program in 1921 to develop the child guidance movement with the ultimate aim of preventing juvenile delinquency.

"If children commit crimes out of emotional frustration and rejection, was it possible that adult criminals could be approached in the same way?" [58]

With the child guidance movement, psychiatry stepped out of the hospitals and into the kitchens and living rooms of the citizenry. The "problem child" was discovered. Castel tells us, "New methods, mainly relying on outpatient clinics, were developed to deal with the personality 'disorders' of such children. These methods involved such new services as family counseling. The clinics 'deal not so much with definite psychiatric entities as they do with the socially maladjusted who are personally within reasonably normal limits.' [One psychiatrist] listed the following 'behavioral disorders,' all calling for intervention: 'tantrums, stealing, seclusiveness, truancy, cruelty, sensitiveness, restlessness, and fears.' Later the vocabulary took on an increasingly psychoanalytic cast." [59]

Needless to say, the stated goal of preventing juvenile delinquency was never reached. In fact, psychiatrist E. Fuller Torrey remarks, "Despite the proliferation of child guidance clinics and their popularity, no evidence was brought forth to suggest that the clinics prevented mental illness. The idea of preventing such illnesses, in fact, was largely ignored or forgotten during these years, and when it was raised at all it was done so with embarrassment."[60]

Indeed, in 1932, Frankwood E. Williams, the director of the National Committee for Mental Hygiene, confessed, "The basic question with which psychiatrists and particularly those interested in mental hygiene start is—What are the causes of mental and nervous disease? This question has been repeatedly raised during the twenty-two years of organized mental hygiene until it has almost become a ritual and like a ritual has led to nothing except repetition—not even a start."[61]

To gain some idea of how far the Mental Hygiene movement felt it should intrude into the lives of others, consider this statement from future American Psychiatric Association president William A. White at the First International Congress for Mental Hygiene held in Washington, D.C., in 1930:

"Mental Hygiene is on this account alone more important than ever before, and its significance can be seen to be gradually changing from one of the simple prevention of mental disease, which is a negative program, to the positive attitude of finding ways and means for people to live their lives at their best."[62]

Also participating in the First International Congress was psychiatrist Ernst Rüdin, designer of the Nazi sterilization laws that went into effect in Germany three years after the Congress.[63]

The year 1943 marked an event that should have cast some doubt upon the effectiveness of the mental hygiene movement. Clifford Beers— founder of the movement for the prevention of mental illness—died in a mental hospital after having relapsed into a psychosis four years earlier.[64]

However, by the Third International Congress for Mental Hygiene, held in London in 1948, the grandiose societal aspirations had only grown more pronounced. We get some flavor of its plans from this excerpt of its official statement: "The social sciences and psychiatry also offer a better understanding of the great obstacles to rapid progress in human affairs. Man and his society are closely interdependent. Social institutions such as

76

family and school impose their imprint early in the personality development of their members, who, in turn tend to perpetuate the traditional
pattern to which they have been molded. It is the men and women in
whom these patterns of attitude and behavior have been incorporated who
present the immediate resistance to social, economic and political changes."

Still, the statement claimed that this "resistance" could be overcome:
"Perhaps the most important contribution of the social sciences in their
joint approach to the urgent problems facing mankind is the recognition
of the plasticity of human behavior and social institutions and of the resistance of each to change. In order to be effective, efforts at changing individuals must be appropriate to the successive stages of the unfolding personality, while in the case of a group or society, change will be strongly
resisted unless an attitude of acceptance has first been engendered."[65]

At the 1948 Congress, the mental hygiene movement formed a global
organization called the World Federation for Mental Health (WFMH).
After the activities in Germany, the term "mental hygiene" had become a
public relations liability. Its first president, a man who helped in its creation and who helped write the above statement, was psychiatrist John
Rawlings Rees.

Rees had clear views on how to implement psychiatric intervention into
society, views that are worth quoting at some length: "We can therefore
justifiably stress our particular point of view with regard to the proper
development of the human psyche, even though our knowledge be incom-
plete. We must aim to make it permeate every educational activity in our
national life: primary, secondary, university and technical education are all
concerned with varying stages in the development of the child and the
adolescent. Those who provide the education, the principles upon which
they work, and the people upon whom they work, must all be the objects
of our interest, for education that ignores the commonsense principles that
have been more clearly evolved of recent years is likely to be of indifferent
quality. Public life, politics and industry should all of them be within our
sphere of influence."

He goes on to say, "...we have made a useful attack upon a number of
professions. The two easiest of them naturally are the teaching profession
and the Church: the two most difficult are law and medicine.... If we are
to infiltrate the professional and social activities of other people I think we

must imitate the Totalitarians and organize some kind of fifth column activity! If better ideas on mental health are to progress and spread we, as the salesmen, must lose our identity.... Let us all, therefore, very secretly be 'fifth columnists.'... Don't let us mention Mental Hygiene (with capital letters), though we can safely write in terms of mental health and commonsense.... I should like to see us go beyond these more obvious points and set out on a campaign to get certain points and ideas which are of importance stressed by well-known novelists in their books.... Many people don't like to be 'saved,' 'changed' or made healthy. I have a feeling, however, that 'efficiency and economy' would make rather a good appeal...certainly we can 'sell' mental health under these headings as well as under any other."[66]

Active as a vice-patron of the 1948 Congress in London was G. Brock Chisholm, the Canadian psychiatrist quoted earlier. Chisholm, who served as a president of the Canadian National Committee for Mental Hygiene for four years was one of the many eugenicists who found a home in the mental hygiene movement. Like Rees, he served as president of the World Federation for Mental Health (1957-58).

A classic Chisholm statement: "If the race is to be freed from its crippling burden of good and evil it must be psychiatrists who take the original responsibility."[67]

The purpose of the World Federation for Mental Health, according to Chisholm, included "responsibility [among] mental hygienists, for a co-ordinated attack on world problems of inter-relationships."[68]

The words of these men may well have smacked of delusion, but for the fact that by the 1950s the mental hygiene movement had sprawled into virtually every aspect of living. Psychiatrist Walter Bromberg notes with pride, "A half century of mental hygiene effort convinced many that human behavior could indeed be modified. In the process, what had been considered 'personal' and the concern of parents, clergymen, and law enforcement agents, now became the substances of mental health programs.... Psychiatrists talked of dealing with 'social realities' a harbinger of Community Psychiatry—the minority problem, housing, youth work, integration, social welfare, senior citizens, etc."[69]

In 1950, the National Committee for Mental Hygiene merged with several other organizations to become the National Association for

Mental Health.

In 1970, the journal *Mental Hygiene*, after fifty years of publication, changed its name to *M.H.* Its new aim: "to involve the 'growing number of citizens faced with major policy decisions' in public situations that affect mental health. These can be population control, abortions, ecology, civil rights, pollution, and social planning of many descriptions."[70]

Today the mental hygiene movement is still propagating its aims as the yet again renamed National Mental Health Association, carrying out its agenda to teach others how to live their lives. Psychiatrist E. Fuller Torrey tells us: "Over the years it [the Committee] has championed for the promotion of 'mental health' despite the fact that nobody knows what it is or how to do it.... The National Mental Health Association promotes mental health through posters asking "Have you hugged your kid today?" This is very nice for children who need hugging, but for the seriously mentally ill it is about as relevant as the work of the American Dairy Association."[71]

CHAPTER IV

THE TENDRILS
OF INFLUENCE

WORLD WAR II MAY HAVE BEEN A NIGHTMARE FOR THE CIVILIZED world, but for psychiatry it was—at least in part—a time of opportunity for those willing to grasp it. And grasp it they did, for the period became the springboard for the most explosive growth in the profession's history.

The number of psychiatrists in the U.S. would increase tenfold in the ensuing forty years.[1]

The amount of government-funded research would grow more than a hundred times over.[2]

Psychiatry would become the only medical specialty in America to regularly receive federal monies to support the education of its members.

And, of course, in view of all this, psychiatry's influence upon society at large would leap commensurately ahead, forwarded by government support.

The story of how this came about is rife with political wheelings and dealings, backroom wrangling, and clever public relations coups.

It begins in 1939 when the outbreak of hostilities in Europe sent rumblings into America about the possibility of future U.S. involvement. Several psychiatric groups—the American Psychiatric Association, the Southern Psychiatric Association, and the William Alanson White Psychiatric Foundation—appointed committees to determine how psychiatry might fit into a future war effort.[3]

The simple truth of the times, however, was that the government, and the military specifically, saw little need for psychiatry. Not only was there no desire for it, but it was actively disliked in many circles. This is abundantly clear in the literature of the time.

When Albert Deutsch, the most famous pro-psychiatric journalist of the mid-twentieth century, wrote on military psychiatry for the American Psychiatric Association's book *One Hundred Years of American Psychiatry*, he opened with, "Military psychiatry has been the subject of widespread and often bitter debate from the onset of the war emergency up to the time of this writing (October, 1943)."

Even the war did not change the fact that, "A marked coolness toward psychiatric advice and assistance began to be manifested in certain high Selective Service and army circles."[4] Advice from psychiatrists for "incorporating sound psychiatric procedures in the draft process were held in abeyance."[5] And, not unjustifiably as it turned out, members of the military considered civilian psychiatrists and their associations to be "'outside' psychiatric sources suspected of self-interest." In addition, "...certain high officials stubbornly turned a deaf ear to the warnings sounded by alert individuals and groups on the consequences of neglect of psychiatric procedures...."[6]

William Menninger, who became the highest ranking psychiatrist of the war, reported that trying to sell psychiatry to the military of World War II was like "trying to hew a foothold in solid granite, and only by the dint of the tremendous effort of many people could we increase that hold by a fraction of an inch."[7] He tells us that psychiatrists were not permitted to attend high-level military organizational meetings until 1943, and when they finally were, it was "against determined opposition from the Army Ground Forces."[8]

It is clear then that psychiatry did not enter World War II because of any demand for its services. Its official offers of assistance were, in fact, commonly spurned. When psychiatrist Harry Stack Sullivan found someone in the Selective Service who would listen to his ideas for screening out mentally unfit draftees, it turned out to be Dr. Clarence Dykstra, the first director of the Selective Service, who "showed a most sympathetic attitude toward psychiatrists."[9] Appointed as Dykstra's psychiatric consultant, Sullivan then spent a year touring the country only to find the authorities would not adopt his proposals. After enough rejections, he resigned.

It is hard to say how much of Sullivan's rebuff was because he was a known homosexual—hardly a credential in those days for a man trying to sell his ideas about screening out undesirables. It did little to advance psychiatry's credibility with the military.[10] Apparently, however, Sullivan was no stranger to having his ideas rejected. In a book written 14 years earlier, he stated that an extended period of active genital homosexuality during late childhood and early adolescence was an essential prerequisite for sound mental health—otherwise a person would probably become a schizophrenic and be socially and mentally incapacitated for the rest of his life. Friends advised him not to publish.[11]

The real turning point for World War II psychiatry—and the entire profession—came in February, 1942. The Surgeon General of the U.S. Army created a neuropsychiatric branch in his office, naming psychiatrist Roy Halloran as its head. Halloran, in turn, took advice from the APA. Deutsch reported, "In response to a suggestion from the American Psychiatric Association's three-man committee, neuropsychiatric consultants were appointed to several Service Commands."[12] One of these appointees was Lieutenant Col. William Menninger.

Although Halloran was able to slowly extend psychiatry's meager presence in the face of military disinterest, it was his successor, Dr. Menninger, who stepped in when Halloran died suddenly at age forty-nine in December 1943, and who grabbed the laurels as the man who launched psychiatry into every corner of the armed services.

MENNINGER'S RISE TO POWER

Bernard H. Hall, editor of a compilation of Menninger's works and his biographer, wrote, "When you met him, he greeted you with an eager handclasp and a quiet smile; he made you feel relaxed, appreciated, a bit more highly valued than you had felt just a moment before."[13] This demeanor of "Dr. Will," as he was known by many, would prove to be one of his finest assets.

Before he entered the service in 1942, Menninger's life was not particularly enviable. Most people knew him from his connection with the Menninger Clinic, a well-known psychiatric institution of the time, where Dr. Will and his more famous brother Karl acted as directors.

Will was not a psychiatrist by initial training, but began a formal study of it in 1927. In 1933, while working in London, he became a personal friend of two psychiatrists we have already quoted: John R. Rees ("Let us all, therefore, very secretly be 'fifth columnists'") and G. Brock Chisholm, the man who claimed that any child who believes in Santa Claus has had his ability to think permanently injured.[14]

In the mid-1930s, William Menninger began an extensive extramarital affair with his nursing superintendent Isabel Erickson. When he went to Chicago in 1934 to study Freudian theory and practice and to undergo personal analysis by famed psychiatrist Franz Alexander—highly regarded by Freud himself—he continued the affair with the encouragement of his analyst. Indeed, when Menninger's wife Catharine met Alexander that same year, he urged her to do the same, as he did when he psychoanalyzed Karl Menninger, who himself had several extramarital flings before divorcing his first wife.[15]

When the Clinic staff got wind of Menninger's unfaithfulness, it raised uncomfortable questions. Lawrence Friedman, biographer of the Menninger family, relates, "Will's second in command, Dr. Norman Reider, wondered why the head of the hospital required a mistress if he had completed successful training analysis under Alexander. Other staff shared in this puzzlement. Should they be operating a hospital built upon psychoanalytic principles if psychoanalysis had not given Will a satisfactory home life?"[16]

Another sidelight which casts doubts on the effectiveness of the Menninger brother's personal psychotherapy was that afterwards they fought even more about Clinic matters, adding fuel to an already volatile relationship.[17] The antagonism between them remained the rest of their lives. In fact, when newsman Walter Cronkite interviewed the brothers in 1961, they refused to sit together, and the film crew had to use camera tricks to lend the appearance that Cronkite and the brothers were conversing around a table.[18]

William Menninger's family life was further wanting as well. His middle son claimed the man "had problems communicating with his own children." And Friedman tells us Dr. Will's three sons "wanted him around to inspire them, as he inspired his hospital staff, but he rarely obliged."[19]

Friedman also reports that the Clinic itself was not exactly a cathedral of propriety: "The separation of the hospital family from the personal family carried obvious sexual implications. 'I suppose most of us made passes at the secretaries or nurses at Clinic parties with wives excluded and bourbon very much included,' Douglas Orr [staff doctor] acknowledged. Catharine Menninger [Will's wife] and Margaret Stone [wife of a Clinic director] felt the parties were scheduled so that doctors could dance with female staff instead of their wives. Charles [Menninger, the father—founder of the Clinic] was known by staff secretaries as a 'fanny pincher.' Nurses, activities therapists and doctors frequently conducted surreptitious liaisons in defiance of hospital policy that precluded staff dating. Senior female staff, like administrator Mildred Law, were encouraged to stay unwed. In fact, Law felt pressured to break off her engagement. She feared that she would disappoint men on staff if she wed an off-campus man, and she might even feel compelled to resign. It was somewhat veiled, but there was an erotic side to hospital community life."[20]

Ironically, despite William Menninger's infidelity and strained domestic relations, he saw fit to advise others on the art of home life through such means as writing a 1939 article, "The Mental Health of the Family."[21] His affair with Erickson finally ended when he was called to military service in the Army Medical Corps in late 1942.

Menninger's first commanding officer, physician Colonel Sandford French, had a clear-cut view of psychiatry. He thought it was "for the birds." But when Dr. Will paid a social call to first meet French, he discovered they both were avid stamp collectors. The customary fifteen-minute visit turned into a chat session that lasted nearly three hours.

Menninger biographer Hall wrote, "And thus stamps changed the future of psychiatry in the Fourth Service Command [Menninger's unit]. After that afternoon of working on stamps, Colonel French gave Doctor Will the green light to do what the latter saw needed to be done. He gave the okay, but he added, 'Bill, I don't understand what you are doing; you are changing the whole Service Command, but go ahead.'"[22]

Despite the lack of public or military desire for psychiatric services, Menninger made it one of his first acts to push for authorization to treat the mental patients in his command. Prior to this, most were simply discharged. He then went on a campaign teaching his Freudian views on mental illness and promoting psychiatric treatment to Medical Corps personnel and the psychiatric staff. Hall tells us, "And for the first time, what psychiatry had to offer was felt throughout one entire Service Command."[23] As we shall see, this was not necessarily a good thing.

In late 1943, when the top-ranked psychiatric consultant for the Army, Dr. Roy Halloran, suddenly died, colleagues—keenly aware of Menninger's propagation of psychiatry in his Command—recommended Dr. Will for the job in the Surgeon General's office. However, the Surgeon General's attitude toward psychiatry differed little from that of Colonel French. He "saw no reason to push its use in the Army."

But shortly after his arrival, Menninger attended a dinner party with the Surgeon General, Norman Kirk. As the evening passed, some of the guests wanted to sing but there was no one to play the piano. Dr. Will volunteered. By the end of the evening the Surgeon General was calling him Bill. It was not long before Menninger presented plans to his new comrade—plans to mobilize psychiatry for the entire Army. They were approved.[24]

However, even with this, Menninger faced opposition from top brass. His opportunity to sell them with his "eager handclasp and quiet smile" came at a dinner party for General Paul Hawley, head of the Medical Department in the European Theater of Operations. Some fifty top-ranking officers attended. During a lull, after the Surgeon General had made a few remarks, he called on Menninger to tell the crowd a humorous story.

Despite the levity of the moment, Menninger's intentions were quite specific. "I was acutely aware that psychiatry was right there on the block, for sure. Either I had to produce for psychiatry, or fumble an opportunity for psychiatry." He told a mildly off-color story about cows and bulls that set the room laughing.[25]

Menninger was in.

The Chairman of the Department of Psychiatry at UCLA, Dr. Norman Brill remarked, "Perhaps more than ever will be realized, that story was responsible for making the opportunity for the tremendous accomplishments that Bill and the Army psychiatrists under him were able to achieve in World War II."[26]

How valid these "accomplishments" actually were is debatable.

THE SPRINGBOARD TO POWER

What followed was the inundation of the U.S. Army by psychiatric thought and practice. Nor was it only the U.S. Army. It paralleled coinciding drives in the Canadian military led by that army's Director General of the Medical Services, G. Brock Chisholm, and in Great Britain by J.R. Rees—both friends of Menninger.

One U.S. Labor Party publication reported, "It is absolutely no exaggeration to say that Rees from 1938-42, proceeded to take over the effective command of the British army. The military, according to Rees, was the ideal place to test out his theories: 'The army and other fighting services form rather unique experimental groups since they are complete communities and it is possible to arrange experiments that would be very difficult to do in civilian life.'"[27]

Not everyone was happy. In December 1942, Winston Churchill warned against the use of psychiatrists: "I am sure it would be sensible to restrict as much as possible the work of these gentlemen, who are capable of doing an immense amount of harm with what may very easily degenerate into charlatanry."

Meanwhile, in the U.S. Navy, Commander Francis Braceland, that branch's top-ranking psychiatrist and also a comrade of Menninger, helped lay similar groundwork. In mid-1943, he proclaimed, "Psychiatry now has a place in every step of the navy man's career from his induction to his eventual separation from the service."[28]

So what "tremendous accomplishments," as Norman Brill called them, were achieved by all of this psychiatric expansion, or was the expansion itself the accomplishment?

As an indication of the impact psychiatry had on the military, the rejection rate of inductees for psychiatric reasons was 7-8 percent in 1942 and 1943, when the major psychiatric influence began.[29] By the end of the war this had doubled to 16.4 percent—so high that it raised the rate for the entire war to *12 percent.* In World War I, the screening rate had been a mere 2 percent.[30]

While psychiatric rejections in WWII increased dramatically, those for other reasons did not. For every 100 people screened out, 28.4 were for psychiatric reasons in 1942. By 1944, it had risen to 45.8.

Despite the fact that more than six times as many would-be soldiers were rejected on psychiatric grounds as compared to the first World War, World War II psychiatrists *dismissed* more than twice as many actual soldiers with a "psychoneurosis" discharge (0.8 percent in WWI compared to

1.8 percent in WWII).[31]

The total number screened out or discharged from the Army alone totaled 387,000—more men than were assigned to the Pacific Theater of Operations during the war.[32]

This "accomplishment" begins to sound more and more like a total failure—at least as far as the good of the nation was concerned. The figures indicate that not only did the screening procedures not work, but they may well have screened out the wrong people.

What makes these figures even more intriguing is this: One of psychiatry's major selling points was that it could save the country money. Claims were made that from 1923 to 1940 the U.S. government paid out nearly a billion dollars for the care, treatment, and upkeep of World War I veterans with service-connected psychiatric disabilities. "Every psychiatric casualty of World War I," it was reported, "had cost American taxpayers over $30,000."[33]

This works out to about 35,000 psychiatric disabilities. Yet in World War II there were 380,000 psychiatric discharges—more than ten times as many—even though there were only 2.5 as many service personnel. An additional 130,000 were psychiatrically discharged for administrative reasons (as compared to medical grounds)—e.g., homosexuals, drug addicts, bedwetters, etc. Again, this was *after* screening out six times as many inductees as World War I.[34]

And how much was the country saved? The billion dollars spent on World War I veterans became billions. As just one indicator, compensation for psychiatric disabilities was costing the country $3.4 million a month in 1943 for World War I vets. By 1953, World War II vet psychiatric disability compensation was costing $23.1 million a month—more than seven times as much, even though, as stated, there were only 2.5 times as many personnel involved.

And to further show how backward the psychiatric effect was, the National Guard units had *no* psychiatric screening at all, and their psychiatric discharge rate was 40 percent *less* than the rest of the military.[35] The psychiatric concept of "mentally unfit" had swept into the war effort like a prairie fire, refusing inductees entry and ejecting soldiers on a level that was inconceivable in the previous war.

As we shall see later, this phenomenon was a pattern that would prove common when psychiatry is introduced into an area: The number of "psychiatric cases" suddenly increases in proportion to the number of psychiatrists present—as though previously disregarded problems are now promoted to the status of full-blown mental diseases. It also brings back to mind Twain's comment that to the man who badly wants to use a hammer, a lot of things look like nails that need hammering.

Menninger, on the other hand, complained petulantly, "To my personal knowledge there are still too many officials of high rank who ignorantly chatter about 'shell shock being an excuse for not fighting' or how the 'psychiatrists decimated the ranks of fighting divisions.'"[36]

The wool was not pulled over everyone's eyes. The effects of the psychiatric invasion did not go unnoticed by Col. L.G. Rowntree, Chief of the Medical Division of National Headquarters, Bureau of Selective Service. He remarked on seminars being given by psychiatrists on how to screen inductees. "These psychiatric seminars, like psychiatry in general, were planned and operated by psychiatrists, and were morally and financially supported by Selective Service. Despite their merits, they engendered much criticism. This criticism came to Selective Service Headquarters from outstanding leaders of medicine, from military authorities, but above all from other psychiatrists. After a trial test, extending well over six months, the Director was disappointed in the results. He was quite uncertain as to whether all rejections were justified and somewhat discouraged to learn that despite this psychiatric screening, considerable numbers of men were subsequently being discharged from the Army because of mental derangement."[37]

Apparently undaunted by the facts, psychiatrists made great public hoopla, boasting of their service to the war effort by screening out so many unfit draftees. They openly claimed and promoted the "significant success" they were having in the treatment of "psychiatric casualties" on the battlefront, giving the impression that psychiatrists could, in fact, cure just about anything mental.

Menninger wrote, "Remarkable results were obtained through a plan of treatment of combat casualties. From an initial start of no plan except for removal to the rear area hospitals with a 5 to 10 percent salvage, treatment centers were set up near the front line, utilizing division psychiatrists and others 'stolen' from evacuation hospitals. With prompt treatment 60 percent of casualties were returned within two to five days to duty for combat or service in the forward area."[38]

What Menninger failed to note about his "remarkable results" is that better results were obtained in World War I with little or no psychiatric care. Psychiatrist Edward Strecker, who served in World War I, outlined the simple rules followed by the staff in a psychoneurosis ward near the front lines: "1. Each patient on admission to have a hot drink. 2. Each patient to have three full meals a day unless otherwise ordered. 3. *Do not discuss the symptoms with the patient.* 4. No one is permitted in these wards unless assigned for duty. 5. The rapid cure of these patients depends on food, sleep, exercise, and the hopeful attitude of those who come in contact with them."(Emphasis added.)[39]

Strecker goes on to quote results: "Of 400 war neuroses, embracing all types and occurring in different operations at the front, approximately 65 percent were returned to frontline duty after an average treatment period of four days. During the second half of the Meuse-Argonne operation, the recovery rate amounted to about 75 percent."[40]

Psychiatrists so inflated their accomplishments to the public, that in 1946, American Psychiatric Association president Karl Bowman had to caution his peers. "Remember that following World War I there was a similar flood of popular interest in psychiatry, and a rather general assumption that psychiatry could now solve all human problems. When, as was to be expected, psychiatry failed to measure up to this impossible standard, much antagonism arose, and many claimed that psychiatry had little or nothing to offer."[41]

But there were those in psychiatry who *wanted* to ride this false tide of public optimism. There were new worlds to conquer. Using a clever leap of logic, they claimed the high number of psychiatric induction rejections—*a situation psychiatrists themselves created*—was indicative of a far greater social problem. "If these young men were representative of the Nation as a whole," wrote psychiatrist Robert Felix, a close friend of Menninger, "what would be the absolute figures for the mental and nervous impairments of the entire population? Certainly that proportion of our population between eighteen and forty-five years of age should represent the flower of our manhood. The prevalence of such disorders in the rest of the people was very likely no less."[42]

Thus psychiatrists fed the press (as they still do today) with such alarming statements as, "One American in ten needs psychiatric help."[43] The true statistic, proven in many studies and as reported by Felix himself, is that at any given moment about 0.6 percent of the population suffers from a disabling mental problem.[44]

Pro-psychiatric reporters such as Albert Deutsch and Mike Gorman (who became a psychiatric lobbyist after World War II), pushed the wonders of psychiatry to an unwitting public. The APA's PR man, Robbie Robinson remarked how the Association, seeking more funding from state and federal governments, "worked closely with some of the leading journalists" to write "snake pit" articles on the conditions inside state mental hospitals.[45]

Mary Lasker, a wealthy proponent of social change through psychiatry and birth control, funded the banner-waving of psychiatric causes through her Foundation set up in 1942. She awarded William Menninger the first Annual Albert and Mary Lasker Award in 1944.[46]

Another wealthy socialite, Florence Mahoney, a friend of Lasker, used her husband's ownership position in the Cox newspaper chain, the largest Democratic chain in the country, to light the psychiatric bonfires for all the public to see. And she hired Mike Gorman to write for her Miami paper. "He came for two weeks and stayed for six weeks," she recalled. "He wrote a sensational series—headlines every day. Then Mike went to the state legislature to lobby them, and he got $6 million for mental health within six weeks."[47]

The iron was hot.

Madness and Government, a book written by Henry Foley and Steven Sharfstein and published by the APA, tells us, "By the time of the war's end, public revulsion against state mental institutions and concern about the extent of mental disability in the country coincided with a favorable view of psychiatry. National mental health leaders determined to seize their advantage. These leaders were committed to replacing the few score state mental institutions with a system in which any number of small communities would provide comprehensive mental health care services to their local populations. Knowing that political leverage was needed to carry a social and public policy change of this magnitude, they proceeded methodically to cultivate political power for the purpose of developing a national mental health enterprise which would stimulate and support the radical rebalance they hoped to effect."[48]

It was a new day for psychiatry.

Psychiatrist Robert Felix, the assistant chief for the Public Health Service and the man credited with placing "psychiatry solidly in the program" at the Coast Guard Academy[49], a man who had grown up in Kansas with the Menninger brothers, met with cohorts in 1945 to design a national mental health program with the intent of getting the federal government to fund it. (Such a program was unprecedented—a previous effort to pass one in the 1800s was found unconstitutional.) Felix assembled three of his friends, the chief psychiatrists of the military services: William Menninger, Francis Braceland, and Jack Ewalt. The following year all would also be members of an upstart radical offshoot of the APA, the "young Turks" known as the Group for the Advancement of Psychiatry (GAP)—the group that would take over the leadership of the APA within the next few years. And, in time, Felix, Menninger, Braceland, and Ewalt would each go on to become presidents of the APA.

The four took a national program Felix had designed earlier and reworked it into a draft legislative bill in a few months. The bill called for a federally funded psychiatric research institute, grants to the states to help improve mental health services, and federal financial support to train more psychiatrists.

The legislation was introduced to Congress in early 1946, sponsored in part by Senator Lister Hill—a man who worked closely with Mary Lasker and her mental health lobby. (The Hill and Lasker group were known on Capitol Hill as the "Health Syndicate"—the APA's Foley and Sharfstein called it "Big Brother.")[50] Once again, psychiatrists used the myth of their war success to advance their cause. Foley and Sharfstein tell us that with many of them sporting the authority of military uniforms, their Congressional "testimony focused on the large number of wartime psychiatric casualties and the acute shortage of people, notably psychiatrists, trained to care for them. Much testimony was heard in praise of the new, more effective methods of care developed during the war. [Nothing was said of their failure, of course.] Also worth noting is that, although psychiatrists predominated and uniformly testified favorably for the bill, the absence of a representative of the American Medical Association indicated that organization's tacit disapproval."[51]

In support of the bill, Francis Braceland, a devout Freudian, quoted a report from the Rockefeller Foundation, stating: "It is not too much to assert that in its actual and potential contribution to general medicine, to education, to sociology, indeed to the general business of living, psychiatry, without claiming omniscience in itself, is cast for a role of fundamental importance in helping to shape any world which may come out of the present one."[52]

Signed into law in mid-1946, the Act established the National Institute of Mental Health (NIMH), a federal arm designed to 1) foster and aid psychiatric research, 2) provide grants for the training of psychiatrists and psychiatric personnel, and 3) aid the states in the prevention, diagnosis and treatment of psychiatric disorders through grants and technical assistance.

And appointed as the first director of NIMH was the man who was to hold that position for the next eighteen years: Dr. Robert Felix. He became a consummate bureaucrat. As Foley and Sharfstein point out, "Felix was making the federal government the prime mover in research and training."[53]

In carrying out the second objective above, psychiatry became virtually the only branch of medicine to have its training subsidized by federal funds, and remains so to this day. Training grants increased eightyfold from 1948 to 1972.[54] As a result, while the general population less than doubled, the number of psychiatrists in the United States grew tenfold between 1945 and 1985 as did the number of psychologists.[55]

As to NIMH "fostering and aiding psychiatric research," Foley and Sharfstein tell what actually happened. Again, these authors are trying to tell the APA's side. Sharfstein was on the APA staff when he wrote: "Naturally, the public expected a return on its investment. Felix and his top staff had to manage the institute's resources so as to produce meaningful advances in order to maintain credibility among the public and their peers. In this, they were only partly successful. The extravagant claims of enthusiasts—that new treatments were highly effective, that all future potential victims of mental illness and their families would be spared the suffering, that great economies of money would soon be realized—were allowed to pass unchallenged by the professional [psychiatric] side of the professional-political leadership. Promising more than could reasonably be delivered

93

became a way of life for this leadership."[56]

The failure to deliver, however, did not prevent them from asking for more and more funds from Congress. Working with the APA leadership and the Health Syndicate, which Elizabeth Drew in the *Atlantic Monthly* called "unparalleled in the influence that a small group of private citizens has had over such a major area of national policy," Felix drove the NIMH budget to greater and greater heights.[57]

The syndicate was represented in Washington by Mary Lasker, Senator Lister Hill, Representative John Fogarty, and Dr. James Shannon, the director of the National Institutes of Health (NIH), of which NIMH was a part. "In the raising of the [NIH] budget," wrote Drew, these four "performed each year like a highly polished quartet."[58]

The syndicate's connections within the APA were, according the Association's PR director, "Daniel Blain, Robert Felix, Francis Braceland, and Jack Ewalt—and in a measure, me since I helped to orchestrate the testimony they presented to Senator Hill and Representative Fogarty. By 1960 the budget for the National Institute of Mental Health had increased from about $3,000,000 to a few hundred million dollars...."[59]

First, the White House submitted a budget request—lower than what NIH suggested. Then, holding hearings, Fogarty reprimanded the Administration for the "cutbacks", and asked NIH officials how much they originally wanted (which he already knew). Then Fogarty asked for medical opinion from "citizen witnesses," and lobbyist Mike Gorman brought him a panel of favorable experts who made the case for more money. Gorman liked doctor witnesses who had "the evangelic pizzazz. Put a tambourine in their hands and they go to work."[60]

With due regard for the mood of the Appropriations Committee, Fogarty then raised the NIH budget and wrote a justifying report to which Gorman and Shannon usually contributed.

But the fattened purse was not filled yet. The budget then went to the Senate where Senator Hill ran it through the same dog-and-pony show, including the "citizen witnesses" to drive the numbers even higher. "During this time," writes Drew, "Gorman and Mrs. Lasker would be making their rounds, doing what they could to assure the success of Fogarty's and Hill's budget-raising performances."[61]

Gorman liked to refer to their fancy footwork as a "high class kind of subversion, very high class. We're not second story burglars. We go right in the front door." [62]

And it *was* successful. The NIMH budget exploded. But, of course, Felix had to pay the devil his due. The extra money did not come without stipulation. Foley and Sharfstein tell us, "...Felix had to negotiate with members of the syndicate in order to obtain increased appropriations," and he "had to accommodate his interests to those of Mahoney, Lasker and Gorman." [63] In one instance, in the mid-'50s, the trio wanted Felix to undertake a massive NIMH study of a new concept that European psychiatrists had been working with: drugs. Felix was opposed to the idea and NIMH had actually been decreasing its drug research. But Gorman bypassed him and got Hill and Fogarty to earmark $2 million of the 1956 budget for drug research. Felix relented and became a drug advocate, creating a pharmacological boom in the psychiatric industry that has yet to peak, launching drugs into every aspect of American living. It became the number one choice of psychiatric treatment and not long after, when it reached the streets, became the number one cause of social instability and crime.

Psychiatrist E.L. Torrey remarked in his book *Nowhere to Go*, about how the psychiatric leadership used NIMH for their own theories and whims and not for the one real problem the country had to deal with, the chronically insane. "The 1945 and 1946," he wrote, "congressional hearings on the proposed National Neuropsychiatric Institute [later named National Institute of Mental Health] set a pattern that would be repeated many times during the next thirty years. Psychiatrists and other interested parties first got the attention of lawmakers by focusing on state hospitals and the plight of the seriously mentally ill. Once this had been accomplished, testimony shifted to preventing mental diseases and eventually to promoting 'mental health.' It was a seductive vision that was not easily resisted; the nation's foremost psychiatrists were claiming that they had the knowledge to make a better world by eliminating the organism responsible not only for mental diseases but for delinquency and unhappiness as well." [64]

THE YOUNG TURKS REVOLUTION

There had been yet other changes in post-war psychiatry. May 26, 1946 was the eve of the 102nd Annual APA convention in Chicago. In William

Menninger's smoke-filled room at the Palmer House hotel, fifteen psychiatrists, including such luminaries-to-be as Daniel Blain and Robert Felix, gathered to discuss their increasing dissatisfaction with the APA. Their purpose: "To discuss ways and means to promote action for the advancement of psychiatry in the current scene."[65] They wanted an organization that would take a more aggressive approach to implementing psychiatry in society—what one East Coast doctor termed a "Young Turks movement" that would shake things up.

The next night they met again, joined by eight more psychiatrists, including Francis Braceland, head of Navy psychiatry. The gathering—mostly of Freudian leanings—unanimously elected Menninger as its chairman. The Group for the Advancement of Psychiatry, or GAP, was born.

As their first act, GAP decided to make a dramatic gesture at the APA convention the following evening. Elections were being held and on the ballot were three men nominated to be elected to the nine-man APA Council. Each year a third of the council was chosen for rotating terms of three years. Normally this was a very routine activity, but on May 28, GAP members nominated an opposition Council slate from the convention floor. Remarkably, all three GAP nominees, one of whom was William Menninger, took the election.

According to the APA's director of press and public relations for thirty years, GAP members "contrived to elect Dr. Menninger president [of the APA] in 1947. Sorely disenchanted with the performance of APA during the war, they were determined to capture control and to use APA as one of their instruments in spreading the influence of psychiatry into the nooks and crannies of American life. They proceeded to do so with no small success."

He goes on to say the GAP membership believed, "...if only we could analyze enough of the gatekeepers or leaders of society, we could change the world...."[66] Indeed, the group would make its political intentions clear in such notable publications as *The VIP with Psychiatric Impairment* and *The Right to Abortion: A Psychiatric View*, in which it explains why it would be psychiatrically correct to support abortion rights.

The GAP elite ruled the APA for the next fifteen years, pushing hard on the idea of "preventive psychiatry"—the concept of getting psychiatry into homes, schools, churches, and the rest of society to cure—through Freudian theories—mental illness before it happened. It was a recipe for social intervention that attracted as members such people as British psychiatrist John Rees, Franz Alexander (the man who so unsuccessfully psychoanalyzed the Menninger brothers), and Eugene Meyer III, the influential brother of *Washington Post* publisher Katherine Graham. Ironically, Graham's husband committed suicide after being placed in a Washington, D.C., institution.

PSYCHIATRY AND THE COLD WAR

GAP did not waste time getting into the "nooks and crannies." Since psychiatrists had entrenched themselves in the military of World War II, it was only a matter of time before they convinced government officials they could be useful in other areas of policy making.

In 1947, with the U.S. standing in the shadows of a Soviet Union with A-bomb technology, the American government sought solutions on how to deal with this conundrum and the obvious panic it might produce. The Psychological Strategy Board—a federal advisory group—formed and gathered for a number of meetings, with psychiatric and government representatives among those in attendance.

A key board member was Dr. Daniel Blain, a man whose name would show up often at significant psychiatric gatherings during the 1940s and 1950s. In October 1945, in Washington, D.C., he took part in a panel discussion with G. Brock Chisholm, the U.S. Secretary of Commerce, the Federal Security Administrator, and the Deputy Director of War Mobilization and Reconversion. This followed on the eve of Chisholm's infamous speech, which we have quoted several portions of, in which he called for the abolition of the concepts of right and wrong and morality as we know it.

In May 1946, Blain attended the first GAP meeting, as noted, and became a pioneering member of that radical offshoot of the APA. Then, in May 1949, when William Menninger gave his presidential address to the APA, he spoke of Blain's appointment as Medical Director, where he served the following ten years essentially to improve the APA's PR. "Under the presidency of Dr. Winfred Overholser," Menninger said, "by vote, the Council took constructive action to alter the status of psychiatry which had provoked the repeated and sincere criticism that we were isolated, inarticulate, and incoordinated. The Council counted itself very fortunate in being able to employ an individual of the stature and ability of Dr. Blain."[67]

In his 1950s book *Every Other Bed*, lobbyist Mike Gorman tells of running with Blain through the hallowed halls of Congress on lobbying forays—a task Blain was not unfamiliar with by this time. Blain was rewarded with the APA presidency in 1964.

His meetings in 1947 with the Psychological Strategy Board represented a budding new role for psychiatry—that of policy-maker for the U.S. government. The gatherings were not only attended by psychiatrists. They were, in fact, sponsored by them. At the October 21 meeting, the topic under discussion was how to get the public to "respond" the way the government wanted on the issue of the Soviets having an A-bomb.

Minutes from the meeting show Blain stating they must, "Find out ways to convince. Plan ways to convince. Includes knowing what to tell them." He goes on to say that catchy words are needed to sell the message, as in a "sizzling steak." As a psychiatrist, he points out that people are motivated by anger, fear, and desire. "...it is possible to plant 'guide posts' in people's minds, to condition them so that when action is possible it will be directed in the right channels." He then cautions: "We can't scare to point of panic. We must scare only to point of mobilizing their energies."[68]

Thus, out of the minds of psychiatrists the Cold War was born, not from the public's natural response to the unfolding of events, but through an organized plan to keep the populace in the clutch of anxiety. "...Public reaction to Russia producing a bomb..." one Board member remarked, "requires application of psychology."[69]

A BRAVE NEW WORLD

By the half century mark, psychiatry had its roots sunk deep into the state and federal governments. Unlike other successful enterprises which earned their daily bread and repute in a capitalist society by delivering what the public needed and wanted, the psychiatric profession had, prior to World War II, been unable to garner much social acceptance or demand for its services. But after learning the art of obtaining federal funding, it had found a way to not only survive but prosper.

Nor did it care where the money came from.

One lucrative source of federal financing for psychiatrists in the early 1950s was the Central Intelligence Agency (CIA), although the seeds of their involvement in the "secret world" had actually been planted in the previous decade during the war. Governments, particularly the intelligence/ military arms of governments had long sought to develop methods to bring unwilling subjects under their control. Thus it was, that while German doctors were experimenting with mescaline on prisoners at Dachau, the Office of Strategic Services (OSS)—the wartime predecessor of the CIA—formed a secret research program to find a "Truth Drug," that could be used during interrogations.

Chairman of the research committee was Dr. Winfred Overholser, head of St. Elizabeth's Hospital in Washington. Among other members was Dr. Edward Strecker, president of the American Psychiatric Association. After testing a number of drugs, including peyote and scopolamine, the committee concentrated on marijuana. However, it proved inconsistent as a truth serum.

Also on the OSS "want list" was a method to control a German prisoner so that he could be programmed—such as through hypnosis—to kill Hitler. Among those consulted were the Menninger brothers, Karl and William, and Colgate University psychologist George Estabrooks.

After the war, the Navy was first to pick up the gauntlet with its project CHATTER. Here, at the Naval Medical Research Institute in Bethesda, Maryland, mescaline was the drug of choice as an interrogation agent. The CIA was not far behind. It started work in the area in the late 1940s and made it official in the spring of 1950, when it institutionalized its first mind control program, an operation dubbed BLUEBIRD which had a mission to investigate drug/hypnosis.

By 1950, U.S. psychiatrists had started to experiment with LSD, an hallucinogenic that produced "a transitory psychotic disturbance"[70] in normal subjects. CIA interest was immediate, and it wasn't long before the agency began to fund psychiatric researchers who were working with the drug.

Among these was Dr. Harris Isbell, Director of the Addiction Research Center, a huge federal drug hospital in Lexington, Kentucky. The good doctor put the word out to the inmates that volunteers for his experimental program would be rewarded either with the drug of their choice or reduced sentences. Most of the addicts opted for drugs, either heroin or morphine of a high quality uncommon in the streets.

What the inmates didn't know was that Isbell would also be giving them LSD. In one chilling experiment, he kept seven men on LSD for 77 days. One 19-year old who took the LSD only once claimed he hallucinated and suffered for 16 or 17 hours. In other tests Isbell tried out a broad spectrum of unproven drugs from the CIA and NIMH, of which the inmates knew neither the names nor the probable effects. Apparently, he tested some eight hundred compounds. As an example of what little regard was given to his actions, Isbell once informed his Agency contact, "I will write you a letter as soon as I can get the stuff in a man or two."[71]

According to *Acid Dreams*, by Martin A. Lee and Bruce Shlain, the directors of the National Institute of Mental Health and the National Institutes of Health were fully cognizant of the Agency's "interest" in Isbell's work and offered "full support and protection." Perhaps coincidentally, NIMH head Robert Felix had also served at the Lexington research center before the war.

Lexington was only one of fifteen penal and mental institutions used by the CIA for its drug experiments on unwitting and captive populations during that period.

Also working with the CIA was Eli Lilly, major producer of psychiatric drugs in today's world, including Prozac. In 1953, Lilly found a faster way to manufacture LSD and became the first U.S. drug company to do so.

That same year, Dr. Ewen Cameron was finishing his stint as president of the American Psychiatric Association. He had been working on his own theories on mind control, including a concept he called "psychic driving." Utilizing CIA funds, he had his assistant rig up a continuous audio tape loop that played negative messages about a patient 16 hours a day for several weeks while the patient lay in a drugged stupor. Some patients received a shock to the legs at the end of the message. Cameron then switched the patients over to two to five weeks of "positive" messages run the same way. With certain subjects he used a combination of LSD and "psychic driving."

The Scottish-born doctor also tried a technique he called "depatterning." The treatment began with 15 to 30 days of drugged "sleep therapy." The patient was awakened two or three times every day for an electroshock treatment. These were not ordinary shock treatments but 20 to 40 times more intense, using a higher voltage and giving additional jolts while the patient was still convulsing from the original one.

John Marks, author of *The Search for the Manchurian Candidate* tells us, "The frequent screams of patients [usually women] that echoed through the hospital did not deter Cameron or most of his associates in their attempts to 'depattern' their subjects completely. Other hospital patients report being petrified by the 'sleep rooms,' where the treatment took place, and they would usually creep down the opposite side of the hall." One doctor told stories of stuporous patients, incapable of caring for themselves, often groping their way around the hospital and urinating on the floor.[72]

Patient L. McDonald, who was 23 when Cameron "depatterned" him, had this to say—twenty-five years after his treatment: "I have no memory of existing prior to 1963, and the recollections I do have of events of the following years until 1966 are fuzzy and few.... My parents were introduced to me... I did not know them. [My five] children came back from wherever they had been living. I had no idea who they were."[73]

None of this prevented Cameron from sharing his knowledge with his peers by writing of his experiments in medical journals. He claimed the typical depatterning subject went through three stages. First was the loss of much of his memory, yet he still knew where he was and why. Secondly, he lost his "space-time" image—did not know where he was or why and had considerable anxiety about it. Stage three the doctor described as follows: "...what the patient talks about are only his sensations of the moment.... His remarks are entirely uninfluenced by previous recollections—nor are they governed in any way by his forward anticipations. He lives in the immediate present. All schizophrenic symptoms have disappeared. There is complete amnesia for all events in his life."[74]

But depatterning was not Cameron's only claim to fame. He also experimented with sensory deprivation. Patients—and all of Cameron's subjects were people who had come to him as paying patients seeking help—were placed in chambers for periods as long as 35 days. (The CIA had been told anything beyond six days would cause irreparable damage.) On one such subject, Cameron coolly wrote, "Although the patient was prepared by both prolonged sensory isolation (35 days) and by repeated depatterning , and although she received 101 days of positive driving, no favorable results were obtained." The woman had come to him for help getting through menopause.[75]

Dr. Donald Hebb, a psychology department head at Montreal's McGill University when Cameron was doing his work, explained how his colleague managed to carry out such hellish experiments with no censure from the psychiatric community: "Look, Cameron was no good as a researcher.... He was eminent because of politics."[76]

Of Cameron's research, attorney Leonard Rubenstein—who successfully sued on behalf of the doctor's patients—commented in 1988, "Indeed, the picture it paints of the psychiatric community is as disturbing as was the CIA's support for this research."[77]

For the final ironic note on this brief look at psychiatric/intelligence atrocities, we must look to Cameron's past: Dr. Ewen Cameron was a member of the Nuremberg tribunal that judged Nazi war criminals who committed inhuman crimes during the war.

THE POLITICS OF POWER

In February, 1955, legislation was introduced in Congress calling for a mental health study act to fund a survey of the nation's handling of the mentally ill. The bill had been drafted not by legislators, but by the APA and psychiatrists from the AMA. The APA president had called for such a study back in 1953. Among those testifying in support were Robert Felix, former APA president Winfred Overholser (of Truth Drug fame), professional mental health lobbyist Mike Gorman, and Leo Bartemeier, chairman of the AMA Council on Mental Health, past APA president, future GAP president, and personal friend of the Menningers as well as trustee at the Menninger Clinic.

The testimony was obviously not unbiased. As psychiatrist E. Fuller Torrey pointed out in his book *Nowhere to Go*, "These professional organizations, although given to periodic hand-wringing and expressions of anguish about the plight of the seriously mentally ill, have rarely represented anyone's interests other than their own. The organizations are nothing more nor less than professional unions and function primarily to serve their members' economic interests. One should no more expect such organizations to provide leadership on care for the seriously mentally ill than one would expect the Teamsters or AFL-CIO to do so."[78]

The bill was passed, calling for a Joint Commission on Mental Illness and Health to conduct the study. Named as the director of the commission was—once again—the head of NIMH, Robert Felix. He appointed to lead the commission his friend, co-author of the 1946 bill, treasurer of the APA, and former GAP president, Jack Ewalt.

In later years lobbyist Gorman implied that the recommendations of the Commission had been predetermined from the very beginning: "I was very happy to be a member of that [Commission] and really made only one contribution although it was a five-year study; I had the good fortune to write my suggested recommendations for Senator Hill in 1956. Old Chinese proverb—'If you appoint Commission, have all the recommendations finished before you appoint it.'"[79]

When the Commission's report was finished in 1960, Foley and Sharfstein admiringly tell us, "Ewalt wisely decided to solicit the help of the American Legion to defuse any charge that the commission's final report was part of a 'commie plot.' He obtained a grant from the Legion to publish the final report. In the congressional hearing in which Ewalt presented the final report, one congressman indeed raised such a charge. But since Ewalt could point out that the American Legion had paid for the publication of the report currently before the congressmen, the charge was completely deflated."[80]

The commission boldly declared that federal, state, and local governments' spending for public mental health services should be doubled in five years and tripled in ten.[81]

Ewalt described the intent of his brainchild, a community mental health system: "Its purpose is to coordinate efforts to improve the community in ways that will enhance mental well-being, decrease to bearable limits the occurrence of personal stress, relieve troubled persons, prevent mental illness when possible, and treat and rehabilitate those who become ill or disturbed. The program should serve the troubled, the disturbed, the slow, the ill, and *the healthy* of all age groups...."[82] (Emphasis added.)

Ewalt was not alone in his dream of communities teeming with psychiatric advisors. It was, in fact, a common push by organized psychiatry in the 1940s and 1950s, which is why so many institutions of society today—schools, courts, social work to name a few—are steeped in psychiatric thought.

Some sample statements. Francis Braceland: "Psychiatry in the future will not content itself with the belief that it is doing a full job when it merely provides care for disease. The job of tomorrow's psychiatry is... large-scale prevention. In the same manner in which medicine has overcome such diseases as lockjaw and smallpox by prophylaxis, psychiatry can do likewise by providing information and a public understanding which will prevent much unnecessary unhappiness. We believe that the technique of more successful living can be taught."[83]

William Menninger: "As psychiatrists we are expected to provide leadership and counsel to the family, the community, the state, welfare workers, educators, industrialists, religious leaders, and others."[84]

Felix urged his fellow psychiatrists to become involved with "education, social work, industry, the churches, recreation, the courts," so that "mental health services" would be "fully integrated into, and a regular and continuing part of, the total social environment."[85]

Psychiatrist E. Fuller Torrey points out, "The end result, in Dr. Felix's thinking, was a vision of a brave new psychiatric world."[86]

The 1960 Commission report, *Action for Mental Health*, was held until after the 1960 presidential election, since it was known that through the efforts of lobbyist Gorman, the Democrats had developed a pro-commission platform: "We will provide greatly increased Federal support for psychiatric research and training and community mental health programs...."[87]

When Kennedy captured the White House, he read the Commission's report and appointed a committee to review it. Once again, the committee chairman called for assistance in the deliberations—people who would submit to him proposals for consideration. He called in the leaders of NIMH. Again, Foley and Sharfstein: "Felix told his staff in the spring of 1962 that assisting the president's interagency committee was the most important job the institute faced.... In committee deliberations, Felix consistently represented the professional concerns of psychiatrists.... Thanks to the leadership of Gorman, Ewalt, and Dr. George Tarjan (future GAP and APA president who served the Kennedy family in the White House), the National Advisory Mental Health Council [part of NIMH] collaborated... in the design of the community mental health centers [CMHC's] proposal."[88]

"The strategy of the mental health alliance was to de-monopolize the states' position in favor of a shared-government support (federal, state, local) for mental health services. Their intention was to obtain a degree of control over the renewal and expansion of the system of public mental health care."[89]

Ultimately the proposal was to call for a mental health center for every 100,000 population—2,000 centers at the time.

The president's committee accepted the CMHC proposal from NIMH and submitted their recommendations to Kennedy.

To push all this through Congress, it was known that the support of the states would be needed. A Governors' Conference on Mental Health was held in Chicago in November, 1961. Yet again, sitting in as consultants to the policy committee of this conference were Felix, lobbyist Gorman, and PR man for the APA, Dr. Daniel Blain.

In January, 1963 William Menninger became the first psychiatrist to meet with President Kennedy. It is not known whether it was his "eager handclasp," his stamp collection or an off-color joke that won the day, but Menninger did it again.

A friend of Menninger relates: "[Menninger] had a lengthy interview with President Kennedy at the White House, the first psychiatrist ever to have achieved such distinction. That interview, more recently described in his *Collected Papers* was, I think, directly responsible for President Kennedy's subsequent address on the mental health needs of our country: the first President in history to have ever taken up our cause."[90]

On February 5, 1963, the President took the matter up with Congress, saying: "I am convinced that, if we apply our medical knowledge and social insights fully, all but a small portion of the mentally ill can eventually achieve a wholesome and constructive adjustment. It has been demonstrated that two out of three schizophrenics—our largest category of mentally ill—can be treated and released within six months...."[91]

Why would a polished statesman like Jack Kennedy make such a political blunder as to promise something to Congress that neither he nor the mental health professionals could possibly (then or now) deliver?

The key is in the first three words in his statement. "I am convinced..." He was told it was possible and he believed his advisors. It is hard to say why they would make such claims, given the obvious disastrous consequences that would follow when they failed, but psychiatric professionals gave the President promises of what psychiatry hoped it could do, when there was no evidence at all to support their position.

It is ironic that Kennedy, of all people, was not more leery of their offerings. In 1941 his sister Rosemary, mildly retarded and prone to wild moods and wandering the streets at night, had been given the best in new treatments to handle it: a prefrontal lobotomy. The operation, as one family member claimed, "made her go from being mildly retarded to very retarded." She no longer realized who she was and her capacity to speak was almost entirely gone. Rosemary Kennedy has been confined to a nursing convent ever since.[92]

Six days after JFK's speech, Senator Lister Hill introduced the community mental health bill to Congress and the hearings began. Foley and Sharfstein point out, "Dr. Jack R. Ewalt, speaking on behalf of his colleagues on the joint commission and in the organizations they represented, told the subcommittee that he supported the CMHC program, describing it as well-planned and based on existing technology. Ewalt's testimony was crucial...This was an excellent finesse by the mental health alliance, which also arranged for favorable testimony from the American Psychiatric Association, American Hospital Association, American Public Health Association, the AFL-CIO, pharmaceutical interests and others as well."[93]

After considerable political wheeling and dealing, Congress passed the bill and Kennedy signed it into law on October 31, 1963, a scant twenty-two days before his death.

Torrey remarks, "In the end...it was not evidence of the efficacy of community mental health centers that carried the day but blind hope. Dr. Felix said he could 'see a new day dawning.'"[94]

Legislation authorized the appropriation of $150 million in 1963 for the construction of new Community Mental Health Centers. Staffing grants of $735 million followed two years later. Ultimately Congress would invest over three billion dollars into the project.

The results? Authors Rael Jean Isaac and Virginia Armat spent a considerable part of their book *Madness in the Streets* chronicling the ensuing debacle and waste. One representative statement: "The CMHC program was so poorly supervised by NIMH that many centers failed to provide the specified services. In March, 1990 a congressional committee issued a report estimating that CMHCs had diverted between $40 and $100 million to improper uses, and that a quarter of all CMHCs had so thoroughly failed to meet their obligations as to be legally subject to immediate recovery of federal funds. Centers in Minneapolis, Boston, Orlando, and many other cities built swimming pools with their CMHC federal construction money. Orlando Regional Medical Center, in addition to a pool, built tennis courts with its federal construction grant and used a federal staffing grant to hire a gardener, lifeguard and swimming instructor."[95]

The remarks of Lawrence S. Kubie, professor of psychiatry at Johns Hopkins University School of Medicine, in the *Archives of General Psychiatry* speak for themselves: "Several department heads have stated frankly that they are glad to take federal money (or any other money that comes their way) in order to build the facilities...they need. They admit that in today's climate, if they are to get this money, they are forced to call their new facilities 'community mental health centers.' They do not hesitate to add that within a dozen years the words will have dropped into innocuous desuetude, leaving the department in possession of the additional space it needs."[96]

Consumer advocate Ralph Nader commented after a decade of the CMHC program, calling it a "highly touted but failing social innovation.... The community mental health centers have been neither accountable backward to the National Institute of Mental Health which established them, nor forward to the consumers and citizens in the community they allegedly serve. They have often become regular windfalls for psychiatrists...."[97]

Franklin Chu and Sharland Trotter did a complete investigation of NIMH and the CMHC program for the Nader Study Group in 1974, compiling their findings in the book *The Madness Establishment*. They found that "the community mental health centers program was vastly oversold.... The short life of the community mental health centers program already bears the familiar pattern of past mental health reforms that were initiated amid great moral fervor, raised false hopes of imminent solutions, and wound up only recapitulating the problems they were to solve.... Amid flowery orations intended to generate great excitement and renewed hope, they were initiated as a reaction to the scandalous degeneration of state hospitals. Had NIMH or Congress responded to the underlying lessons of past failures...a far more sober approach might have been adopted. There are no known, foolproof answers as to how best to care for those labeled 'mentally ill'—just as there are no widely accepted answers to the question of what 'mental illness' *is*."[98]

Dr. H. G. Whittington, former director of psychiatry for the Denver Department of Health and Hospitals, referred to as "one of the half dozen intellectual architects of the community psychiatry movement,"[99] commented in 1983, "I was already beginning to feel very much like a parent must feel who has a badly handicapped child. Should I smother it in its sleep, or should I help the poor little deformed bastard grow up to do the best it can in life? The deformed creature that has developed from the original community mental health center movement does not arouse much enthusiasm in any of us, I am sure, who had some more grandiose visions."[100]

E. Fuller Torrey puts it succinctly. "Community mental health centers...are almost complete failures."[101]

Even Foley and Sharfstein were blunt about the disastrous results in *Madness and Government*. "In no other aspect of the CMHC program was the oversell more egregious, the rhetoric more exalted than in its promised elimination of the need for state hospital services. Hospitals would close, it was claimed, and humane care would prevail; costs would even be reduced if only the CMHC legislation were enacted. Exactly how, and how soon, CMHCs would accomplish this was never explicated, but in so exuberant an atmosphere such sober considerations were set aside...psychiatrists gave the impression to elected officials that cures were the rule, not the exception. As a result...inflated expectations went unchallenged.... In short CMHCs were oversold as curative organizational units."[102]

Harry Cain, who helped write the CMHC program, shruggingly stated years later, "There was a lot of wishful thinking.... We were federal bureaucrats on an NIMH campus talking about the community, but really from some conceptual level as opposed to hands-on experience."[103]

But the CMHC program was more than just a three-billion-dollar failure. The net result of it was that many state hospitals—the traditional solution for housing the insane—were closed down on the promise that patients would get "community" care that never materialized. As a result, many of the chronically disturbed had no place to go and ended up living in the streets. The very people psychiatry was purporting to serve became homeless.

Not surprisingly, in 1985, when APA president John Talbott remarked about "this unsavory episode in our history," he assigned its causes elsewhere. "It is both tragic and ironic that at the very time when psychiatry is so fertile with ideas and pregnant with promise, its public image is so closely linked to a 30-year-old failed public policy which we had so little power to influence."

The title of his speech demonstrates the reason for this unwillingness to accept responsibility: "Our Patients' Future in a Changing World: The Imperative for Psychiatric Involvement in Public Policy."[104] Nor is it surprising to note that psychiatry's "pregnancy" existed in 1945, 1985 and is still with us in 1995. While promise is fertile and continues to grow in the womb, it has never been delivered.

Despite the debacle of the psychiatric-created mental health programs of the Kennedy era, there has been no sign that psychiatry and the mental health lobby has materially learned from this experience.

It is unlikely, when President Jimmy Carter spoke to Congress in 1979 for yet another mental health plan by organized psychiatry, that anyone in the country noticed the shadows of deja vu in the president's first three words: "*I am convinced,*" he said, "that…the passage of the Mental Health Systems Act will reduce the number of Americans robbed of vital and satisfying lives by mental illness."[105] (Emphasis added.)

PART TWO:

THE TOOLS
OF
PSYCHIATRY

CHAPTER V

VOLTAGE THROUGH THE BRAIN

WHILE IT MAY NOT SAY MUCH FOR EITHER MAN'S COMPASSION OR HIS ingenuity, the fact is the problem of the madman and the disordered mind has been so unsolvable that for centuries virtually every conceivable device and torture has been visited upon the insane to stop their ravings.

In 1810, for example, Johann Reil, Professor of Medicine at the University of Berlin in 1810, gave his characteristically Teutonic recipe for handling the mentally disturbed: "Through strong, painful impressions we capture the patient's attention, accustom him to unconditional obedience, and indelibly imprint in his heart the feeling of necessity. The will of his superior must be such a firm, immutable law for him that he will no more resist it than he would rebel against the elements."[1]

Nor could the English method be considered an improvement. One historian noted that in the 1800s, "The old 'treatment'…was supplemented by the so-called Darwin chair (invented by Charles Darwin's grandfather; the physician Erasmus Darwin).… In this chair the insane were rotated until blood oozed from their mouths, ears and noses; and for years most successful cures were reported as a result of its use. Castration and starvation cures were also employed."[2]

The very phrase *snake pit*—slang for "mental hospital"—stems from the days when the insane were thrown into a serpent-filled hole to shock them back to their senses.

Thank goodness, some might say, that today our mental health professionals have developed different, more modern methods for dealing with problems of the mind. Unfortunately, they should also realize that while technology has provided man valuable benefits, it has also given him the ability to destroy with even greater power and efficiency. And in light of this, many will argue that these modern therapies have served only to bring us to a new peak of scientific barbarism.

TYPES OF TREATMENT

There are essentially only two types of treatments in psychiatry today, *psychological* and *somatic*.

Psychological treatments are direct approaches to the mind and the person's problems and take the form of counseling or psychotherapy of one sort or another, as discussed in Chapter II.

The other type of treatment, *somatic* (also called "organic" or "biological"), does not address the individual's problems or mind at all. Somatic treatments are rooted in the basic materialistic concepts of psychiatry—man is an animal; he has no soul or spirit; all of his thoughts, feelings, and aspirations are mere electrochemical reactions in his brain and neurons.

Lobotomists Walter Freeman and James Watts disdainfully expressed the essence of this approach very clearly in 1944. "There is still a tendency to consider the brain as the 'temple of the mind,' the 'seat of the soul,' and the 'greatest gift of God,' and to decry any suggestion that such a holy structure is being tampered with. The shackles of medieval thought are difficult to strike off."[3]

The primary somatic treatments are electroshock therapy, psychosurgery, and drugs. The reader may be surprised to learn, however, that these treatments do not "cure" the individual's troubles. In fact, it is a rare psychiatrist who would even try to make such a claim. Rather, the acknowledged fact is that these treatments "blunt" the problems, as psychiatrists say. What they actually do is interfere with the individual's current emotional and thought processes to such an extent that when the treatment "works" it commonly means the patient is suppressed from responding to life situations with natural, though sometimes unpleasant, feelings such as sadness, fear, or anxiety.

114

Philosophically and practically, then, this biological approach to human problems is in direct conflict with the basic moral tenets in most civilized societies. These are the same tenets that form the basis of our entire legal system and which most of us learn from childhood (and pass on to our children) as necessary to successful living—that we are each self-determined moral agents responsible for our lives, for our actions, and for dealing with our problems.

Remarkably few educators, legislators, and even parents see the striking similarity between what psychiatry is espousing—in our newspapers, on our televisions, and in our classrooms—and the "philosophy of no responsibility" that is damaging our society. Yet while it may seem incredible at first thought to associate organized psychiatry with social chaos, inspection reveals that psychiatry is the *only* authoritative source of that philosophy in modern times.

Does any other official voice promote the biochemical, non-responsible nature of man—presenting the human as a soulless entity at the mercy of DNA, cellular and hormonal dictates?

The somatic treatments of psychiatry are premised on the idea that our bad feelings are chemically and genetically induced. There is nothing we can personally do about them. And there is no moral agent involved.

As an example, if a man cheats on his wife, it would not be unexpected for him to feel guilty and depressed afterwards. A common psychiatric solution would be to give him drugs or electroshock to make him stop feeling sad. This would be a successful "cure." But what *actually* happens?

The man is prevented from experiencing the normal life processes involved in his actions: thinking the matter through, confronting the guilt, deciding whether or not to tell his wife in order to clear his conscience, etc. He has circumvented life and all its lessons. The pain that makes most of us stronger from having weathered it, that, in fact, builds character, is "blunted" for this man.

Even the so-called success of the cure is in question. Psychiatrist Lee Coleman describes this phenomenon as it relates to the typical "recovery" of a patient treated with shock treatments: "The brain, for a while, is so injured (even children know that electricity is dangerous for them and living things) that the patient is too confused to know or remember what was troubling them. Unfortunately, when the brain begins to recover somewhat, the problems usually return since electricity has done nothing to solve them."[4]

The somatic viewpoint of psychiatrists often comes as a shock to patients and their families—if they ever become aware of it. After being subjected to the unrelenting public relations campaigns, many people go to these doctors with the assumption that they are about to place their lives in the hands of those who understand the deepest workings of the mind, men who by virtue of their training know something about their problems that mere mortals are not privy to. There is no truth to this belief. In fact, they are placing their lives in the hands of men who specialize only in the suppression of certain mental phenomena through the application of force.

In the next few chapters we will be examining these somatic treatments in detail. You will see that they are not noticeably different from the cure of 1810 when, "Through strong, painful impressions we capture the patient's attention...."

ELECTROSHOCK THERAPY

As recently as 1991, Max Fink, the leading advocate of electroshock therapy in America stated, "Electroconvulsive therapy (ECT) remains a controversial treatment in medicine." It is somewhat of an understatement, but to fully grasp the scope of that controversy, some historical background is needed.[5]

Shock treatment was first performed in Italy in 1938 by Dr. Ugo Cerletti. He was fascinated to learn that hogs prepared for slaughter were first shocked through the temples to render them unconscious. Initially, Cerletti thought the jolt itself did the killing and this "seemed to confirm my doubts regarding the danger of electric applications to man." But when he found the hogs survived the shock, he decided to try it on a human.[6]

Impressed by the jarring effect the jolts had on patients, Cerletti and his staff soon began promoting the new "therapy" to other doctors. Obsessive and difficult patients grew meek and manageable. And those troubled by past events were no longer so troubled. Some doctors were equally impressed by such changes and quickly adopted the new therapy.

By January, 1940, electroconvulsive therapy had arrived in the U.S. Heated opposition arose almost immediately. During a 1941 meeting of psychiatrists, Dr. Roy Grinker of Chicago said about electric and insulin shock* treatments, "I think it can be stated unequivocally that it is fraught with extreme danger. There is not only an emotional but an intellectual change in the patients.... Careful studies by means of a battery of psychologic tests reveal a definite 'organic' change in memory which does not entirely clear up.... Often the so-called normal alpha rhythm increases greatly in voltage, making one suspicious that irreparable damage to the brain has been produced."[7]

ECT was forbidden in World War II by the U.S. Army, until psychiatrists worked their way into high command in mid-1943.[8] However, in spite of the opposition, civilian psychiatrists liked the quick-fix possibilities of this new treatment and its use spread quickly. It was given to virtually all types of patients, from children to the elderly, for all manner of mental peculiarities. Psychosis, depression, mania, homosexuality—all were under assault by the new procedure. By 1942, some form of shock treatment, electric or chemical, was in use in 85 percent of the psychiatric institutions in the United States. (Chemical shock includes insulin, which produces diabetic coma, and metrazol, which causes convulsions and unconsciousness.)[9]

The Group for the Advancement of Psychiatry—the "Young Turks"— which successfully took control of the APA, made a point of railing against the "promiscuous and indiscriminate use of electroshock therapy" in its first bulletin, issued September 15, 1947. It called for "definitive studies as to the possibility of irreversible brain damage," and complained that "abuses in the use of electro-shock therapy are sufficiently widespread and dangerous to justify consideration of a campaign of professional education in the limitations of this technique, and perhaps even to justify instituting certain measures of control."[10]

And abuse was indeed rampant. The psychiatric literature of the '40s, '50s, and even '60s teems with reports of all manner of drastic ECT experiments. Numerous psychiatrists made little attempt to hide the fact that they were knowingly and willingly trying to damage brain tissue or using shock treatment to quiet patients instead of heal them.

In 1942, Dr. Abraham Myerson said, "The reduction of intelligence is an important factor in the curative process.... The fact is that some of the

---

* The application of large doses of insulin which drastically reduces the sugar content of the blood and ultimately sends the patient into a coma which lasts about an hour.

very best cures that one gets are in those individuals whom one reduces almost to amentia [feeble-mindedness]. It is impossible to conceive of that amentia without an organic base; there must be at least temporarily organic changes in the brain, and the cure is related to these organic alterations."[11]

Lucino Bini, the man who helped Ugo Cerletti develop the first shock machine, also invented something he called "annihilation therapy." Cerletti tells us, "Bini in 1942 suggested the repetition of ECT many times a day for certain patients, naming the method 'annihilation.' This results in severe amnestic reactions that appear to have a good influence in obsessive states, psychogenic depressions and even in some paranoid cases.... The 'annihilation syndrome' has been compared by Cerquetelli and Catalano with the psychopathology following prefrontal [lobotomy]."[12]

Also in 1942, Dr. Theodore Dehne remarked to other psychiatrists at a meeting in Philadelphia that a number of schizophrenic patients had been given this therapy as a palliative* rather than a curative measure. "Nearly all such patients became quieter and were more easily cared for," he claimed.[13]

Dr. W. H. Kayy reported that during his tour of duty in World War II, he found an American psychiatrist using ECT for non-therapeutic reasons. "Electro-shock was indicated to help in the management of insane soldiers, who would become quite meek and manageable after a session with the 'thing.'"[14]

On an even more grotesque note, in 1948, Drs. J.C. Kennedy and David Anchel reported their research on "regressive electric-shock" in the *Psychiatric Quarterly.* "We started by inducing two to four grand mal convulsions daily until the desired degree of regression was reached....We considered a patient had regressed sufficiently when he wet and soiled, or acted and talked like a child of four."[15]

A 1951 report in *Diseases of the Nervous System* was one of many that told the same story: "By the end of this intensive course of treatment practically all [52] patients showed profound disturbances. They were dazed, out of contact and for the most part helpless. All showed incontinence of urine, and incontinence of feces was not uncommon. Most of them were underactive and did not talk spontaneously. Many failed to respond to

---

* Palliative: Serving to reduce the violence of, lessen or abate.

questions but a few patients would obey simple requests. They appeared prostrated and apathetic. At the same time most of them whined, whimpered and cried readily, and some were resistive and petulant, in a childish way."[16]

Shock treatment was a very raw affair during this period. Convulsions were so violent, broken bones were common, particularly in the spine. One researcher of the time, who X-rayed patients complaining of back pain after ECT, concluded that 0.5 percent of all ECT patients had fractures. However, another researcher X-rayed *every* patient after their first course of shock treatment and discovered, more accurately, that *20 percent* had compression fractures of the vertebrae.[17] Perhaps they were too apathetic to notice.

To remedy this problem and the general unpleasantness of patients thrashing about during ECT, psychiatrists began using muscle relaxants and anaesthesia during the 1950s. Prior to this, patients were awake when the electrodes were placed on their heads and the voltage released. This new procedure became widespread by the 1960s and became referred to as "modified ECT" to differentiate it from its violent predecessor. Even today this method is often called the "modern form of ECT" by its proponents, who work diligently on ECT's public image, trying to erase any connotation of the seizure-racked treatments of days gone by.

Of course, the use of muscle relaxants and anaesthesia did not reduce the impact the shock had on the brain and nervous system. If anything, *more* current was now needed to bring about a convulsion. These modifications simply prevented the body from manifesting the force of the current via a full-blown seizure. They also added to the treatment the side-effects and inherent risks of using anaesthesia and a powerful relaxant.

Another change in ECT—first tried in the late 1940s—was the use of "unilateral ECT." Normally shock treatments are given by placing electrodes on each temple. This is called *bilateral* ("two sides"). *Unilateral* is a variation on this in which the electrodes are placed on the same side of the head, one on the temple and the other on the forehead or above the ear. Proponents claim it results in less memory loss—a puzzling and contradictory position, since all ECT proponents refuse to admit there is any significant memory loss. The bilateral school says it is less effective, therefore requiring more treatments. An APA survey of psychiatrists in 1978 on this subject—the most recent we found available—showed that 75 percent of psychiatrists still give only bilateral shock.[18]

By 1970, one sampling of U.S. psychiatric hospitals showed 91 percent were administering ECT,[19] in spite of the fact the controversy had not quieted over the years:

1954—Dr. Maurice Grimes: "Shock therapy never builds. It only destroys, and its work of destruction is beyond control. A hundred and fifty years ago a well-recognized shock treatment method was to flog or frighten the patient, and in some instances the results were excellent. Now we 'do it electrically,' and we get about the same percentage of good results, but with some breaking of bones and memory losses which frightening and flogging never produced."[20]

1966—Dr. Robert Morgan: "In summary, even one or two ECT treatments risk limbic damage in the brain leading to retarded speed, coordination, handwriting, concentration, attention span, memory, response flexibility, retention, and re-education. On the psychological side, fear of ECT has produced stress ulcers, renal disease, confusion, amnesic withdrawal, and resistance to re-educative or psychological therapy. The research thus indicated that ECT was a slower-acting lobotomy with the added complications of shock-induced terror."[21]

1974—Dr. Karl Pribram: "I'd much rather have a small lobotomy than a series of electroconvulsive shocks.... I just know what the brain looks like after a series of shocks—and it's not very pleasant to look at."[22]

By the mid-'70s, however, ECT was sparking more than just catcalls and controversy. Physicians, ex-patients and others decided to take legal action. In 1974, they lobbied in California for a bill prohibiting, among other things, ECT without patient consent. The bill flew through both houses of the legislature with only one dissenting vote. When psychiatrist Gary Aden successfully sued to have the new law revoked, *another* law was passed in 1976 restricting the use of shock treatments. This one stuck and remains in effect to this day. Over thirty-five states have followed suit with similar legislation.

At the same time, prompted by the new ex-patient organizations and psychiatric watchdog groups, public outcry arose against ECT in the mass media. Neurologist John Friedberg published *Shock Treatment Is Not Good For Your Brain* in 1976. 1978 saw the publication of ex-patient Leonard

Frank's remarkably well-researched volume, *The History of Shock Treatment.*

Between 1975 and 1980, ECT use plummeted 46 percent nationwide.[23]

But there were those in psychiatry who wanted shock treatment to survive. At the 1975 annual APA meeting, six such psychiatrists joined together to form the International Psychiatric Association for the Advancement of Electrotherapy. Their purpose: to defend and promote the use of ECT and publicly assert its "harmless" nature. Dr. Gary Aden, the psychiatrist who sued against the 1974 California ECT law, was among them.[24]

The war continued. In 1983, the citizens of Berkeley, California—by a 62 percent vote—made it the first city in America to ban the use of ECT within the city limits. Once again, ECT proponents fought back and the courts rescinded the law in less than two months as being a local infringement on a matter of statewide concern. Similar efforts to ban ECT occurred elsewhere in the U.S., Canada, and around the world—endeavors which remain active to this day.

1985 saw the creation of the journal *Convulsive Therapy*, edited by Max Fink, today's leading ECT advocate. The magazine gave a stage and a sanctum of legitimacy to the minority of psychiatrists who continued to promote and use shock treatment. (A 1978 APA survey showed only 16 percent of psychiatrists actually gave ECT, and when they included as "Users" those who had advised psychiatric residents to use it, the total still only rose to 22 percent. Sadly, only 32 percent "expressed some degree of opposition to the treatment.")[25]

In 1991, the San Francisco Board of Supervisors, in a 7-4 vote, passed Resolution 129-91 opposing the use and public financing of ECT.[26] Signed by Mayor Art Agnos, it declared, "…The Committee concluded that ECT should not be used in the City of San Francisco due to the serious doubt that ECT is safe and effective."[27]

Today the battle rages on. Patient watchdog groups, outspoken doctors, and groups such as The Committee for Truth in Psychiatry—a collection of 500 ex-shock patients—decry ECT's effects and use, while die-hard ECT advocates push the continuous message that shock treatment is a good thing. As a result of their efforts, shock treatment has made something of a comeback in recent years.

WHAT IS SHOCK TREATMENT?

Modern shock treatment is a relatively straightforward procedure.

The patient is not allowed to eat or drink for four or more hours prior. This reduces the likelihood of vomiting during the treatment.

A half hour before, he is given a drug such as Atropine or Robinol, a medication that reduces secretions in the mouth and air passages, thereby cutting down the risk of suffocation and other complications that could arise from the patient swallowing his own saliva.

Patients are encouraged to use the bathroom prior to treatment to prevent accidents from loss of bladder or bowel control. Dentures, sharp jewelry, and hair ornaments are removed to avoid mishaps during the convulsion.

The person is placed on a bed. A "crash cart" is kept nearby. This is a cart supplied with a variety of life-saving devices and medications, including a "defibrillator" for jumpstarting a heart in cardiac arrest.

A jelly is applied to the temples. This helps improve electrical conductivity and prevent burns.

An anaesthetic is injected into the vein, rendering the patient unconscious in seconds. This saves the person the anxiety of feeling his body suffocate from the upcoming muscle relaxant and from watching the doctor place the electrodes on his head.

A muscle relaxant is then injected, causing a virtual shutdown of muscular activity, including breathing. From this point forward the subject is on artificial respiration until he resumes breathing on his own after the treatment.

A rubber gag is placed in the mouth to prevent the person from breaking his teeth or biting his tongue.

The electrodes, commonly round discs affixed to an elastic headband, are placed against the temples.

The psychiatrist pushes a button on the electroshock machine, and 70 to 170 volts of electricity are sent from one electrode through the brain to the other electrode. The shock lasts from 0.1 seconds to 1.5 seconds.

The convulsion begins. The body may quiver slightly or, more commonly, simply lie there, while in the brain and nervous system a seizure reaction takes place for 30 to 45 seconds or more. The muscle relaxant masks the body's normal response to the shock, which is a grand mal (French: "great illness") seizure, exactly like that seen in epileptics. Before "modern ECT," the person was awake when the shock was administered and writhed violently in the bed, requiring the presence of attendants to hold him down to prevent bone breakage.

The patient lies unconscious for a few minutes after the shock under artificial respiration, then begins unassisted breathing, and sleeps for 15 to 30 minutes. Upon awakening, he commonly feels any or all of the following: amnesia, disorientation, headache, nausea, dizziness, confusion, muscle ache, or physical weakness. Additional complications have included breathing irregularities, combativeness, delirium, heart irregularities, terror, vomiting, and wild excitement. After a few hours the immediate adverse effects usually begin to diminish, except for a certain amount of amnesia, confusion, and weakness, which varies considerably in intensity and duration. Many patients have claimed to have experienced permanent damage to memory, mental skills, and personality.[28]

Dr. Michael Chavin, an anesthesiologist who has assisted with "hundreds" of shock treatments, described to us what happens in the brain during ECT: "There is a shock wave through the brain, causing the brain to discharge energy in a very chaotic type of state. And this increases metabolism to a very high level which deprives the brain of oxygen and can actually destroy cells and destroy some of the intricate connections."[29]

Here is one psychiatric nurse's perceptions of post-shock treatment patients returning to the ward: "After the ECT treatments the patients were generally very confused and unsure of what happened to them. They were fearful. The treatments had brought on much anxiety and doubt. These patients would oftentimes have accompanying memory loss. They would ask the staff, 'What is happening to me?' 'I can't remember what happened.' 'What happened yesterday?' 'When will I get better?' 'Have my relatives come up to see me?' When such questions were answered, ECT-related amnesia had caused a memory loss so severe in some persons that these persons repeatedly questioned us and failed to recall the answers just obtained.

"I recognized a strange sort of apathy in these post-ECT people. A feeling of a sort of surrender or resignation to their fate overcame them. They would have a certain number of ECT treatments and become deeply depressed and very quiet and distant rather than whatever they had felt before treatments."

They are no longer feeling what they felt before treatments. Another successful cure.

THE MOST OBVIOUS THING ABOUT SHOCK TREATMENT

"It is a very bizarre notion that the passing of electricity through the brain can help someone," remarked Dr. Harold Sackeim, a leading ECT advocate, in 1994. "It sounds ludicrous and it frightens people."[30]

Frightens people, indeed. Of all the things that can be said about electroshock, one fundamental aspect stands out like a beacon. There is a visibly clear, natural repugnance to shock treatment in the average person, even among those who may not know there are seizures involved. This distaste goes beyond what some people feel toward dental work, surgery, or witnessing death and gore. The mere mention, description, or sight of shock treatment invokes an abhorrence unlike any other. Raw survival impulses come to the fore. There is immediate revulsion and outrage at the concept of electricity ripping through the brain, the mind, the self. On a very primitive level, the body and mind seem to *know* that this is something that can cause damage to the core of one's being.

And this reaction is not new.

"I saw something terrible today—I never want to see that again!" According to his wife, these were the words of a "very pale" Lothar Kalinowsky, who went on to become one of the world's leading ECT advocates, when he returned home after watching Ugo Cerletti administer the world's second shock treatment.[31]

The man who *received* that treatment had already made his own feelings known. After the first one, according to Cerletti, the patient said clearly and solemnly, "Not another one! It's deadly!"[32]

Cerletti himself was not free of the specter his actions raised. "Cerletti," Kalinowsky recalled, "had been worried that something might go wrong with the first treatment, and it was given in secret."[33]

Cerletti wrote how he felt after giving the initial jolt. "Naturally, we, who were conducting the experiment, were under great emotional strain and felt that we had already taken quite a risk."[34]

Psychiatrist and ECT advocate David Impastato relates about that first shock treatment, "The Professor [Cerletti] suggested that another treatment with a higher voltage be given. The staff objected. They stated that if another treatment were given the patient would probably die...." [35]

Cerletti later relayed his own gut reaction. "When I saw the patient's reaction, I thought to myself: This ought to be abolished! Ever since, I have looked forward to the time when another treatment would replace electroshock." [36]

In 1956—eighteen years after that first electroshock—it was evident he could still not shake the personal sense of darkness that hung over his actions. "It was not long after I had first witnessed electrically produced convulsions in man," he wrote, "and had confirmed that they had a practical application that I came to the conclusion that we must get away from the use of electroshock. When subjecting unconscious patients to such an extremely violent reaction as these convulsions, I had a sense of illicitness and felt as though I had somehow betrayed these patients." [37]

The man who gave the first metrazol shock treatment was no less spared. "On 23 January 1934 he induced the first convulsion in a patient by the intramuscular injection of 25 percent camphor in olive oil," wrote R.M. Mowbray in the *Scotland Medical Journal*, "and at the end of this successful experiment he was so distressed himself that he had to be supported to his room by nurses!" [38]

When researchers studied 96 mental patients receiving ECT in Los Angeles in 1963, they reported finding at least some fear in all the subjects. "Reactions ranged from strong denial of fear, such as 'I'm glad to take it,' to fear of total mental destruction or death, such as 'Shock will destroy my mind,' 'My heart will stop,' 'I will die.'... Often the S [subject] revealed under questioning a high degree of fear after first denying any fear, such as a depressed S who admitted 'I'm scared to death every time. I never know if I'm going to come out of it or not.'" The researchers noted the level of fear "remained relatively constant throughout the series of treatments." In short, personally experiencing ECT did not make it any less frightening. [39]

American poet Sylvia Plath wrote in her 1971 book *The Bell Jar* about her first shock treatment. "'Don't worry,' the nurse grinned down at me. 'Their first time everybody's scared to death.'" [40]

The American Psychiatric Association is acutely aware of the natural aversion people have to shock treatment. And it did something about it. Its 1978 Task Force Report on ECT states, "The Task Force is concerned that the terms 'shock therapy' and 'to shock' are neither appropriate nor helpful descriptions of the treatment and elicit unnecessary anxiety in patients and families. We recommend that the use of such terms be discouraged." This is why the term "ECT" is used in psychiatric circles rather than the common term "shock treatment."[41]

Something else in this report reveals that even psychiatrists have a sense of revulsion toward ECT that they perhaps prefer to hide beneath their clinical veneer. It is one thing to shock adults and become numb to it, but what about shocking children? If shock is so harmless and helpful, then why not? Yet only 16 percent could bring themselves to disagree with the survey statement, "ECT should not be administered to children 16 or under." 57 percent agreed when the disturbing thought was put to them.[42]

More than fifty years after that first "terrible" shock treatment, the response of horror has not diminished. "Belief that ECT affects the brain," acknowledged proponent Max Fink in 1991, a man who has given many of the treatments, "arouses primitive fears that the soul of the individual, one's inherent individuality and uniqueness, is affected."[43]

So what are we to think of this? Are we to believe, as some psychiatrists prefer, that this is all just an irrational fear? It is hard to believe that such a universal disgust can, with the sweep of a hand, be attributed to weak stomachs and overactive imaginations.

Doesn't it seem more likely that this feeling of revolt people have toward shock treatment is a survival reaction based on common sense? Electricity, after all, *burns*. It alters chemical and physical structures. After contact with it, most humans and animals will go to great lengths to avoid it. It is a pain that rakes through the body and senses and hammers them like no other. Multiply that effect by the added factor of electricity cutting through the most sensitive, critical organ of the body—the brain—the only organ nature saw fit to surround with bone—the seat of the mind and personality—add that factor and we have a recipe for terror.

And it is a terror that would seem to be quite justified.

So although it is important that we look closely at all aspects of ECT—including the psychiatrist's complicated explanations—so that we may evaluate it rationally, we must be wary of those who would like to steer us away from observing the obvious. And the above is something plainly—and painfully—obvious about shock treatment, though to the doctors who have given hundreds or thousands of them, this conspicuous terror in the eyes of their patients may no longer be visible, having become as over-looked and commonplace as the blood on a butcher's apron.

THE SECOND MOST OBVIOUS THING

In a 1980 study by C.P.L. Freeman and R.E. Kendell, published in the *British Journal of Medicine*, a group of ECT patients were surveyed to determine their attitudes toward the treatment. When they were asked, "How does the treatment work?" 32.7 percent answered, "Gives you a jolt or shock." This was, in fact, the *leading* explanation by far. ("Makes you forget" came in a distant second at 7.3 percent.)[44]

The second most obvious thing about shock treatment, aside from the aversion it generates, is that it "works" by violently jarring the individual. This is directly observable. Examinations of post-ECT individuals and descriptions of these patients by themselves and others paint a distinct picture of people who have been stunned.

So while some psychiatrists may try to portray, as did Dr. David Richmond in 1990, that "this treatment is far more complex in many ways than other medical or psychiatric treatments,"[45] the truth is the ignorant layman does not find this to be complicated or hard to understand at all.

One could take a group of even relatively low-IQ people and have them watch a person being given shock treatment. It is highly unlikely the observers would be surprised to find the shock recipient awakening stuporous and confused. It is a rather natural outcome of force being applied to the head. We all have some level of personal experience with head blows so it is easy to relate to. When that force is electricity, it is not hard to extrapolate that the impact will reach deep internally, will be pervasive, and will be harsh. And, most of all, it is not difficult to grasp that the recipient will be likely to come out of it *changed*.

"The changes one sees when electroshock is administered," wrote psychiatrist Lee Coleman in 1977, "are completely consistent with any acute brain injury, such as a blow to the head from a hammer. In essence, what happens is that the individual is dazed, confused, and disoriented, and therefore cannot remember or appreciate current problems."[46]

In 1942—four years after the advent of ECT—one anonymous psychiatrist needed little medical jargon to state the matter clearly in the *American Journal of Psychiatry*: "From the cases I have seen treated by shock therapy I believe better results could have been obtained by devoting the time and energy towards a more constructive program. To put it bluntly, I do not believe that we can scramble brains and expect to have anything left but scrambled brains."[47]

In an incisive 1990 article in *The Journal of Mind and Behavior*, Leonard Frank concludes, "One doesn't need a medical degree to recognize the destructive potential of passing 100 to 150 volts of electricity through the human brain. The same amount of current used to produce a seizure in ECT, if applied to the chest, would be fatal."[48]

WHAT PSYCHIATRISTS THINK OF ECT

The psychiatric view of electroshock, according to the 1978 APA ECT survey, runs from total opposition to wholehearted endorsement. Even among those who *give* ECT, there is a disparity of viewpoints. Some think it should be given more, some less. Some believe it should be used only as a last resort. Some consider it a first resort.

But there is a certain core of individuals who actively promote ECT and expend great effort to spread the message that electroshock is safe and effective. "Electroconvulsive therapy is a rapidly acting and highly effective treatment for severe affective illness [e.g. depression]," claimed advocates Richard Weiner and C. Edward Coffey in a 1991 article in *The Archives of General Psychiatry.*[49]

"[ECT's] efficacy is equal or better than alternative treatments for many mental disorders," wrote proponent Max Fink that same year.[50]

What these doctors see is that when shock therapy is applied to a given patient—usually for depression—that patient's attitude and mental view often *changes*, as one would expect after such a head trauma. If the patient is no longer depressed after a series of electroshocks, the treatment is deemed "effective."

And that is essentially the sole criteria used in evaluating the efficacy of ECT.

A 1974 article in *World Medicine* clearly indicates, however, that this "effectiveness" may exist more in the mind of the psychiatrist than in actual fact. Written by J. Easton Jones, the anaesthetist of a hospital in northern England, the article tells us the institution had to replace its old shock machine with a modern, more complicated, one. This machine was used for the next two years, until a new nurse came into the ECT room and remarked that the patients were not "twitching" as they should. Upon inspection it was discovered *the shock machine never worked*. "All the patients had been getting for two years," wrote Jones, who had administered the treatments, "was thiopentone [anaesthetic] and a shot of Scoline [muscle relaxant]—and no one had noticed."

The author commented, "In my innocence I supposed that there was some sort of rational scientific basis for the treatment."[51]

Despite such evidence, hardcore ECT proponents insist the treatment is a necessity. To prove this they often raise the specter of patient suicide and claim if ECT were denied, a great many suicidal patients would end their lives without the treatment. Such statements are often made when ECT's usefulness is challenged, yet they do not have any proof of this. In fact, from 1975 to 1980, a period when ECT use dropped 46 percent and one would expect a commensurate increase in suicide, there were actually *fewer* suicides recorded in the United States, despite population growth.[52] Also statistics routinely show that men suicide three times as often as women. Yet following the argument that they utilize ECT to prevent suicide, why is it that psychiatrists consistently shock twice as many women as men?[53]

What *is* known, however, about suicide and ECT is that patients sometimes take their lives *after* receiving shock treatment. A 1982 study of 90 patient suicides showed that 10 percent had had shock treatments within the previous four months. Two ended their lives while still in the hospital and seven did so shortly after being discharged.[54]

Ernest Hemingway's demise is a classic example. Despondent from ECT "ruining my head and erasing my memory," the Pulitzer Prize-winning author put the end of a shotgun barrel to his head and pulled the trigger two days after leaving the hospital.[55]

And of course, the truth is a great many doctors and non-physicians manage to deal successfully with suicidal patients without ever resorting to electroshock.

THE EFFECTIVENESS OF ELECTROSHOCK

While a handful of ECT users express pleasure with the "effective" results of electroshock, outsiders to this process see other things besides a patient who is no longer depressed. They see a person walking about in the murk of mental befuddlement, docile and uncertain. But these things will likely not be noted in his medical chart as they are normal "side effects." What will be noted is that the patient's depression is "responding" to the treatment. (As a case in point, in one study 50 percent of the ECT patients claimed memory impairment was the worst side effect they experienced, but this was noted in only 7 percent of the charts.) [56]

The patient is returned to his family and friends. They, too, notice the forgetful, dull-witted behavior. They may assume the doctor knows best and simply say nothing. They may be happy to see the patient is less of a problem to them and accept his state. Or the family may ask the doctor about it. If so, the doctor will explain the situation in a variety of ways.

The common physician response is, "It's all temporary." This will handle a large percentage of queries—families that will return home, await improvement, and abandon the matter in the hustle and bustle of living. They or the patient may occasionally remark after that about how his mental faculties haven't been the same since "those shock treatments."

But again, psychiatrists who promote ECT regard these "cognitive effects," as they call them, to be almost irrelevant. That the patient is too confused or disoriented to be depressed is also considered irrelevant. They look primarily at the fact that the depression is "gone." This is their trophy and *this is the entire basis for the claim*, "Electroconvulsive therapy is a rapidly acting and highly effective treatment."

While this may sound too incredible to believe, Dr. A. E. Bennett explained this "recovery process" in 1977 in a published letter, protesting an unfriendly ECT article. "Improvement in affective disorders," he wrote, "follows the induction of transient mental confusion which appears after treatment, depending upon spacing of treatments and the patient's age. This confusion coincides with recent memory impairment. This transient, induced, organic, psychotic reaction makes the patient forget his worries, breaks up introspection and obsessive thinking and reverses the affect, frequently changing depression into mental elation." [57] The "elation" Bennett refers to is a common aftereffect of a blow to the head. A 1991 article in *Special Report* tells us, "It's known that a trauma to the brain, whether induced by an electric current or a 12-car pileup, can leave the recipient feeling remarkably relaxed and comfortable. That's why nurses and orderlies have long joked that at any hospital the head-injury ward ranks with the maternity ward in having some of the most cheerful patients around."[58]

As to the "cognitive effects," some take the tack of justifying them, like psychiatrist Frank Guerra. "Depression is like cancer," he told the *Denver Post* in 1990. "It's a potentially fatal illness. Nobody says we shouldn't be treating cancer because of the side effects. Everything in medicine has side effects."[59]

Others avoid the subject by clouding it in completely irrelevant, pseudo-scientific mystery. For example, in 1990, when Dr. Charles Hudson tried to defend the charge that ECT causes memory loss, he stated, "I believe that their [ex-ECT patients] complaints are real but their complaints are difficult to understand medically. Usually, I think subjective memory is a very different thing from objective memory, just as subjective pain can be a very different thing from objective pain."[60]

Still others tell us these side effects simply are not there. "Thousands of patients receive ECT each day in this country with obvious benefit and no readily demonstrable adverse effects," wrote Dr. Fred Frankel in the *Massachusetts Journal of Mental Health* in 1973.[61]

It is puzzling to many how psychiatrists can look at a post-ECT patient who is weak, stumbling and muddled and yet only remark that the patient is now "recovered" as he is no longer depressed. We asked several doctors how it could be that their colleagues miss the obvious picture.

Thomas Szasz pointed out that psychiatrists don't see the full impact of electroshock "because it would be inconsistent with their efforts to use it as a treatment. People magnify or minimize what suits their interests."[62]

Michael Chavin told us it is not so much that psychiatrists become deadened to the obvious. "It's not quite even that," he said. "They don't even know what they are doing. They don't have a basis of understanding of what the human being is. I would meet psychiatrists and talk to them because the mind fascinated me. They had nothing to say, I mean nothing to say. If you would ask them how would you deal with a person, why would a person have an anxiety attack, what would be the genesis or origin of voices in your mind, why would a person act in a disturbed manner— they couldn't even begin to tell you about that. All that they can do, all that they are taught is the person is depressed and what do you do. Boom, you give them ECT, you give them Thorazine, you give them Elavil or antidepressant. This is what their creed is."[63]

THE MEN BEHIND ECT?

In reviewing extensive amounts of literature on ECT, within and outside the medical journals, it became apparent that there is a relatively small band of hardcore ECT advocates in the U.S. psychiatric community and abroad. Their names come up repeatedly in psychiatric journals or in newspaper quotes (Max Fink, Richard Abrams, Harold Sackeim, Richard Weiner, to name a few), reporting their allegedly unbiased scientific findings on the effectiveness or safety or best uses for ECT. Harmful findings by these proponents are rare indeed.

This kernel of supporters then spreads the message to others through teaching or articles or speeches on the subject. The message is constant: "ECT is safe and effective." We found a certain percentage of psychiatrists then assume the message is truthful and perpetuate it (they commonly parrot the medical journals).

Money is, of course, a powerful incentive. It has been estimated that 100,000 people a year get ECT in the U.S., generating $2 to $3 *billion* in revenues.[64] Anesthesiologist Chavin, who is quite intimate with the costs of electroshock, having billed for many himself, told us, "It could be easily $2,000 per treatment on an in-patient basis. The psychiatrist charges $300-$400, the anesthesiologist charges between $250 and $500. The hospital charges plenty for the use of the machine, the room, the medications, all the anaesthetic. Medicare and Medicaid pay less, so they do it much less frequently on Medicare patients. In state psychiatric institutions where they are not getting paid this type of money, it is an extremely low rate and in private psychiatric institutions where they get paid $1500 to $2000 per treatment, it is a frequent thing."[65]

Despite the obvious financial motives, possibly some of these doctors are trying to utilize the latest in psychiatric technology to help their patients. While anti-ECT groups have indelicately referred to them as "shock doctors," conjuring images of hunched, wild-eyed professors in lab coats, the truth is that a good number of them are simply following the road of assurance that has been paved by the ECT experts.

However, when we look intimately at these experts—those who actively keep electroshock alive as a treatment—we find *their* intentions may be less than honorable and *their* scientific validity more questionable.

Probably no one performed or promoted ECT with the same zeal as Lothar Kalinowsky until his death in 1992.[66] An icon in the field, he administered countless shock treatments until he was well into his eighties. There can be no doubt that Kalinowsky had seen and heard about the full breadth of effects that shock treatments have on the human mind and spirit. He had started as an aide to Ugo Cerletti. And his familiarity with the private problems doctors have with ECT were evident in a 1956 letter published in the *American Journal of Psychiatry*. He noted being privy to "personal communications on [ECT] fatalities which remain unpublished because of understandable fear of lawsuits."[67]

As to his awareness of ECT-caused memory loss, he once wrote, "All patients who remain unimproved after ECT are inclined to complain bitterly of their memory difficulties."[68] But then how could he *not* notice ECT's effect on memory? It is the number one side effect and has been known to be such since ECT's inception. One 1980 study done on patients six months to seven years after they received shock treatments showed that 30 percent felt their memory "never returned to normal after ECT."[69]

Yet in 1976, when Kalinowsky was asked to give testimony in a deposition for defendant Dr. John Nardini in an ECT-memory loss malpractice suit, the shock expert was noticeably silent on the subject.

The plaintiff was a government economist named Marilyn Rice. Rice wrote: "I have lost the vast edifice of specialized knowledge that I had been adding to almost every day of my adult life. I have lost the pride and self-confidence (and income) that go with being an expert in one's field. I have lost the intellectual joy of utilizing my mental capital. I have lost my value to society in that the work in which I was engaged was dependent on my unique assemblage of knowledge. I have lost much of my general education. I have lost personal memories that I would never willingly have given up—people I have met, places I have been, books I have read, plays I have seen."[70]

While we can understand Rice's memory loss, how do we then explain Kalinowsky's sudden amnesia when he testified to the following, *under oath* and under penalty of *perjury?*

Q: Does any psychiatrist to your knowledge inform his patients that there is a risk of permanent memory loss from ECT?

A: No.

Q: Is permanent memory loss a known or established consequence of ECT treatment?

A: No.

Q: In your practice have you ever experienced or seen a case of permanent brain damage or permanent memory loss caused by ECT?

A: No.

Q: Some people, it's reported, have had in excess of a hundred treatments, is that right?

A: Right.

Q: Then with those patients has there been any demonstrated evidence of permanent brain damage or permanent memory loss by ECT?

A: No.

Q: Have you ever read about an authenticated or documented case of permanent memory impairment caused by ECT?

A: No, except there are schizophrenic patients whose sickness continues and who slowly deteriorate because schizophrenic patients frequently deteriorate....[71]

With Kalinowsky's "expert" testimony to refute her, Marilyn Rice lost her case.

Another leading figure in the world of shock treatment is Dr. Richard Abrams. Author of numerous articles and books on the subject, Abrams defends ECT doctors when they are sued. He promoted the 1985 National Institute of Mental Health Consensus Conference on ECT and had input into the APA's 1990 Task Force Report on ECT—a report that squelched virtually all of the many concerns raised in the APA's previous (1978) report. Abrams has also been a key figure in pushing the recent trend in psychiatry, the shocking of the elderly. (Most of the patients receiving electroshock in California and other states are over 65.)

What was generally *unknown* about Abrams, until he was questioned in a deposition in 1991, was that he is *president* of a shock machine manufacturing company called Somatics, Inc. He also makes up half of its two-person board of directors and receives about 50 percent of his income from the company. Starring in Somatics' ECT videotapes, which sell for about $350.00 each, is Abrams' close colleague and editor of the only medical journal on ECT, Max Fink.[72]

And then there is the unholy triad, the fate of whom makes one wonder about the character of these ECT proponents. One of the key efforts to save ECT from extinction came in 1975 when the treatment was under serious threat from the ex-patient movement, concerned legislators, and budding psychiatric watchdog groups. As mentioned, at that year's annual meeting of the American Psychiatric Association in Anaheim, California, six shock treatment proponents united to found a bastion against the assault: the International Psychiatric Association for the Advancement of Electrotherapy (later renamed the Association for Convulsive Therapy).[73]

In an uncanny act of fate, *three* of the six founders were the subjects of public scandals in ensuing years. H.C. Tien of Michigan gained notoriety when it became public that he had used shock to destroy the memory of a woman so that she could be programmed to become a better housewife. Shervert Frazier, it was learned, had plagiarized a number of papers he had published. He lost his professorship at Harvard because of this.

And then there was the third member of this group, Dr. Gary Aden, the man who sued to have the California's 1974 ECT law struck down. He had his medical license revoked in 1989. According to the *San Francisco Examiner*, Aden had a fondness for instructing his patients to read pornography. But he went further. "Aden also ordered them to dispense with underwear, masturbate during phone calls from him, submit to beatings with a riding crop, and allow themselves to be penetrated with foreign objects and branded on their private parts, records show. His patients complied, then complained."[74]

The San Diego Union reported that three of Aden's female patients alleged the doctor "had sexual intercourse with them, drugged them and/or physically abused them" between 1972 and 1980.[75] This was the same period in which Aden was actively promoting ECT. Another article in the same newspaper reported he allegedly beat the women and branded two of them "with heated metal devices, including an iron that bore his initials."[76]

The prosecutor, who went on to become a judge, claimed Aden's case was "absolutely" the worst he'd ever seen.[77]

Aden himself refused to undergo psychiatric examination.

BRAIN DAMAGE

"Until recently electro-convulsive therapy was used on a fairly wide scale. The method, however, involves gross interference in the bodily functions and entails pin-point hemorrhages in the brain tissues. Its application, therefore, is restricted to cases where all other methods of treatment have failed. A course of convulsive therapy is followed by a memory loss of the type of retrograde [events prior to the shock] or anterograde [events after the shock] amnesia, which is a clinical manifestation of both the functional and the organic changes occurring in the brain due to the electric shock."[78]

This matter-of-fact description comes from the Russian textbook, *Psychiatry*, published in 1969. Decades ago—as far back as the 1950s—there was ample evidence in the U.S.S.R., as there was in America and Europe, that shock treatments cause cerebral damage and memory loss. Unlike their American and European counterparts, however, Soviet psychiatrists found no "controversy" in these findings. Nor was there any professional effort to hide or obfuscate the facts, perhaps because there was no financial incentive to do so.

Another book from that country, *The Structure of Psychiatry in the Soviet Union*, by Edward Babayan and published in 1985, tells a similar story and is quite specific as to why electroshock was rarely used in the U.S.S.R. "Another harsh method used in clinical psychiatry, that of electroconvulsive therapy, was also repeatedly subjected to critical analysis. Special tests were staged in animals at the Laboratory of Pathological Anatomy of the Institute of Psychiatry, U.S.S.R. Academy of Medical Sciences, to study the effect of electroconvulsive therapy and convulsive attacks on the central nervous system. Convincing proof was submitted pointing to grave changes in the central nervous system, the nerve cells, the glial-tissue apparatus, and the interoceptors of the brain and spinal cord of animals after electroconvulsive therapy; following single and repeated convulsive attacks induced by various methods, effects were observed ranging from changes in the functional character of the type of swellings of the interoceptors of nerve fibers down to their complete destruction (i.e. to degeneration of nerve cells and the nuclear apparatus).... A study into the clinical data of these experiments determined with precision the narrow indications for this method and imposed the strictest limitations on the use of electroconvulsive therapy in psychiatric practice."[79]

In discussing how Soviet law "limits and proscribes [psychiatric] methods that have failed to justify themselves," such as ECT, Babayan is bemused by its use in the U.S. where, he says, "it is very widely used and has become all but a repressive measure applied even to healthy people."[80]

In posing the question, "Does ECT cause brain damage?" research readily reveals that answers are not difficult to find. The official Soviet answer was obviously an unequivocal *yes*. Yet recognition of shock-induced brain tissue destruction was also common in American and European medical journals during the 1940s, '50s, and '60s when psychiatrists freely discussed brain-damaging treatments without fear of reprisal (or litigation). As early as 1946, American neurologist Bernard Alpers commented on the blatant evidence of ECT-caused brain damage to be found in the medical literature. "A survey of recent reports relative to this problem would lead one to believe that the matter is settled and that there is nothing further to be said."[81]

Then, in a notable example of the pot calling the kettle black, America's leading lobotomists, Walter Freeman and James Watts wrote in 1944, "The evidence assembled from the various fields of investigation in regard to shock therapy points definitely to damage to the brain. Perhaps the majority of authors tend to minimize the significance of this and attempt to find some explanation more satisfying to their consciences."[82]

A 1942 report on the autopsy of a post-ECT patient states, "The importance of the case lies in that it offers a clear demonstration of the fact that electrical convulsion treatment is followed at times by structural damage of the brain."[83]

When the facts are irrefutable, one can always take another approach. As Dr. Paul Hoch—one of Kalinowsky's colleagues—remarked in the *Journal of Personality* in 1948, "This brings us for a moment to a discussion of the brain damage produced by electroshock.... Is a certain amount of brain damage not necessary in this type of treatment? Frontal lobotomy indicates that improvement takes place by a definite damage of certain parts of the brain."[84]

In 1959, I.M. Allen published a report in the *New Zealand Medical Journal* on numerous studies on the effects of shock treatments. He concluded, "They confirmed the appearance of irreversible physical changes in the brain after and as a result of electric shock treatment."[85]

Years later, a 1973 study in the *American Journal of Psychiatry* casually concludes, "The ECT patients' inferior [test] performance does suggest that ECT causes permanent brain damage."[86]

But then, suddenly, in the mid-1970s, a strange silence descended upon the land. Psychiatric journal reports on brain damage and other negative effects mysteriously dwindled. This happened to be coincident with the fact that psychiatric practices had started to fall into greater disrepute, with a simultaneous rise in malpractice suits and the protests of the ex-patient movement. "There has been a dramatic drop in the number of published accounts of any problems with the practice of ECT, especially deaths," wrote neurologist R.J. Grimm in 1978. "There is an erie silence in a literature that hitherto was substantial and extremely useful in questions of morbidity and mortality."[87]

A clear example of this reticence is seen in a 1982 letter to the editor of the *British Journal of Psychiatry*. It is written by two doctors who are dancing on hot coals after making a disturbing discovery. "We wish to disassociate ourselves," they write, "from the unduly stark comment [in an article] by our co-authors, Drs. Calloway and Dolan, that "'we found a statistically significant association between frontal lobe atrophy and previous treatment with ECT.'" Though they admit "the statement is correct," they tell us, "All that can be said at the moment is that the results are sufficiently interesting to warrant further investigation. They cannot, in our view, be taken as definite evidence either for or against the suggestion that ECT may cause permanent cerebral damage."[88]

Another example of scientific sleight of hand occurs in the APA's 1978 and 1990 Task Force reports on ECT. In the 1978 Task Force report, 41 percent of the psychiatrists surveyed agreed with the statement, "It is likely that ECT produces slight or subtle brain damage," and only 26 percent disagreed with it. (There was no question asked regarding ECT causing *greater* than slight or subtle damage.)[89] The report also freely discusses postmortem cerebral destruction found in ECT patients.[90]

Yet in the APA's 1990 186-page report, the subject of brain damage is virtually non-existent, brushed off with the whisk broom of a single sentence: "In light of the available evidence, 'brain damage' need not be included as a potential risk."[91]

While the APA is obviously culpable, much of this vanishing act is attributable to the public relations efforts of ECT proponents. It is good Madison Avenue technique but hardly science. They continue to make such authoritarian claims as the 1991 remark in an ECT text, "There is no scientific controversy about ECT.... We know that it works well and with a high degree of predictability and safety."[92]

The fact that shock treatment was considered so destructive that even an oppressive totalitarian regime such as that of the Soviet Union refused to countenance it apparently does not qualify as sufficient scientific opposition to be considered controversy. The fact that Japan will not use it and that numerous European countries have restricted its use appears to be equally undaunting.

Is this ignorance or arrogance? The evidence of brain damage has been so widely published over so many years that ignorance is highly unlikely.

Factually, in 1990, even the Food and Drug Administration (FDA), notorious for standing silently on the medical sidelines, stated, "FDA does not believe that ECT has been shown to be without risk of injury, even though changes in brain tissue may not be observable."[93]

In 1991, the year the "no scientific controversy" claim was made, *Neurology* magazine described a woman's death due to cerebral hemorrhage clearly caused by ECT. The writer wrote, "It is controversial whether ECT causes structural brain damage."[94]

An extensive and "impartial review of the literature" on ECT in *Clinical Neuropsychology* concludes—as did the Soviets—"A wide array of research and clinical based facts that provide suggestive to impressive evidence in isolation, provide compelling evidence when viewed in a composite fashion.... ECT has caused and can cause permanent brain pathology."[95]

So where is the controversy? Well, consider by contrast, a similar extensive, but not necessarily impartial, review of the literature in 1984 by unabashed ECT advocate Richard Weiner, which concludes, "Evidence that ECT, given in a contemporary fashion, typically leads to the development of brain damage and its lasting physiologic and cognitive correlates is weak."[96]

While a number of psychiatrists have busily tried to hype "modern ECT" and smooth over and nullify the damaging evidence against ECT already accumulated in years past, the simple truth is, as psychiatrist Lee

Coleman put it, "Since neither the brain nor electricity has changed since the Thirties, the result is still the same—brain damage."[97]

But microscopic inspection of gray matter is not the only evidence of brain damage created by shock treatments. Clearly the reason so many different scientists have carried out post-ECT brain examinations is because they *suspected* cerebral tissue destruction *by seeing the behavior of patients after shock*. Such patients visibly manifest severe head trauma. And the issue of brain damage keeps coming up after fifty years of study—despite persistent denial by ECT advocates—because patients continue to show *symptoms* of brain injury.

Their personality is blunted, they appear dull-witted, they are in a fog. These manifestations are widespread, clear-cut, and easily seen by even the untrained observer.

To compound the problem, patients themselves are commonly unaware of how much mental damage has been done. "As in other forms of brain injury," wrote neurologist John Friedberg, "the subject is often oblivious to the residual deficit."

Linda Andre, an ex-shock patient herself (ECT in 1984) and the head of the Committee for Truth in Psychiatry, an organization of former ECT recipients* told us, "This is what happens with the brain damage. There is just less of you for quite a long time.... I don't think you fully recover either. But especially right after—I didn't have the word 'no' in my vocabulary. Everyone remarked on it, too, because I had never been that way before. It was really strange, and I've seen it in other people: 'OK, whatever you say; whatever you want, I don't care, I don't mind.' That is a physiological thing that happens with the brain damage....Very scary."[98]

The 1980 Freeman and Kendell study of ECT patients concurred remarkably with Andre's experience. In questioning the patients, the interviewing psychiatrists noted, "We found this area of the questionnaire

---

* While there are organizations of ex-patients in Canada and the U.S. who are opposed to current ECT practices, there is no such organization of ex-patients in favor of electroshock. In fact, it is uncommon to find former ECT recipients who are willing to promote it as a therapy. Rarer still is the psychiatrist who has undergone the treatment. In researching thousands of pages, we came across one or two. During the 1991 ECT Hearings in San Francisco, when a pro-ECT doctor tried to explain away this scarcity of patients willing to promote electroshock, Supervisor Angela Alioto listened incredulously. "With all due respect," she told the psychiatrist, "if I received medicine that made me well, I would go out and advocate for it." There were *no* satisfied ECT recipients at the hearings.[99]

[regarding consenting to ECT] the most unsatisfactory and we were left with the clear impression that patients would agree to almost anything a doctor suggested. Many people could not remember ever having signed a consent form, didn't regard it as particularly important and seemed quite happy to have other people, such as relatives, give consent on their behalf." This docility was evident, even though ECT had been given *six months to seven years prior.*[100]

The same report says, "Many subjects had little idea how many treatments or how many courses of ECT they had had, and the information they gave was quite unreliable when checked against case-note records.... Forty-nine percent were sure they had been given no explanation at all [about ECT] and stuck to this view even when it was suggested to them that they might have forgotten. Twelve percent said they couldn't remember being given any explanation but one might have been given."[101]

A rare recorded interview before and after ECT, reported in 1950, shows how closely the effects of shock treatments match what you would expect to see with a severe head injury:

"Before ECT (Q. How did your illness begin?).... About four years ago, right after I lost my child...I took thyroid then which caused palpitations. I didn't know, at the time, that that caused it. I felt terrified by them. It was a real panic, as if I were on railroad tracks with a train coming. I was trying to be very brave about the death of my baby, going to work in the hospital where it died, collecting legal papers on it, and so forth, trying to be the super-woman. Then I had the palpitations; a friend told me I should get psychiatric help. I saw my family doctor and he sent for a neurologist. I spent the night at my doctor's office and then I went to the H Sanatorium for a week. I was hopeful of getting all better. They didn't feel I was really ill. After that, I began analysis."

The above information required no prompting by the interviewer. Here is the same woman 3½ weeks after completing a series of 10 shock treatments:

Q. Did you take some medication after the loss of your child?

A. I don't remember.

Q. Thyroid?

A. I think so.

Q. What reaction did you have to it?

A. I don't know.

Q. During that period did you have any special symptom which disturbed you?

A. I felt depressed.

Q. Anything else?

A. I don't recall.

Q. Did you have palpitations?

A. I vaguely remember having palpitations now that you mention it.

Q. How did you feel about them at the time?

A. I don't recall how I felt.

Q. How did you feel at the moment when you had the palpitations?

A. Probably not too well.

Q. Did you ever go to a sanatorium?

A. Yes, I remember going to one.

Q. What was the name of it?

A. I don't recall the name.

Q. What were the circumstances that led to your going there?

A. I don't remember why I went or what happened; I remember being there though.

Q. How long were you there?

A. I don't remember. I don't think it was for very long. I really can't reconstruct that whole period." [102]

MEMORY LOSS

Clearly the primary complaint one hears from shock treatment patients is that they cannot remember things. In the Freeman and Kendell study, 63.9 percent of the patients complained of memory impairment after ECT.[103] In a 1982 study, when 35 patients were asked three years after receiving ECT, "Do you think your memory now is as good as it is for most people your age?" 58 percent said "no." All but one attributed the difficulty to ECT.[104]

Memory function, however, is not a mental faculty that works independently of all others. Memory difficulties are normally associated with a host of other problems, such as mental acuity, reasoning ability, and learning skills. Indeed, one's very personality is founded considerably on past experience.

These more fundamental ECT-incurred losses (as well as psychosurgery-incurred) prompted Pope Pius XII to warn in 1952, "A man may not undertake or permit medical acts, physical or somatic, which doubtless eliminated serious physical or psychic stains or infirmities, but which at the same time involve permanent abolition, or a considerable or lasting diminution of liberty, that is to say, of the human personality in its typical or characteristic function. The result is the degradation of man to the level of a being sensitive only to acquired reflexes or of a living automaton."[105]

Psychiatrist David Richman wrote in 1978, "The personal testimony of many who have undergone shock treatment attests to the fact that it can and does cause permanent memory loss. Languages, special skills, recollections of personal experiences can be blotted out of the mind as if an eraser had swept across a blackboard. Despite the psychiatric party line that ECT causes only temporary memory loss and no permanent memory or intellectual loss, there is no hard evidence to back up these claims."[106]

When we asked Linda Andre what happened when she received shock treatments, her immediate remarks were of the memory loss. "I lost years and years of my memory," she said. "I would say about five years altogether. So I've had difficulty in life not knowing who I was. You *don't* regain it. That is one of these really cruel myths. Psychiatrists have said that, but it is absolutely not true. Nobody regains any of it."

She has also found that, among the ECT patients in her group, learning difficulties stemming from the treatments are common. "I hear it all the time. We sort of get together and figure out ways of making life easier by living with the problem, because we all have the same problems.... But it is very common for people to have learning disabilities after shock. People can't remember things. I don't mean just not remember what happened to them, but they can't remember an ongoing thing, like where they put things, where they knew something that they used to, or forget people's names or how to get places. Everyday memory becomes poor. Mine is like that. It is very frustrating, but there is nothing I can do about it. It's just there."[107]

Obviously this is a very real loss to those who experience it. Some wonder how psychiatrists live with themselves, knowing they are creating such devastating effects. One answer may be simple denial. When ECT supporters discuss this exact same memory loss, it loses something in the translation. In a book sponsored by NAMI (National Alliance for the

Mentally Ill), authors Isaac and Armat coolly remark, "While few mind forgetting the period immediately preceding ECT when they were profoundly depressed, acutely psychotic, or both, a small number complain of severe, long-term memory deficits."[108]

It is one of the great paradoxes of the ECT camp that many proponents make little of the memory impairment (words like "spotty" or "transient" are common in the literature), yet a great number heartily endorse the use of *unilateral* shock treatment for the sole reason that it allegedly creates less memory loss.

Unilateral, as earlier noted, involves running current through one hemisphere of the brain as compared to bilateral which shocks both. A continuous dispute among ECT proponents, however, is the argument that unilateral is less effective than bilateral. Isaac and Armat tell us that giving only bilateral "is deplored by such experts on ECT as Max Fink and Richard Abrams. Conceding that from 10 percent to 20 percent of patients respond only to bilateral placement, Dr. Fink believes that because memory loss is so much reduced with unilateral placement, it should be tried first, except in special circumstances (for example, when the individual is actively suicidal). Dr. Abrams has recent data suggesting that unilateral can be as effective as bilateral ECT if the electrical dosage intensity is raised to approximately two and a half times threshold (the minimum electrical dosage necessary to obtain seizure)."[109]

So unilateral shock, an allegedly improved form of shock treatment, actually requires stronger current through the brain to be as "effective." *Or* it requires more treatments to produce the same effects as bilateral.

Remarkably few psychiatrists seem to question the notion that a shock through one side of the brain is somehow going to create less physical damage than a lesser shock running a different direction through the same gray matter.

Common sense would seem to indicate that if a different section of the brain is damaged, a different set of adverse mental and motor effects would result. Neurologist Friedberg concurs. "In this [unilateral] variant," he wrote in the *American Journal of Psychiatry* in 1977, "the current path and most of the damage is confined to the nonverbal side of the brain, usually the right hemisphere. This exploits the well-known phenomenon of anosognosia, or denial, that is associated with right hemisphere lesions—

victims can't verbalize their difficulties. They complain less. Cohen and associates, however, using design-completion tests proved that shock to the right hemisphere produces its own kind of memory loss—visual and spatial. Inglis found in 1970 that the effects of unilateral ECT were comparable to those of a right and left temporal lobectomy, with identical impairment of memory and learning."[110]

THE CHELMSFORD STORY

It is rare indeed for the public to get an intimate look at the inner workings of the ECT rooms within a psychiatric hospital. The residents of the state of New South Wales in Australia, however, have seen more than any citizenry could ever desire or imagine.

The hospital was Chelmsford. The chief psychiatrist, Dr. Harry Bailey. In the 1960s Chelmsford was a tiny private facility with only 14 beds, expanding to 40 in 1971. Yet the horror stories that fermented in this unassuming little place would ultimately rock the front pages of Australia's newspapers for a decade; require 288 days of oral testimony in a two-year, $15 million government investigation; headline Australia's largest newspaper with an unprecedented series of stories, running every day for two weeks; and result in the first permanent ban on a psychiatric treatment (outside of psychosurgery) in the English-speaking world.

It started in mid-1963 when Bailey began to practice a technique he called Deep Sleep Therapy (DST). This involved the intensive administration of barbiturates and other drugs to induce a 2-3 week state of continuous unconsciousness and semi-consciousness. The patient was then given *daily* ECT, without anaesthesia or muscle relaxant. *The Report of the Royal Commission Into Deep Sleep Therapy*, the summary of one of the longest-running government-directed inquiries in Australia's history, explains, "Patients rendered unconscious were generally fed through a naso-gastric tube although they did have periods of semi-consciousness from time to time when they were able to take some sustenance. The manner of toileting was to permit the patients to wet or soil the beds although again, during periods of semi-consciousness, a commode was used. The level of unconsciousness required manual, periodic, repositioning of the patient and routine suctioning of the airway."[111]

One woman described her boyfriend after his treatment with DST. He had been brought to Bailey for drug abuse, but otherwise had no history of mental problems. "When I saw Ashley again, shortly after he had been released from [the] hospital, he had completely changed. He was very subdued and had lost most of his confidence. He did not want to see any of his friends anymore and had no interest to do anything. He was very lethargic and would just sit quietly, although he was obviously very anxious and withdrawn...he couldn't think straight and would become very distressed when he tried to say something and couldn't formulate his thoughts clearly. Physically he had deteriorated. He had lost a lot of weight and was very thin, his skin had become blotchy and pimply. He had become very introverted and lacked the confidence to do even basic things—like organize himself to go somewhere or talk to someone. He had become very suspicious of people, something he had never done before. We continued our relationship but he was obviously very confused and depressed. His health had deteriorated and he had very little appetite. Ashley used to love to eat, but after coming out of the hospital it was just one more thing that he had lost interest in."[112]

On December 17, 1970, twenty-four days after his last DST treatment, Ashley James Adams, aged 20, killed himself.

He was one of 24 people who suicided within a year of receiving DST. This was 2 percent of the 1127 patients who had endured deep sleep. Another 24 died as a direct result of the treatments.

So many of the survivors—hundreds of them—were crippled by the treatment with memory damage or other mental and physical impairment that a government fund—normally used for *crime victims*—was used to compensate ex-patients for their losses.

When it was discovered that over 15 percent of Bailey's patients had received ECT without written consent and a great many more received it without adequate explanation, the Royal Commission ruled that the ECT "doctors and the nurses who treated patients without the patient's consent, contrary to the patient's consent, or on the basis of a consent obtained by fraud or deceit, committed a trespass to the person of each of these patients and were responsible for an assault on them." This classified the giving of ECT without consent as a crime, punishable by jail time.[113]

Inquiries into Bailey's activities unearthed even more sordid details.

Although fellow psychiatrists who knew him for many years testified that Bailey was "most dedicated and the most skilled physician"[114] and "the Master," and "a very significant member of the psychiatric profession,"[115] those outside the psychiatric profession seemed to see a different side.[116]

One police officer was assigned to investigate the suicide of one of Bailey's patients, Sharon Hamilton. He found the married DST doctor was having sex with the woman, had beaten her, had borrowed tens of thousands of dollars that were never repaid, was left a hundred thousand dollars in her will, had tried to involve her in a sexual "threesome," and probably drove her to suicide. The officer's evaluation of Bailey: "He was a very, very low form of life."[117]

It was discovered that sex with numerous patients and sexual advances toward others was part of Bailey's routine. A head nurse reported, "In his speech he would be very raw and anything but a gentleman. Sometimes of female patients he would be most rude and refer to them sexually. What they needed was a 'f.' He told the patients that."[118]

Sure enough, a patient testified, "Every time I went to see him he would say to me, 'What you need is a good fuck'; nobody had ever spoken like that to me ever in my life, and he also commented on my big boobs and also felt them and it was a bit embarrassing."[119]

The Commission wrote, "It is difficult to comprehend the vileness of Dr. Bailey's behavior."[120]

The final report also made a comment not unlike some of the questions we have posed here. "It seems inconceivable," they wrote, "that someone of Dr. Bailey's talent could not have been aware of the defective nature of his treatment."[121]

Deep Sleep Therapy was banned in New South Wales, Australia, in 1983, the same year Bailey was brought up on manslaughter charges.

The Commission concluded its inquiry on December 21, 1990. But there was one key witness they were unable to interview. At the height of the scandal in 1985, Dr. Harry Bailey committed suicide with his own barbiturates.

The Chelmsford inquiry was the most in-depth investigation of its kind, one that not only peered into a questionable therapy, but inspected the institution and doctors involved. The primary impetus that prompted government action was the public horror that arose when the stories of deaths and mentally and physically damaged (including paralysis) patients would not go away.

Little did the public know, however, that similar rates of deaths (2 percent or more) have been reported in past medical journals as a result of *ECT alone* with no newspaper or government commission taking notice.[122] As to post-ECT suicides, there are many known incidents, but no known figures.

And as we saw earlier in the scandal-riddled shock treatment association of 1975, half of its founders were "anything but a gentleman." In light of these similarities, is it possible that if we were to inquire deeply enough into the lives of those who hold shock treatment so dear and portray it as so scientifically sound that we may find other Harry Baileys—who, like "the Master," deftly invoke the authority of science, yet who, in truth, "live in a delusional state"—"not aware of the defective nature of his treatment?"

The victims of these men—while they may suffer memory loss and other trauma—have no such delusions. They know without doubt that they have been subjected to brutality under the guise of science.

CASE HISTORIES

Over the past quarter century the Citizens Commission on Human Rights (CCHR™) has devoted its efforts to exposing harmful practices in the field of psychiatry. In the process, it has received thousands of reports from ex-patients and family members who have experienced the effects of shock treatments firsthand. A case in point: One day in September, 1994, following the appearance of CCHR representatives on a small national talk show discussing shock treatment and involuntary commitment, the phone began ringing in the Los Angeles CCHR headquarters at 6:00 AM and calls continued to flood in, keeping up to eight lines occupied until late in the day. More than 500 calls were received.

The following case histories were selected at random from CCHR files to give some flavor of what these people experienced. Where available, dates and ages are given. Names and identifying data have been withheld.

While ECT proponents would deride such evidence as "anecdotal," who is more qualified to describe the effects of ECT than its victims? And who has more right to make his voice heard?

Case A: A report on a woman who received 20 shock treatments in

1965. "[She] had no choice but was given these treatments after refusing to go along with a psychiatrist's group therapy. On the 19th shock [she] did not go under the anaesthesia but was fully conscious. Even though she told the psychiatrist and nurses that she was not under they gave her the shock anyway.... Afterwards, in terror, she begged the psychiatrist to not give her more shocks. The psychiatrist told [her] that since 20 shocks had been ordered she would receive 20 shocks.

"After the shocks [she] found that her artistic abilities were virtually gone. Before the ECT she had been a talented artist, but she now has no memory of that talent and cannot draw or paint."

Case B: A report on an 18-year-old woman depressed after losing a premature baby. "The psychiatrist did not tell [her] of any dangers or problems that ECT would cause and [she] did not question the psychiatrist as she had been taught all her life to trust doctors.

"[She] checked herself into a psychiatric hospital of her own will. She had her first shock that same day. When [she] woke up she was in agony and terrified. She describes it as knowing that something was very wrong. However, when [she] told the nurses that she did not want any more shock and that she was checking out of the hospital, they would not let her leave. [She] was instead grabbed by hospital attendants, force-drugged, strapped to her bed and kept locked up in the hospital. While there, she was forced to undergo approximately 12 more shocks in a week's time. [She] says that her recall of events after being grabbed by the attendants when she wanted to leave is very vague and hazy as the shocks destroyed her memory.

"After [she] was released from the hospital her family described her as having gone from a bubbly and alive young woman to a zombie who acted like a whipped puppy dog. It took [her] years to recover from the ordeal. She had trouble talking and connecting her thoughts and had to struggle to come back physically and emotionally to a point where she could function normally. According to [her], what helped her recover more than anything was when she learned that others had had similar experiences and that she needed to speak out against these abuses to make people aware of the damage and harm that shock and psychiatry does to people."

Case C: A report on a woman suffering from insomnia due to stress. She was placed on drugs, then "persuaded to try shock as she was 'not responding to drug therapy.' [She] received seven shocks before she finally realized

149

that she was only getting worse with the drugs and the shock. At that point she left the psychiatrist, never went back to the hospital and eventually got off all of the drugs.

"However, [she] has had permanent memory damage due to ECT. Fortunately she did not lose her job skills but she has very little recall of the time during which she was under the psychiatrist's care. [She] also cannot recall certain events and memories in her life and has had to have family tell her these things. She does not recognize some people who are friends and her memories of them have never returned."

Case D: A woman who claims her sister, a psychiatrist, mistakenly considered her suicidal and contacted a colleague who had her committed for a "72-hour hold" in 1989. "Once at the facility, [she] contacted her attorney and was making arrangements to get released. The psychiatrist then drugged [her] and had her sign papers consenting to ECT. [She] was then given ECT and so has only vague memories of what happened once she was in the hospital.

"She says her memory was permanently damaged and she suffered in her career as a dentist since she could not remember patient names or details and her staff had to continually remind her of these things. [She] states that she was drugged up and given ECT to prevent her from leaving the hospital on her own.

"Several months later [she] did try to commit suicide as she was in despair over the damage the ECT had done and felt that she was losing her career due to this damage."

Case E: A woman who went to see a psychiatrist in 1986 about her anxiety over a heart condition she had developed. "The psychiatrist placed [her] on drugs which brought about a decline in her mental and physical condition. [She] was hospitalized several times as a result.

"During one of these hospitalizations, another psychiatrist suggested ECT for [her]. This psychiatrist did not tell [her or her husband] that ECT can create problems for someone with a heart condition. Instead [they] were convinced that this treatment would be safe and [she] received some 38 shocks. After a while [the husband] began to notice that his wife was getting worse with each shock but the psychiatrist persuaded [her] to continue in spite of [the husband's] concerns. [She] experienced a loss of memory and became frailer and more submissive as a result of the shock.

150

"In 1988, while receiving her 38th electroshock, [her] heart stopped and had to be restarted. From there she was rushed to an intensive care unit where she underwent a series of tests and operations to restore her health. [She] never recovered and died later that year.

"[The husband] feels that the psychiatrists with their drugs and shock treatments ended his wife's life prematurely and he wants shock to be banned as a barbaric and destructive practice."

Case F: An affidavit signed in 1987 by a woman who had exhibited unusual behavior in 1968 while withdrawing from alcohol addiction. "My husband could not understand my behavior, not being familiar with withdrawal from alcohol, and thought that it would be best to take me to see a psychiatrist, as he thought a psychiatrist would know what to do.

"Rather than being helped by the psychiatrist, I was confined in the _____ Hospital…and while there was given electroshock against my will. In total I was given twenty-three treatments which have devastated my once clear memory. Since receiving the shocks, I have a hard time concentrating, and I cannot remember many important parts of my life, such as what happened on my child's last birthday.

"Prior to the electro-shock I was a waitress, which is actually a difficult job, requiring an excellent memory and an ability to think quickly. Since getting the shocks my ruined memory prevents me from working as a waitress again.

"Also, my ability to learn new information has been seriously damaged. I have a hard time retaining things and I have to go over and over my checkbook before completing balancing it."

Case G: An affidavit from a man who was awarded a full scholarship to attend Julliard School in New York. He received ECT in 1970. He went to a psychiatric hospital for light-headedness and an inability to concentrate (which he later attributed to malnutrition brought on by his meager budget).

"At this hospital I was given a battery of shock treatments. I don't know how many shocks I had there, although I know that it was more than one. I believe that my wife managed to stop the treatments after the third one.

"I never gave anyone permission to shock me. My wife had given a general permission that the psychiatrists could do what had to be done to make me better, but she did not give permission for them to shock me, and my understanding is that she stopped the treatments when she saw me in a daze after the third one.

"I have lost a lot of memory due to ECT, and have lost permanently the recollection of many fine experiences from my days at Julliard. I don't remember a lot of the instruction that I was given in school, although I'm convinced that if I had been given more shocks my recollection would be far worse."

Case H: An affidavit from a senior electronics engineer with two masters degrees who worked on a critical military project for a major high tech firm. In 1982 he became greatly troubled when his girlfriend abruptly left him. When he discussed the matter with his supervisor, a psychiatrist was recommended. The doctor first gave drugs.

"The drugs did not improve my condition, and this psychiatrist then told me that ECT was the only alternative, and that it would bring me out of my depression. I knew nothing about ECT at the time and didn't know that it permanently destroyed memory. I was required to sign certain forms which...provided some limited information regarding the side effects of ECT, including *temporary* memory loss.

"I was given 12 ECT treatments in 1983. After the treatments I went back to work...but was not able to work as I could not remember the electronics principles and formulae necessary to my job. I went back to the psychiatrist and told him that I could not remember what I had learned. He told me that my memory would return within six months. I waited six months, and my memory did not return. When I asked the psychiatrist about it, he said it would return within the following year.

"My memory of my electronics training did not return within another year, and in fact has not returned to this day [about five years later]. I have no doubt that my memory was destroyed by ECT treatments. I am now on a disability pension, not having been able to hold a job since I received the shock treatments. I have no doubt that I will never be able to go back to work again.

"In my view ECT is a barbaric treatment with a tremendous potential for destruction. The current protections regarding informed consent and due process are vital, while in my opinion are inadequate to give the full truth of the destructive power and permanent disabilities caused by this treatment. I don't feel that I was fully informed, and if anything, the protection against people being destroyed with ECT should be strengthened to where there is a true disclosure of what ECT does. If I had full knowledge of the effects I would have fought being given ECT or even being put into the hands of the psychiatrists.

"I feel that my career, my education, and my brain were utterly destroyed by ECT."

Case I: An affidavit by a man who at 21 became depressed by life problems and a breakup with a girl friend and subsequently spent a year in a psychiatric hospital. Upon release, he was still depressed. "I went to see Dr. _____, the former head of _____ Hospital and a reputed leader in his field. [He] recommended electro-shock treatments as "the only thing" that would help me. He presented it as something that I had to receive or I would never be happy, and represented to me that if I did receive ECT I would do much better in life. Accordingly, in 1965 I consented to a number of ECT treatments.

"In fact, the electro-shock treatments I received did not improve my depression, but instead destroyed my memory of my education, particularly my accounting training, which had been my major in school.

"Fortunately, I was very young and was able to relearn some of what I had lost. I feel that the major part of my education was stripped away by the ECT at that time, and this has not come back. I have had to relearn a lot of it, and this has been hampered by the reduced ability to remember and concentrate which I believe is due to the ECT as well.

"I asked the psychiatrist when my memory was going to return and was told that there was no reason to worry about that. The psychiatrist explained his certainty that my memory would return in this manner: 'In Russia, where ECT is given as torture to political prisoners, people's memories return even after hundreds of shock treatments. As you have gotten much less than that, your memory will definitely return.'"

"Prior to ECT I was given a full scholarship to _____ Law School, primarily due to my having had the second highest score on the law aptitude in _____ College and partially due to having good grades in school. After ECT I failed the US Army IQ test. My score put me in the 29th percentile.

"Also, after ECT my ability to operate in life generally was so severely hampered, that I was actually afraid that I wouldn't be able to get any kind of job, and was willing to take just about any job. The ECT treatments have affected me adversely through to this day [22 years later].

"I do not feel I 'volunteered' for ECT. I had no concept of what I was getting into. If I had, I would never have allowed it, and every citizen in this country is entitled to the right to full disclosure and refusal of this destructive 'treatment.'

"If a person's arm is cut off, only his body is hurt. The damage is visible and can be comprehended and dealt with. But with ECT, the mind is assaulted, affecting a person's certainty about himself. It is incredible to me that in this day and age ECT is still done in this country."

Case J: A 35-year old woman who received 25 treatments at age 25 for "bad depression." She was interviewed by phone. Notes taken include the following:

"They said it helped me, but it gave me real bad headaches. It was real scary. My friends tried to kidnap me from the hospital because I looked so bad. Epilepsy popped up after when I was 28.... Very traumatizing. Real bad headaches."

Question: Any long-term effects? "Memory loss. For five years after lots of holes in memory—most of it came back eventually. Don't know what memory I lost from just before shocks."

Question: Any effect on your personality? "Very confused. Friends said I was violent just after. I ended up in state psych hospital for one year after."

Question: Did the treatments affect your intelligence? "Yes. Had diagnosed learning disabilities. Dropped out of school. Math subjects hardest for me."

Question: Did the treatments affect your emotions? "Yes—flat. I lost my spark."

Question: Did the treatments affect your ability to deal with life? "Completely disabled me at the time. I was totally scrambled and disoriented. Ran down the street in my hospital gown. Long cycle of major recuperation—over two months.

Question: Is there anything else you'd like to mention about your experience with shock treatment? "It made me more depressed. Tried to commit suicide after ECT. Didn't do me any good."

Question: If you had it to do over, would you take shock treatment again? "Never. I'd kill myself first."[123]

THE FUTURE OF SHOCK

Although the supporters of electroshock have worked hard to promote it for more than a half century and reported on its effects with great optimism, it only seems reasonable to wonder if such a practice can ever find broad acceptance in a civilized society. Civilization—by definition—eschews force over reason. And the rendering of electroshock upon suffering minds is—to most—a shuddering act of force.

So while we may hear such remarks as that in a 1991 ECT text that "ECT is now rejoining the mainstream of sound medical psychiatric practice," the truth is there are far fewer fans in the bleachers than ECT advocates would have us to believe.

In the same text, Max Fink gives us a glimpse as to how little support ECT actually has. He bemoans the fact that "this negative perception of ECT is still held by many mental health professionals; some, in an allegiance to a faith in the psychological basis of mental illness; some in the belief that the public perception of brain damage is indeed true." He tells us, "The [anti-ECT] movement also finds passive support in the ambivalence of leaders of American psychiatry, who are insecure about the role of ECT in their practice, teaching, and research." He adds, "ECT remains a stepchild of psychiatry, being taught in a limited number of medical schools and residency training sites."

The shock expert goes on with the litany of rejection ECT has undergone. It is ignored by psychiatric learned societies. It is paid no heed by national organizations dedicated to somatic treatments. "Only one association," he says, "the Association for Convulsive Therapy [the current name of the notorious 1975 "electrotherapy" organization], encourages research and teaching in ECT." Federal, state, and municipal hospitals hardly use it. The pharmaceutical industry does not encourage it. No large foundations will support ECT research. "The few psychiatrists who become interested in ECT find that it is difficult to obtain local approval for experimental studies and almost impossible to obtain financial support from governmental or private fundings sources."[124]

Clearly, electroshock's chapter in history is finite. But judging from its past record, it is highly unlikely that organized psychiatry will police its own ranks and write the final page. It will doubtless be written by alert legislators after enough crippled ECT patients have come forward and told the story of shock treatment's legacy.

After a half century and millions of electroshocked people, only two questions remain: How many more minds will it take? And why has it taken so long?

CHAPTER VI

DESTROYING THE BRAIN TO SAVE THE MIND

MOST READERS WILL NO DOUBT WONDER WHY WE ARE INCLUDING a chapter on psychosurgery. After all, this notorious form of mental treatment vanished from the psychiatric scene in the 1960s and '70s.

The simple answer is that psychosurgery has, in fact, *not* disappeared. It has, instead, gone underground.

In her 1992 book *Psychosurgery*, Joann Rodgers noted that because of fear of legal, political, and regulatory repercussions, those who continue to work in this field tend not to offer information either to the public or to journalists who report to the public on health and medicine. "For example," she writes, "some of the psychiatrists and surgeons who made headlines calling for an open mind about psychosurgery in the 1970s would not respond to repeated requests for interviews…. One neurologist at a prestigious East Coast medical center made anonymity for himself and his hospital the price of cooperation and access to information."[1]

Indeed, the mere *mention* of the subject to these doctors creates anxiety. Just as psychiatrists of today try desperately to banish the phrase *shock treatment* from the public's vocabulary, so does the word *psychosurgery* rattle the nerves of those performing the operations. "Without exception," wrote Rodgers, "every surgeon and psychiatrist I interviewed requested that the word *psychosurgery* be expunged from the text in favor of such phrases as 'brain surgery to treat psychiatric diagnoses' or 'functional neurosurgery.'"[2]

So secretive is this field that the precise number of psychosurgeries being done is unknown. While there are 200 to 300 recorded operations per year around the world[3], the actual figure may run into the thousands, with many being performed out of the public eye or under the guise of other forms of brain surgery.[4]

Call it what you will, surgical tampering with the brain for psychiatric reasons is still with us.

THE BIRTH OF PSYCHOSURGERY

Medical historians often trace the beginnings of modern psychosurgery to 1848 and an accidental explosion involving a railroad worker named Phineas Gage. The bright and easygoing Gage had an iron rod driven through his cheek and into the frontal lobes of his brain, yet to the amazement of many, lived to tell the story. Lived, but did not survive all that well. According to his physician, the formerly religious Gage became "fitful, irreverent, indulging at times in the grossest profanity (which was not previously his custom), manifesting but little deference to his fellows...." He noted "his mind was radically changed, so that all his friends and acquaintances said that he was no longer Gage." Unable to hold his job, the railroad worker found employment as a freak for P.T. Barnum's circus.[5]

But this and similar incidents did not go unnoticed in the medical community. Here was living proof of a remarkable phenomenon: you could remove or damage the frontal parts of a man's brain without altogether killing him.

In the 1880s, Swiss asylum superintendent Gottlieb Burckhardt became the first known psychosurgeon when he removed cerebral tissue from not one, but six, patients, hoping "the patient might be transformed from a disturbed to a quiet dement."[6] Although one died and others contracted epilepsy, paralysis, and aphasia (loss of ability to use or understand words), Burckhardt was pleased that several did indeed become easier to manage.[7] Severely criticized by fellow doctors, the psychiatrist stopped the operations, but defended his actions.

In 1910, similar surgery was attempted on three patients by Lodivicus Puusepp, an Estonian physician, who also then abandoned the idea.[8]

But 1935 marked the true birth of psychosurgery. That year Egas

158

Moniz, a Portuguese neurologist, attended the Second International Neurological Congress in London, where he heard reports on two chimpanzees which had had their frontal lobes removed. Postoperatively, the animals showed little or no concern for matters that had previously frustrated them. They had become calm and passive.

Perhaps, Moniz hypothesized, the same treatment could be applied to pacify human emotions. Given the obvious dangers of the ground the doctor was treading, one would expect such a theory to be painstakingly researched and carefully tested before its application to the public. Moniz did not perform one operation and then methodically scrutinize the short-term and long-term results—despite the fact that after the first surgery, as one writer notes, "…The woman was reported as being less agitated, but more apathetic."[9] Less than 60 days after the conference, the neurologist, with the help of a neurosurgeon, carried out a succession of 20 psychosurgeries in a span of two months.[10, 11]

He dubbed it the *leucotomy* (leuco: "white"; tomos: "cut"), because it involved slicing out white matter. To perform the surgery, he developed a unique tool called a leucotome. The shaft probed into the white matter of the frontal lobes. A plunger on the leucotome was pressed by the surgeon. A loop of wire came out the end of the tool into the brain. The leucotome was then turned, coring a section of the patient's cerebral tissue.[12]

Moniz—the man who coined the word *psychosurgery*—claimed a third of his patients cured, a third improved, and a third remained unchanged.[13, 14] This assertion—which was nothing more than the doctor's unverified opinion—would become the basic assumption behind thousands of leucotomies to follow. Dissenting opinion was not well tolerated. Author Joann Rodgers says of Moniz in *Psychosurgery*, "He used personal connections to quash criticism in the popular press."[15]

The inevitable footnote one finds in any discussion of Moniz' life is that he was ironically shot and permanently paralyzed by one of his leucotomized patients in 1944. What one rarely hears, however, is that twelve years later he was attacked again by another grateful patient—this time with fatal results.[16]

WALTER FREEMAN AND THE LOBOTOMY

Moniz's work ushered in an era that American Psychiatric Association President Alan Stone called "a tragic and unfortunate chapter of psychiatry."

He added, "I found it shocking when I was a medical student back then and I still do. There was no excuse for what was done."[17]

"What was done" was that Moniz's claims of cures set in motion a chain of events that would result in more than 100,000 psychosurgeries around the world over the next 20 years.

On September 14, 1936, within three months of the publication of the Portuguese doctor's work, an American psychiatrist and neurologist named Walter Freeman teamed up with neurosurgeon James Watts to perform the first such brain operation in the United States. Freeman gave the surgery a new name—a name that, unbeknownst to him, would live in infamy: the frontal lobotomy.*[18]

The patient was a woman who, before surgery, "showed uncontrollable apprehension, was unable to sleep, laughed and wept hysterically." She was held down while a drug was administered, rendering her unconscious. "Four hours later after the anaesthetic had worn off," wrote Freeman and Watts, "her face presented a placid expression and she admitted that she felt much better...."[19]

During the next five years, Freeman and Watts carried out 108 operations on a variety of mental patients. Four died. Freeman claimed 63 percent had sustained worthwhile benefit. One "complication" they noted in some patients was what Freeman called the "frontal lobe syndrome," a vegetative condition described by one modern psychosurgeon as "nonchalance, inability to carry out tasks, and loss of social control."[20]

Freeman's idea of "benefit" or "improved," however, was similar to Moniz's. Where others saw "zombies," Freeman saw patients who were "less anxious, less concerned about their inner experiences, and more responsive to the environment."[21] When the lobotomy was performed on patients in chronic pain, the psychiatrist thought it a success that they no longer cared or, as he put it, "the patient was enabled to face disability and death with equanimity."[22]

This is a key point, for it applies across the boards to all psychiatric treatments today. When you read the numerous self-serving newspaper quotes from psychiatric spokespeople claiming they can successfully con-

---

* The frontal lobotomy was called the "prefrontal leucotomy" or "prefrontal lobotomy" by Moniz. They are the same operation. Later psychosurgeons preferred "frontal" since the tissue destruction is not in front of ("pre") the frontal lobes, but is within them.

trol or cure or blunt depression, psychosis and numerous other ailments, remember the above paragraph and the ones that follow.

But back to Freeman. In his book *Psychosurgery* (1942), he shows the photograph of a dull-eyed woman with the caption: "Photograph of patient 22 months later when she had gained a lot of weight and was rather indolent but pleasant, making a good adjustment and caring for the home."

A before-and-after set of pictures tells a similar story: Before— "Depression of 4 years duration with constant complaint of painful eye." After—"Patient one year after operation. She was indolent and euphoric, and subject to convulsive seizures, but she made no complaints."[23]

Freeman and Watts' loose interpretation of "better" becomes quite evident when their reports are even cursorily studied. The following letter was written by a patient's son:

"Mar. 24, 1940

"Frankly, Dr. Freeman, I don't know of any way that I might suggest to anyone to more effectively cause the deterioration of an entire family than that operation. Progressively since the operation my father has been regressing toward childhood. He lost his business…dissipated the family savings…and made our home life practically an unbearable thing. Apparently for him the operation was a huge success for he had no worries about the past or future and almost daily suggests that others see you about the operation…."

Notes on the patient show he "became quite unruly and aggressive toward his family and his clients, lost the rest of his business, was faced with lawsuits on account of financial irregularities as well as physical attacks. He turned his son out of his home, changed secretaries every few days, behaved in a very arbitrary manner toward his clients and turned completely against his wife who was ill of cancer."

With this evidence before them, here is how Freeman and Watts interpreted the results: "From the standpoint of the patient's inner harmony, it cannot but be considered an overwhelming success. Here stands a man with his business ruined, his family alienated, facing criminal proceedings, and he insists that he never felt better in his life."[24]

Convinced of the rightness of their cause, Freeman and Watts showed little compunction in asking patients to pay the ultimate price for "getting better." "Patients who undergo prefrontal leucotomy," wrote Freeman, "must sacrifice some of the virtue, some of the driving force, creative spirit or soul."[25]

One patient who had to make this sacrifice was John F. Kennedy's sister Rosemary. The young woman was mildly retarded, occasionally violent, subject to wild mood swings, and had a taste for running the streets at times. One magazine reports, "Eminent medical specialists were consulted and the advice was that the girl should undergo 'a certain form of neurosurgery.'"[26] It is believed Freeman himself performed the operation.[27]

Many years later Rosemary's mother, Rose Kennedy, told what happened: "The operation eliminated the violence and the convulsive seizures, but it also had the effect of leaving Rosemary permanently incapacitated. She lost everything that had been gained during the years by her own gallant efforts and our loving efforts for her. She had no possibility of ever again being able to function in a viable way in the world at large."[28]

And, as mentioned earlier, after her operation, Rosemary Kennedy spent the next half century in a nursing convent in Wisconsin.[29]

Freeman and Watts justified the debilitating results of their work with their own brand of social philosophy. "It is better for [a patient] to have a simplified intellect capable of elementary acts," they wrote, "than an intellect where there reigns disorder of subtle synthesis. Society can accommodate itself to the most humble laborer, but it justifiably distrusts the mad thinker."[30]

By 1948 the duo had performed 623 lobotomies, with a 3 percent death rate. They had refined their technique, using deeper, more accurate cuts and switching from general anaesthetic to a shot of novocaine to the head so the patient would be awake during the operation—allowing them to monitor the patient's behavior as they cut through his brain.[31]

The surgery began with the boring of holes above the temples.

"Apprehension becomes a little more marked when the holes are drilled," they wrote, "probably because of the actual pressure on the skull and the grinding sound that is as distressing, or more so, than the drilling of a tooth."[32]

The patient could feel and hear the scalpel scraping away white matter inside his cranium.

"You could see the change right there on the operating table," recalled

Watts in an interview. "People who were moaning, people crippled with guilt, depression—their face eased and tension left—like that."[33]

In lobotomizing one 24-year-old man named Frank, the doctors took note of his comments as evidence of the operation's success:

"Doctor: How do you feel?

Frank: I don't feel anything but they're cutting me now.

D: You wanted it?

F: Yes, but I didn't think you'd do it awake. Oh, gee whiz, I'm dying. Oh, doctor. Please stop. Oh, God, I'm goin' again, Oh, oh, oh, Ow, (chisel). Oh, this is awful. Ow (he grabs my hand and sinks his nails into it). Oh, God, I'm going, please stop."

Forty-five minutes later:

"Doctor: What happened to your fear?

Frank: Gone.

D: Why were you afraid?

F: I don't know.

D: Feel okay?

F: Yes, I feel pretty good right now."[34]

It is a hideous thought that this monster had control over the minds and bodies of thousands of mental patients—and had the willingness to use it. Modern day psychosurgeon Thomas Ballantine comments on his experience, watching Freeman perform his most famous psychosurgical development—"ice pick surgery": "It was awful. Ugh. I got sick. I couldn't watch it. None of us could very easily.... I had to walk out of the room. I don't have a very good answer to why he wasn't stopped."[35]

What Ballantine was watching—or what he could not stomach watching—was a specialized form of lobotomy developed by Freeman and first performed in secret in his office in January, 1946.[36] Hitherto, the operations were complex and expensive, requiring the adroit services of a neurosurgeon and surgical team. Freeman wanted something simple and easy.

His surgical instrument of choice was an ordinary ice pick he had taken from his kitchen drawer. The patient, a woman named Ellen, was knocked unconscious with electroshocks. Freeman pulled back one of her eyelids to expose the tear duct where the eye socket (the "orbit") met the bridge of the nose. He placed the tip of the ice pick against the thin sheet of bone there. "A light tap of the hammer," he later wrote, "is usually all that is needed to drive the point through the orbital plate."[37] He noted, "In other cases, however the plate is so thick and heavy that the operator risks bending or breaking the instrument. Quite often there is a sudden give or even an audible crack as the...plate fractures."[38]

In the typical operation, the ice pick was driven in about two inches (later up to 3.5 inches[39]) and the handle was swept as far to one side as the orbital plate would permit. Further probing and slashing followed. The procedure was then repeated via the other eye socket. The patient commonly awoke with black eyes.

He called it the transorbital lobotomy (or leucotomy). It was Walter Freeman's gift to psychiatrists, a psychosurgical technique they could perform on their own without the need for a qualified surgeon, or even an anaesthetist.

"I was horrified when I saw it," commented APA president Alan Stone.[40]

Watts, the neurosurgeon, was outraged by his partner's undignified, devil-may-care surgical methods and the two ultimately parted company.[41, 42] Freeman himself noted the technique was "favored by psychiatrists but frowned on by most neurological surgeons."[43]

There was also another source of friction between Watts and Freeman. At the outset of their early surgeries, the pair had agreed that lobotomy should only be used as a last resort on hopeless cases. Gradually, however, Freeman saw things differently. "Lobotomy should be considered in a mental patient who fails to improve after six months of conservative therapy," he told doctors in 1951. "It is safer to operate than to wait."[44]

Freeman's new quick fix for the hopeless cases of mental hospitals catapulted him onto the world's stage—a place he found most endearing. According to his ex-partner, he was "a good speaker, almost a ham actor. He was so good, people would bring their dates to the clinic to hear him lecture." The lobotomist became a media icon, backed up by praises from the top names in psychiatry, as he traveled from state to state (and ten foreign countries) touting the inflated results of his "ice pick surgery" and hawking his service to society with the motto, "Lobotomy gets them home."[45]

His wild claims of success were reported heartily by a servile press, but little else. One day while in the middle of surgery at Cherokee State Hospital in Iowa, Freeman released his grip on his surgical tool to take a picture. The ice pick sank into the patient's brain up to the hilt. The matter was shrugged off and received scant attention.

Like shock treatment, lobotomy was hailed as a cure-all for every mental disorder. Psychosis, homosexuality, willful behavior, alcoholism, depression —there were few restrictions. *Psychosurgery* author Joann Rodgers reports, "Nothing, it seemed, could stop the lobotomy juggernaut, or its apologists. Enthusiasm far outstripped suspiciously bloated results."[46]

What was commonly *not* reported were the overwhelming tragedies left behind:

1. Post-operative death and suicide—mortality rates as high as 10 percent have been reported.[47]

2. Epileptic seizures. Studies have found convulsions in up to nearly half of patients who have received lobotomy.[48] Freeman himself noted, "The seizures may begin soon after operation and come under control easily, or they may first appear five to ten years after operation."[49]

3. Weight gain—sometimes leading to obesity. "The lowering of activity and of pride in appearance makes for overindulgence in food," wrote Freeman.[50]

4. Loss of bowel and bladder control—something "more troublesome to the family than the patient," says Freeman.

5. Bizarre behavior: Hyperactivity, distractibility, irritability, profanity, rudeness, loss of social restraint, hypersexuality, laziness. And alcoholism —"The family has a responsibility to…prevent the development of a taste for alcohol."[51]

6. The hallmark of lobotomy: the deterioration of intellect, the loss of personality, the loss of self. In Freeman's words: "Isn't it true that when these poor devils stop suffering, it is through a loss of what you call psyche.…What happens to the psyche if it is not 'mercy killed?'"[52]

Even children were not taboo. Freeman and Watts commented on one mother's review of her reckless and hostile 6-year-old after lobotomy. "She has not had one temper tantrum since the operation…it is a pleasure to dress her now."[53] A 1949 study on over 20 lobotomized youngsters reported "a somewhat mixed result." It discussed the case of one "wild, destructive" boy: "the child was docile…obedient, though irresponsible. The mother states that she now has on her hands a child of nine years physical growth but of only three years mental growth."[54]

Freeman took his show on the road, traveling about the country, lecturing and lobotomizing in theatrical fashion, selling his promise of emptying out the nation's back wards. In August, 1952, he roared through five state hospitals in West Virginia, performing or supervising 228 psychosurgeries in 12 days. The press dubbed his tour "Operation Ice Pick."[55]

One report tells us, "He performed his operations not only for a packed house but also for the cameras. He set up lights and provided himself with a backdrop, posed with his golden ice pick in hand, ready to poke it into somebody's head. He often operated on ten patients in a row, sometimes two at a time."[56]

One patient, a huge black woman, Freeman reported as being violent and unsociable. After lobotomy, however, "We could playfully grab Oretha by the throat, twist her arm, tickle her in the ribs and slap her behind without eliciting anything more than a wide grin or hoarse chuckle."[57]

In late 1948, Freeman went to Western Washington State Hospital at Steilacoom, where he performed what would become one of his most infamous operations. The patient was Frances Farmer, a popular, beautiful and vivacious actress who had earned a five-year stint in mental facilities for her rebellious, reckless, and often whimsical behavior.

Farmer's biographer, William Arnold, describes Freeman's visit:

"The tormented actress was held before him. He put electrodes to her temples and gave her electroshock until she passed out. Then he lifted her left eyelid and plunged the ice pick shaped instrument under her eyeball and into her brain. [After doing a number of other patients, Freeman left. William Keller, superintendent of the hospital walked out sickened.]... An hour later, Keller returned to the operating theater and found everyone gone. He walked into the anteroom and looked at the postoperative patients resting on cots. One woman was silently weeping and several others were staring blankly at the ceiling. Near one end of the row of patients was Frances Farmer. She was, for all purposes, ready to be released. She would no longer exhibit the restless, impatient mind and the erratic creative impulses of a difficult and complex artist. She would no longer resist authority or provoke controversy. She would no longer be a threat to anyone."[58]

Walter Freeman was not the only lobotomist plying the trade, however. Others followed suit shortly after the first operations in the 1930s. With the advent and banner-waving of the simple "ice pick surgery" in 1946, though, non-surgeons (primarily psychiatrists) stepped into the fray. The numbers tell the story. Up to that point—ten years after the operation's introduction—approximately 2,000 had been done. Within three years the total had reached 10,000. By 1949 the number of lobotomies performed mushroomed to 5,000 per year.[59]

In a state hospital in Logansport, Indiana, Dr. Jack Ferguson studied Freeman's methods and modified the transorbital lobotomy into a three-minute procedure. He carried out hundreds of the operations, claiming a two-thirds success rate, the only drawback—in his eyes—being that after the surgery the patients "couldn't plan ahead."[60]

By 1955, the Lobotomy Era had peaked. New tranquilizing drugs quieted patients with much greater efficiency. But for countless mental patients, the damage had been done. As medical writer Joann Rodgers noted, "The grim reality is that between 1936 and 1960, an estimated 50,000 mutilating lobotomies were performed in the United States alone."[61]

Another 15,000 were carried out in England.[62] Worldwide the number reached 100,000.[63] Freeman himself was responsible for carrying out 4,000 of the procedures.[64]

In the end, as with Moniz, lobotomy proved to be Freeman's undoing. In 1967, he performed his last transorbital lobotomy at Herrick Memorial Hospital in Berkeley, California. The woman died. Embarrassed hospital officials did what many before them had desired, but none had dared. They pulled his surgical privileges.[65]

But this did not put an end to lobotomy. Though the numbers were reduced to a trickle and the procedure became clandestine, there have always been a handful of physicians who insist the operation is simply maligned and has a rightful place in the psychiatric arsenal.

A 1994 report on psychiatry and human rights in Europe by the Council of Europe Parliamentary Assembly stunned the world with the news that lobotomies are, in fact, still being done in France, Ireland, the Netherlands and the United Kingdom.[66]

THE UNTOLD STORY OF PSYCHOSURGERY

When the subject of psychosurgery is posed to psychiatrists, the usual response, if they are willing to talk at all, is to acknowledge that the Lobotomy Era of Freeman and Watts, was indeed a black period in psychiatry's history.

What is almost *never* heard in the public arena, however, is that Freeman and Watts did only a fraction—less than 10 percent—of the psychosurgery in the U.S. and almost none of it abroad. Their highly publicized atrocities have allowed the profession to use them as whipping boys, without discussing the bigger picture.

The truth is *many* doctors besides Freeman and Watts—including leading figures in psychiatry—participated in lobotomies and many more performed—and have continued to perform—other forms of psychosurgery. But most are not talking, because as one psychosurgeon stated, "It is not professionally safe."[67]

When we interviewed retired New England surgeon Robert Shaw, he said he was one of a multitude who helped perform lobotomies in the early years. "I did them as an assistant. It wasn't my decision. I assisted the resident and I helped the knowledgeable staff.... When I became junior staff...I started to look a little more closely and I had nothing to do with it."

When we asked him how these operations turned out, a palpable darkness came over the doctor's voice. "Oh, Christ—terrible," he said. "It made them so they were socially conventional. They lost all their pizzazz. They lost their individuality. They no longer became feisty. They were easily managed. That's a hell of a thing."[68]

Dr. Shaw's honesty is rare in the extreme. Factually, similar scenarios were played out by quite a number of doctors in the '40s and '50s, but the details are buried along with their patients. Some discontinued the practice out of conscience, some out of social pressure. Others continued for years, attracting less attention than the flamboyant Freeman, yet desirous of riding on his coattails.

Guy McKhann, director of the Krieger Mind-Brain Institute at John Hopkins University, notes some doctors who hop on such bandwagons "are interested in getting their name in the paper or on radio, and then there are those who recognize this is a way to make a buck. People in my business don't like to talk about it, but that's exactly what happens. And it's exactly what happened with psychosurgery."[69]

In the United Kingdom, one of the patriarchs of psychosurgery is Geoffrey Knight. Interviewed at age 84, the neurosurgeon looked back on his work in the early days. "I cut through to the lower half of the lobe and put a leukotome in horizontally. I moved the instrument downward just until I felt resistance, then swept it laterally, or to the side. That was the first lower segment leucotomy." Knight's ideas on "improvement" were reminiscent of Freeman's: "We helped people with the worst of their symptoms, but certain patients couldn't lead a normal life and didn't enjoy any improvement you might have produced. Many of them became childish in their behavior, retarded, euphoric, irritable."[70]

In the United States military, along with the rise of psychiatrists to powerful positions in 1943 came a dramatic change in the treatment of mentally disturbed soldiers. That year a directive from the Veterans Administration asked neurosurgeons to get trained in the lobotomy techniques of Freeman and Watts. Over the next eight years, almost 3,000 veterans sacrificed their frontal lobes to the knife.[71]

And these sacrifices were made despite the government's own proof that the operations were useless. A report from the National Institute of Mental Health revealed that in 1949 a four-year Columbia University study of lobotomies done at Greystone Hospital in New Jersey showed the surgeries produced *negative* results. A follow-up review ending in 1953 reached the same conclusion. "Neither the original nor the followup," stated the NIMH report, "was able to provide any substantial scientific evidence that these psychosurgical procedures were useful." Furthermore, according to NIMH, the 1949 and 1953 conclusions "had little effect on the psychosurgeons, who continued to ignore or gloss over the side-effects of their procedures."[72]

Ironically, however, the destructive nature of lobotomy did *not* go unnoticed in—once again—the Soviet Union. According to a 1985 psychiatric text, in this land characterized throughout the Cold War as ruthless and calculating, during the early 1950s "Soviet psychiatrists demonstrated that in practice neither leucotomy nor lobectomy produced desirable results in treating mental diseases, while inflicting tremendous damage and trauma on the patient's brain." In 1954, after a brief period of testing, lobotomies were permanently banned in the USSR and remained so until the Union was dissolved in the 1980s.[73]

Dr. Edward Babayan, one of the Soviet scientists who participated in the research that caused the ban, wrote, "In 1949-50 the USSR Ministry of Health thoroughly studied the experience of using leucotomy and lobectomy in the treatment of mental patients.... The Ministry prohibited

169

the application of these methods in the USSR as 'brutal, harmful to the patient, scientifically unjustified, and ineffective.' This was an exceptionally important and humane measure.

"In the USA, for example," Babayan continued, "in spite of protests on the part of patients and their relatives, these operations, which we believe maim the patients, have not been proscribed."[74]

In America, the operations did indeed continue unabated. In *The Mind Manipulators*, authors Alan Scheflin and Edward Opton relay the story of American neurosurgeon William Scoville who experimented by removing sections of patients' temporal lobes (the area just behind and below the frontal lobes). Of course, one would expect the greatest of caution in performing such an operation, perhaps one small step at a time. But as Scheflin and Opton note, "The cautious approach was not how Moniz, Freeman and other well-known psychosurgeons won their fame."

Scoville operated on not one, but *thirty* patients, removing tissue from *both* temporal lobes. No patients improved, but eight of them suffered permanent impairment or total memory loss. One man, whose case was well documented, was completely unable to register new information after the operation. The world and the people around him remained strange and continuously new, a fate he was left to endure for the remainder of his days. Ironically, the man was never even mentally disturbed to begin with—he was simply an epileptic.[75]

Was Scoville censured or ostracized for his actions? On the contrary. He became the president of the International Society of Psychosurgery. And in 1972, when the journal *Frontiers of Psychiatry* needed a pro-psychosurgery point of view for their debate on the subject, Scoville was the man who presented that position. In 1980, the *Washington Post* described him as "one of a handful of psychosurgeons who share the belief…that destruction of selected parts of the brain can favorably alter human behavior and cure mental illness."[76]

Scoville's view on lobotomy? "The results were actually quite worthwhile."[77]

RETURN TO CHELMSFORD

In reviewing psychosurgery's history, one cannot help but feel a sense of the eccentric, the perverse—and even the criminal—pervading it at every turn. We have seen this same pattern crop up in other areas where the psychiatric profession hangs its hat, such as the sexual deviates among Freud's early followers and the reprehensible activities of ECT proponents.

It should, therefore, not be surprising, as we follow the decline of lobotomies in the late 1950s and the rise of *new* forms of psychosurgery in the 1960s and 1970s, that we find less-than-savory characters at the helm, piloting the new wave.

On August 4, 1988, the *Sydney Morning Herald*, Australia's leading newspaper, ran the front page headline, "How they put metal plates in Bruce's brain." The ensuing story detailed the ghoulish accounts of patients Bruce Roach and Gwen Whitty. In 1971 and 1965, respectively, each had received a *cingulotractotomy*, an operation that severs a tract of tissue in a section of brain near the front called the cingulum.

Years afterwards Roach made a grisly discovery. "What came up in the scans was shocking," he recalled. "They found metal clips in the skull, in the front part of my head." This may have offered some explanation for the blinding headaches and sudden, complete memory losses he had experienced since the operation.

Gwen Whitty's ordeal was no less startling. After her psychosurgery, she suffered excruciating headaches and developed a festering, half-egg sized lump on her head. "I've got this horrible stuff coming out of my head from where I had the surgery," she told the doctor who had recommended the cingulotractotomy. "Don't worry about it, Gwen," he replied. "Just wash your hair and it'll go away."

Thirteen years later, bizarre symptoms resurfaced. "I'd get out of bed and vomit. I'd have these dreadful pains like someone was shoving a spear in my head."

In 1984, after six more years, the nightmare returned. In Whitty's words, "Oh my God, not again." A lump oozing pus appeared once more on her head. After visits to several doctors, one specialist asked her a question that no doubt raced a shiver through her spine. "How long have you had a piece of metal sticking out of your head? You've got a piece of metal protruding from your skull."

Gwen Whitty was rushed into emergency surgery to remove the foreign object that had been left lodged in her cranium for 19 years.[78]

The architect of these operations was a man who claimed to be involved with more psychosurgeries than anyone else in the Southern Hemisphere,[79] the same man who escaped criminal charges by ending his own life.

It was Deep Sleep doctor Harry Bailey.

The deaths and horror stories emanating from Bailey's barbiturate and electroshock treatments tend to overshadow the entirely separate, but no less chilling, surgical aspect of his career. According to the testimony of his assistant, Dr. John Herron, Bailey was, in fact, "seen as the centre of psychosurgery internationally."[80] *The Report of the Royal Commission into Deep Sleep Therapy* tells us, "During the 1960s and 1970s, Dr. Bailey's use of psychosurgery, which was more publicly known than his use of DST, was the main matter causing concern to his colleagues."[81]

Bailey's involvement in psychiatric surgery began in the 1950s, when he studied under Sweden's Lars Leksell, Europe's leading experimental brain surgeon. Leksell was one of the developers of "stereotaxic" surgery—a technique that uses an apparatus outside the skull to guide a needle or other surgical instrument through a drilled hole—in the back of the head, for example—and into a pinpointed location in the brain.

Bailey brought the Swedish doctor's techniques and equipment to Australia, setting up the Cerebral Surgery Research Unit in 1957. According to investigators, "Dr. Bailey had problems with patients dying during this period." Colleague Dr. Michael Kennedy Perkins said that more than once Bailey suggested no inquest was needed.[82]

Although the Deep Sleep doctor did not perform the operations himself, he was the driving force behind them and went to great lengths to make this known. He once bragged to his attorney, "We carried out over 350 cingulotractotomies, the largest series carried out in the southern hemisphere."[83]

Like Moniz, Freeman, Scoville, and other psychosurgeons before him, Bailey trumpeted his work in respected professional journals. In one 1973 article reviewing 150 of his "successful" cingulotractotomy cases, the doctor assures us the operation is safe and even produces "slight improvements" in people's intelligence. Bruce Roach, the patient who found metal clips in his head, believes he was among those 150, but he would hardly call the procedure successful.[84]

One of Bailey's colleagues, Dr. John Ellard, commented years later, after the damage had been done by treatments "deserving of severe censure by

[Bailey's] peers": "Remember too that he had published at least once and perhaps twice on his psychosurgery in the *Medical Journal of Australia* with eminent referees [authoritative references], and had been accepted. It looks black and white now but it was not then."[85]

How murder and mutilation could not have looked "black and white" says much about psychiatry. And the psychiatric profession continued to quote Bailey's work as proof of the therapeutic value of psychosurgery, even after his death in 1985. The 1988 text *Physical Treatments in Psychiatry* cited the Deep Sleep doctor's writings repeatedly, despite extensive criminal allegations against him, abundant evidence of record falsification, and even Bailey's own suicide over the matter.[86]

It might be assumed that the book's authors were simply ignorant of Bailey's activities. Nothing could be further from the truth. Two of the three co-authors, Leslie Kiloh and J. Sydney Smith, knew him well and were, in fact, Bailey's local competitors. Bailey's and Smith's were the only two significant psychosurgery groups in all of Australia.[87]

In fact, Smith openly testified *against* Bailey—the man he had quoted as a psychosurgery expert in his text. In 1980, he and a government official claimed the negligent circumstances around the death of one of Bailey's patients "could well justify, in our view, a charge of manslaughter."[88] One has to wonder why Smith would promote to the psychiatric profession the work of a man he personally considered a killer—unless it was simply to give the impression psychosurgery was more successful than it actually is, even if that meant using fraudulent records to prove it.

The documents of the Royal Commission into Deep Sleep clearly demonstrate the rift between the two men. "There was antagonism," the Commission stated, "between Professor Kiloh and Dr. Smith against Dr. Davies [a psychologist who worked with Bailey] and Dr. Herron who were identified with Dr. Bailey. The latter, according to Dr. Herron, were more accepted by those at the Madrid meeting [the Fourth World Congress of Psychiatric Surgery, 1975] who saw Dr. Bailey as the center of psychosurgery in Australia."[89]

In 1977, Bailey co-wrote, with psychosurgical teammates Drs. Davies and John Dowling, several chapters for the book *Neurological Treatment in Psychiatry, Pain and Epilepsy*. One was titled, remarkably enough, "The Ethics of Psychiatric Surgery." In it they explain that the psychiatrist and the psychosurgery personnel "must all converge on the [patient's] problem so that the surgical procedure will result in the maximum of 'the good.'" They then define *the good*: "The view of 'the good' adopted here is that which facilitates behaviors that does not encroach upon or otherwise inhibit the behavioral expression of others."[90]

Like Walter Freeman, the Deep Sleep doctor clearly stated, "The operation should not be carried out as a 'last resort.'" In fact, he considered his cingulotractotomy the "treatment of choice" for numerous psychiatric problems.[91]

As a measure of how *unsuccessful* the operation actually was, however, a survey of Bailey's first Deep Sleep patients showed that 5.6 percent of them (56 out of 1,000) had prior psychosurgery—as recommended by Bailey. Several had had *two*. In a group under another doctor's care at Chelmsford, two of the patients had each had *three* psychiatric surgeries.[92]

In 1977, a moratorium was finally placed on psychosurgery in Bailey's home state of New South Wales. In a letter to U.S. psychosurgeon M. Hunter Brown, the Deep Sleep doctor declared that the operations in Australia were suffering from a "flare up amongst consumerists."[93]

Bailey's connection with Brown—a major figure in his field—was not insignificant. They knew each other for thirty years and it was common for the doctor from Down Under to send his patients all the way to California so Brown could perform his "multiple target" psychosurgery on them.

This relationship is important because it lends us a peek into the hush-hush world of the psychiatric surgeon. Of Bailey we know a great deal—this "very, very low form of life," as one police officer called him. We learn a considerable amount about psychosurgeons in general by observing whether they rejected this bad apple or accepted him as simply another member of the barrel.

M. Hunter Brown—one of the most prominent psychosurgeons in America—not only accepted Bailey, he *testified in his defense* at a trial via a written statement submitted in 1984. And he even defended Deep Sleep: "Deep sedation is needed less often today…. However, severe cases may have a crisis prior to the effective time required for psychotropic drugs to take effect." In the same affidavit he tried to get Bailey off the hook for a Deep Sleep death, even though it is clear Brown never even saw the patient: "I understand in this case the patient suddenly sat up in bed and then expired; clinically this fact seems to exclude the deep sedation as the proximate cause."[94]

Taking a further look we find that Brown was bedfellows with Dr. Gary Aden, the ECT doctor who had his license revoked for sexually abusing his patients (See last chapter). In 1975, Brown joined Aden as a co-plaintiff in suing the state of California to rescind its new ECT law (which also restricted psychosurgery).[95]

If we are to judge men by the company they keep, it seems reasonable that the rule should hold for doctors as well as hoodlums. As to their "scientific" grasp of the nature of the irreversible surgery they were doing, Bailey once wrote to Brown, "The problem of the all consuming mother has been present in just about every case and it certainly seems that [the] multiple target operation allows us to drive a wedge in between the mother and the patient more effectively."[96]

Brown himself fancied their psychosurgical efforts as a cure-all for the violent criminal. "For roughly $6,000," he once claimed, "society can provide medical treatment which will transform him into a responsible, well adjusted citizen."[97] In this same vein, he predicted the demise of our existing penal system: "When this current effort fails, as it will, the state will turn to professionals for well-designed comprehensive programs including chromosome classification [i.e. mass genetic screenings...]....and finally neurosurgical intervention to specific targets as indicated. Until then, humanity must mark time."[98]

The final word on Bailey and Brown—and their psychosurgical aspirations—is politely summarized by the *Report of the Royal Commission*: "[Brown] and Dr. Bailey provided strong mutual support. According to [a colleague] they corresponded regularly. Although there were not many letters found, the tone of those which were examined support this assertion.... The two men shared a similar approach to psychiatric treatment...."[99]

PSYCHOSURGERY TODAY

In recent decades, Walter Freeman's ice pick has been abandoned in favor of more refined techniques. Stereotactic surgery is the way into the brain for today's psychosurgeon. Using a device that guides their surgical instrument into cerebral sites within a millimeter of accuracy, physicians use electrodes, minute radioactive rods, ultrasound, hot needle tips, and other tools to create "lesions" (tissue damage) in the brain.

The area targeted is generally the "limbic system." *Limbic* means "bordering around" and the *limbic system* is that tissue that borders around the brain stem.

Areas around the brain stem are reached by approaching each through a skull hole cut in whatever location will facilitate access.

The cingulum—a popular modern day target of psychosurgeons (including Bailey's team)—is a section of tissue located down inside the area between the two brain halves. The cingulum sits on the outskirts of the limbic system.

Other favored surgical locations in recent decades, such as the amygdala and the hypothalamus, are simply brain structures located near the brain stem.

Psychiatrists and psychosurgeons believe the limbic system to be the "site of the emotions," and therefore assume that tampering with it can alter undesirable mental states. In fact, they often present the impression to the public that the brain is completely mapped and understood—and, of course, one would think they would not be operating inside people's skulls if they did not fully comprehend what they are doing.

Yet if one reads their statements carefully, we find a substantial amount of guesswork involved. "The limbic system and the brain stem, the brain's 'hardware' in computer terminology, most probably constitute the neural basis of emotion," wrote two Japanese neurosurgeons in 1988.[100]

Doctors are not even certain what will happen when they cut. "There is strong evidence that different approaches lead to different results," wrote psychosurgeon L.V. Laitinen in 1988.[101]

Surgery advocate and Belgian psychiatrist P. Cosyns commented in *Acta Neurochirurgica*, "There is no universally accepted understanding of how psychosurgery works."[102]

Even in the basic theory behind psychosurgery—that Man is his brain—we find the surgeons confused. While on the one hand proclaiming that personality is simply neurons and biochemicals and that a well-placed lesion will improve behavior, we find that *when they fail to induce change*, psychiatric surgeons actually speak of an element of personality which is beyond the brain. Call it the soul, the will, the spirit or whatever you will—in a confounding display of academic contortionism, these doctors see it, blame their failures on it, and yet deny its existence.

Recent statements of three prominent neurosurgeons bear this out. American Thomas Ballantine: "Some people, of course, are just bad actors. They have a character disorder that has nothing to do with abnormalities in the brain or psychosis. No surgery can deal with that."[103]

Britain's Paul Bridges: "The demented stop caring and don't do as well even if you stop the depression [with psychosurgery]."[104]

The United Kingdom's Desmond Kelly: "If we didn't wait years and years to consider the surgery, until patterns of behavior associated with the illness were so rock hard and intractable and the patients so frustrated and demoralized, we would do even better, in my opinion.... If you have people who are so deteriorated that they've lost all support systems, all hope, you won't get as good results."[105]

In the mid-1970s, neuropsychologist Elliot Valenstein undertook, at the U.S. government's request, an extensive review of psychosurgery. He concluded that scientists "are quite explicit about not knowing 'how' or 'why' psychosurgery works and they openly state that physiological explanations at this time are pure conjecture, heterogeneous and often tortured sets of arguments."[106]

Discussing his field of expertise at the end of his career, Thomas Ballantine, one of the most active U.S. psychosurgeons in the 1970s and 1980s, gives a rather jarring reality adjustment on just how little is known by him and his modern-day colleagues: "It must be determined [in the future] whether there is really a specific limbic system interruption which is best for a specific disorder of affect or: Is the limbic system such a truly reverberating circuit that the location of a lesion within it is less important than its size and shape?"[107]

Yet Ballantine performed hundreds of operations, specializing in cingulotomies. In *Psychosurgery*, Joann Rodgers reports, "Ballantine recalls that people were very upset with him and others over this kind of work. But he never stopped operating."[108]

When we interviewed surgeon Robert Shaw who knew Ballantine from their mutual work at Massachusetts General Hospital, he gave us some rare insight as to what would motivate a psychosurgeon to perform irreversible operations despite such limited knowledge. "Oh, he's a nice enough guy," Shaw told us. "He married the boss' daughter. He married the daughter of a very, very famous neurosurgeon which helps to get up the line…. He's not sensitive to things as he should be…. He was not sensitive to the responses of his patients."

When we asked Dr. Shaw what he meant by "not sensitive," he said simply, "He doesn't know any better. I like him. He's a good guy. He literally does not know any better. He's not sensitive to what he does. He's insensitive to feedback. I'm sorry, that's the way it is. Some people are bull-headed."[109]

Joann Rodger's 1992 description of Ballantine was remarkably similar: "One who still labors at all this after almost four decades has a sign on his office door that proclaims, 'Tiger Inside.' Behind the door, there is one, with piercing eyes and ferocious energy. He is unapologetic about his chain smoking or his advocacy of psychosurgery…. Even the recent death of his 48-year-old son in a car accident can't subdue the gutsy 'cowboy' impression associated with both his Oklahoma heritage and his long career as a neurosurgeon."[110]

This "insensitivity" is a common charge leveled at psychosurgeons. Walter Freeman and Harry Bailey were notorious for it. This would explain why so few doctors will perform the surgery and why so many report vomiting or fainting when they watch. This is a vitally important matter if one realizes that psychosurgeons are promoting their "successes" in the medical journals and elsewhere, with claims that quite likely omit more tragic details that the doctors don't see, consider "unimportant" or "acceptable tradeoffs," or simply don't want the public to know.

This may explain why researchers—British psychologists O'Callaghan and Carroll—concluded in 1982, "Where sensitive and comprehensive examination has been undertaken, whether of older or newer procedures, a wide range of postoperative deficits and non-specific effects have been revealed. The range of side effects revealed seems mainly to reflect the comprehensiveness of the scrutiny, and to a lesser extent the size and location of the lesion and the technical sophistication of the operation."[111]

It may also explain why reviewers looking over the reported triumphs of modern psychiatric surgeons find the claims so highly questionable. In Elliot Valenstein's aforementioned government study, he found over 90 percent of the medical journal articles he reviewed (written by psychosurgeons, 1970-1976) ranked in categories four to six in a declining scale of scientific acceptability (six being the lowest). Category four was defined as "given only to articles of low scientific value. It is unlikely, for example, that an animal study with such a low rating would be accepted for publication by the editors of a respected experimental journal." Valenstein relegated about half the articles to category six.[112]

O'Callaghan and Carroll came to similar conclusions in their in-depth study of the field. "After 40 years of psychosurgery," they commented, "some agreement on the matter of its efficacy might reasonably be expected. It is clear , however, that no such consensus exists.... There is little to suggest that contemporary studies have substantially transcended dubious methodological practices [of the past]."[113]

All this might make for engaging debate if these were mere matters being bandied about in the halls of academia. But they are not. While psychiatric surgeons guess and argue, human brain tissue is being destroyed. And for each patient, there is no turning back. As authors Alan Scheflin and Edward Opton point out in *The Mind Manipulators*, "When you are dead, you are dead.... But the torture of living with a mutilated mind would continue indefinitely."[114]

THE USES OF PSYCHOSURGERY

Over the past several decades, much of the protest against psychosurgery stems from its potential abuse as an instrument of social control. While supporters like to claim such fears have little merit, the truth is that it not only *could* be used toward such ends, but it *has been and continues to be.*

A study of 70 hypothalamotomies on sex offenders and deviants in West Germany (1962-1975) showed "indications for surgery [were] based on questionable scientific and clinical grounds and practically [excluded] psychotherapeutic...aspects."[115] Similar operations have been used to kill overactive libidos in sex criminals.[116]

In Japan, hypothalamotomies have been used to stop violent, aggressive behavior. One supporter claimed, "Side effects such as hyperactivity and lack of bladder control make this a risky procedure, but in severe cases, worth the risk."[117]

In a 1988 article, Japanese psychosurgeons describe the results of these operations being done on 60 people from 1962-1977, almost half of whom

179

were under age 15. The "sedative neurosurgery" was done to stop aggressive behavior, including among those they referred to as "hyperkinetic children."* Most of the patients were epileptics with some degree of mental retardation. The doctors *guessed* at what they were doing: "The area we have been stimulating and electrocauterizing *probably* involves [either of two small brain sites].... Therefore, it is *quite probable* that destruction of the [tissue fiber] bundle would result in a decrease of...the expression of rage or aggression...." (Emphasis added.)

Postoperative follow-up 10 to 25 years later found *13* of the 60 had died—including three suicides, two drownings, one "unknown cause," and two cases of status epilepticus (continuous seizures). The surgeons would not even consider that they bore any responsibility in these fatalities. "Since any cause of death does not seem directly related to the surgical intervention," they wrote, "this unusually high rate of death may reflect a relatively short life expectancy of those handicapped patients." They conclude, "The experiences of the present group with 29 children seem to support an early surgical intervention."[118] Apparently, the Japanese people did not agree. Psychosurgery was banned in that country in the mid-'70s.[119]

In Czechoslovakia, psychosurgery has been used to treat "hedonia." People with this malady "disturb the existing social order and sometimes endanger social order to considerable extent; some others are even criminal, for instance sexual deviations." Some symptoms include excessive smoking, drinking, and/or eating. One of these surgically altered hedonists was a six-year-old boy.[120]

Children have been vulnerable targets for these operations. Authors Scheflin and Opton report interviewing an American psychosurgeon who "told us that the four to five million children in the United States with 'varying degrees of mental retardation,' hyperkinesis, or autism are also good prospects for psychosurgery. He personally has operated on 'a great number' of retarded children and a few with autism."[121] Mississippi psychosurgeon Orlando J. Andy has also specialized in children—as young as five years old. "Psychosurgery," he told a senate subcommittee in the 1970s, "is preferable to that of having a child with abnormal behavior continue under inadequate control during the formative and development years of his life."[122]

---

* i.e., "hyperactive" children.

Prisoners have also been favorable candidates among psychosurgeons. In 1972, psychosurgeon Ernst Rodin sought to perform amygdalotomies on Michigan inmates with aggressive histories. The resulting court case, known as *Kaimowitz* (after the attorney who filed suit against the operations), effectively banned psychosurgeries in state institutions from that time forward.[123]

Psychiatrist Louis Jolyon "Jolly" West of the University of California at Los Angeles—who holds the distinction of being the only man to ever kill an elephant with LSD—spearheaded a drive to establish a Center for the Study and Reduction of Violence in the '70s. Although West and state officials denied the center had any plans for psychosurgery research[124], their submitted "project description" clearly states, "As the Center develops, and pursues various studies of violent behavior and its control, it will require the services of scientists from such widely divergent areas of expertise as psychiatry, neurology, neurophysiology, neurosurgery,…"

It goes on to say that animals "can be deliberately provoked to violence, or subjected to medication and brain surgery, with the objective consequences of major applicability to homo sapiens."[125] In 1992, West looked back on this period with some rancor. "In the aftermath of Ken Kesey's [anti-psychiatric novel and movie] *One Flew over the Cuckoo's Nest*, anyone who was operating on anyone else's precious brain was a Frankenstein."[126]

As a result of considerable public outcry, the Violence Center never opened. Subsequent U.S. Senate hearings in 1974, however, revealed that for a few convicts it was too late. In 1968, according to testimony, "California officials secretly amygdalotomyzed three prisoners, paying scant regard to legal and ethical issues of informed consent. This serious tampering with the human brain yielded no favorable results for reducing crime or violence. In fact, the prisoner reported by officials to be the most improved is still in prison. His old symptoms have returned, and he now suffers additionally from memory loss and other effects of the brain destruction."[127]

This notion of using psychosurgery for social control has more subtle meaning than these obvious political applications. While some surgeons rationalize their efforts as a necessary evil for the good of society, others take it a step further and consider simply the family's intolerance and their request for ridding the patient of undesired behavior. Here we get into such things as the Rosemary Kennedy lobotomy and Harry Bailey's remarks that psychosurgery should create behavior "that does not encroach upon or otherwise inhibit the behavioral expression of others."

Bailey's own observation that "the problem of the all consuming mother has been present in just about every case" on which he recommended psychosurgery leads us to the almost unthinkable conclusion that a great many of his patients had their brain tissue destroyed not because they wanted it but because Mother deemed it necessary.

The fact that Bailey would—instead of recommending a vacation from Mother—elect to perform brain surgery is not out of line with the thinking of most psychosurgeons. Their entire premise, in fact, is that there is no other solution to solving some mental problems.

Thus in discussing some of the various psychiatric reasons why psychosurgery is done, we must assume that a percentage of the operations—while ostensibly being done to help the patient—are, in fact, not done at patient request but at the prodding of a friend or relative or psychiatrist. Frequently these patients are so weak or demoralized that it takes little external pressure to coax them into the operation. One survey of more than a hundred cingulotomy patients showed greater than 80 percent had already had shock treatment. A fourth had had over 50 ECTs each, along with tranquilizers and antidepressants.[128] As we saw in the previous chapter, docility and submissiveness are common after shock, making it much easier to get "informed consent" on just about anything.

Modern psychosurgeons claim their operations are useful for a variety of psychiatric problems including severe anxiety, manic depressive psychosis, depression and, to a lesser degree, schizophrenia.

One popular use for it is "OCD" or obsessive-compulsive disorder, a situation where the person feels obsessed with recurring thoughts and/or compelled to repeat certain behavior such as hand washing.

There have been other applications as well. In Denmark, psychosurgery has been used to curb the appetites of obese people. In India, surgeons perform their work to alter the habits of addicts and alcoholics.[129]

In all cases, of course, the surgery "works" by interfering with the normal functioning of the brain—an act that has its own consequences.

Modern Side Effects

Modern psychosurgeons like to distance themselves as much as possible from any association with the lobotomies of the past because, of course, even they realize that the lobotomy produced so many horrific effects. Today's surgery supporters like to claim that current techniques are far less destructive than the lobotomy, and are therefore better and more socially acceptable.

While on the surface this argument may sound reasonable, the truth is the tissue damage in modern operations is substantial. Typical cingulotomies create two lesions ($\frac{1}{3}$ inch in diameter and $\frac{2}{3}$ inch deep).[130] Even if this creates $\frac{1}{2}$ or $\frac{1}{8}$ of the harmful effects of lobotomies, we are still talking about dramatic and irreversible changes in mental and physical function and behavior.

To call these changes *side effects* is a misnomer, of course. They are so named merely because they are in addition to the intended effect. Factually, however, they are *primary* effects, i.e. destroying brain tissue creates specific effects—it disrupts the innate functions of that section of the brain.

In their extensive study of today's psychosurgery, O'Callaghan and Carroll state, "Untoward side effects must be expected given the complex functional integration of diverse brain areas and the fact that psychosurgery interrupts...normal brain tissue. It should never be assumed...that the effects of the operation will be specific, modifying only circumscribed patterns of undesirable behavior and leaving unaffected other psychological functions. Indeed, one of the most persistent criticisms of psychosurgery has been that the effects of operations are, in fact more diffuse, leading to a fairly general dampening of function."[131]

Just as with Walter Freeman and the lobotomy, we have a difficult time getting an accurate picture of what effects today's psychosurgeries have because the surgeons often seem to see only what they want to. When Thomas Ballantine reviewed 198 cingulotomy cases he concluded two-thirds showed significant improvement. However, *The Wall Street Journal* reports that a more exhaustive study on another group from Ballantine's hospital reported improvement in only 25-30 percent.[132]

The term "improvement" here is a very subjective one. As with shock treatment, we find doctors will consider the patient improved only because the original symptoms are blunted—even if that blunting was caused by memory loss, disorientation, judgment impairment, or any other mental malfunction created by the operation.

A good example of just how much gets ignored can be seen in the book *Madness in the Streets*. The authors, in trying to make a case *for* psychosurgery tell the story of a woman named Paula Perlstein. We are told Paula is "vibrant" and that her "demeanor and speech give no hint of the terrible illness that dominated her life prior to surgery." This is what the authors claim to see. However, when we read the account we find Paula has a massive psychiatric drug history (it looks like it spans 20 years), has received at least 200 shock treatments, has had *four* psychosurgeries, and at the time of the interview was on antipsychotic medication. How could the authors see "no hint?"

It is obvious from Paula's statements that she has some amnesia. "I was very bad then," she says of the time when she got her first cingulotomy from Thomas Ballantine. "I've read some of the records and I was in restraints." In describing an incident from one mental hospital, she says, "I was in a seclusion room and I don't remember this, this is what they told me."

We also read that Paula's fourth psychosurgery was "the most radical limbic surgery done today," and that after her operations Paula was "much more outgoing." This is strikingly reminiscent of the "unrestrained behavior" Freeman spoke of in lobotomy patients. The authors conclude, "Paula's experience was typical—the surgery had no harmful effects on her personality."[133]

As this account sounds questionable at best, we looked nationwide for Paula to ask her ourselves but we couldn't find her. We *did*, however, find John Barrella, a man who had received three psychosurgeries, including two cingulotomies, in 1980—about the same time as Paula.

John's story requires no embellishment. After receiving his psychosurgery for chronic anxiety, "I blanked out. I was gone. I had no memory of anything.... I was a walking zombie." Seven years later a day came when he found himself becoming vaguely aware of something very unsettling. It began to dawn on him that he had no memory. Prior to this, according to John, his amnesia was so extensive that he was unaware he even had it.

It took another five years, till around 1992, for him to slowly get to the point where he could even grasp what was wrong with him and to take any steps to deal with it. After years of trying to help him recover, John's mother took him to an institute specializing in the rehabilitation of brain-injured people. "From there I was able to understand the extent of my injuries. Otherwise, today I still would not know.... My mother came with me because I was not able to retain information."

The record of his life was erased. He has had to piece it back together through photographs, his medical records, and the accounts of others. Regarding his mother, "I really don't know if I ever remembered who she is.... I know she's my mother...but I cannot recall her whatsoever."

Most painful is the loss of any recall of his wife of three years. "I met my wife and had fallen in love with her and I just graduated from college. ...She married me, from what I understand, because I see my wedding—it was taken on tape—and I don't remember anything about it.... She was not aware I was so severely injured because I looked okay.... I was fearful of everything [after the operations]. I don't remember that...I don't remember that at all. And my wife left me for that reason because I would just go out of it.... In the beginning [after the operations], I had no feelings. My feelings were very, very destroyed. But about '87 I started feeling pains for my wife."

Today John's life centers around index cards. He has a book at home where he keeps a written record of what has occurred each day. He has a marking system that tells him what he has done and not done. At night he fills out an index card telling him what to do the next day. The following morning he takes the card with him if he leaves the house. When he comes home at night, the day's activities are entered in the book and a new index card is filled out for the following day. He informed us that after our interview he would enter what occurred in his book. "Then it will never be forgotten," he said. "That's the only way. There is no other way."

One day on TV he saw the psychosurgeon, Dr. Stanley Stellar, who had operated on him. He had no recall of the face. Then he saw the name flash on the screen, a name he'd seen in his medical records. A quiet rage boiled. "This guy was talking on TV," John told us, "and everybody was listening like he was a good doctor. This guy destroyed me.... Something is not right. Somewhere it's not right."

Around 1993—John cannot recall the date—he confronted Dr. Stellar at the hospital where it all happened. "I had a talk with this guy. 'What the hell did you do to me? I came to you for help, you destroyed me and then you washed your hands.'... He said, 'You're in pretty good shape, I see.' I said, 'Dr. Stellar, you're a quack. I hope you've hurt nobody else.' Then he gets close to me, his hand on my knee, he says, 'Listen, not all these surgeries work a hundred percent.' I said 'Okay, but why didn't you help me after you hurt me?'"

One of the most difficult aspects of rising out of the fog of his psychosurgically-created amnesia is what John calls "the disorientation." He gets a wisp of a memory—a song on the radio or an awareness of a skill he didn't know he had (he wasn't aware he had a college degree in business administration until six or seven years after the operations)—and this snippet of the past gnaws at him like a shadowy key to a door he can never open.

In addition to his short- and long- term memory loss, John Barrella has disorientation of time and place, impaired judgment, and partial paralysis on the right side. He summarizes his psychosurgery experience bitterly: "When I went in for the surgery I was very much in love, I wanted to get rid of this problem, I wanted to start a life—and all of a sudden this guy murdered me."[134]

While such amnesia is common, a host of other side effects have been attributed to modern psychosurgery. The *full* extent of these are impossible to come by unless—as we did—one goes directly to the patient. These *adverse sequelae*, as doctors call them are essentially the same as those which occurred in lobotomy patients, except we are told there are fewer deaths and, with the lesions being more localized, the untoward effects are limited to smaller areas of the brain.

As with lobotomy patients, there are problems with weight gain, seizures, dampened emotions, "unrestrained behavior," concentration, intellectual functioning, loss of bladder control, post-operative suicide—the full spectrum of effects that one would expect after healthy brain tissue had been destroyed, effects the patient often never dreamed would happen. And effects he was never told would happen. Imagine the sense of betrayal. Imagine waking up tomorrow with no memory and no bladder control.

FOR AND AGAINST

The number of psychosurgery advocates today are actually quite few. They consist mainly of a minority of neurosurgeons with financial interests or a small number of psychiatrists, surgeons, and like-minded citizens who literally cannot fathom a better way to deal with certain mental problems.

For example, the book *Psychosurgery* by Joann Rodgers takes a rare pro-surgery stance. A cursory glance shows that Rodgers is the director of media relations for Johns Hopkins Medical Institutions. And what is her organization's position on psychosurgery? Chief neurosurgeon Donlin Long: "If the gross lobotomies of the past actually helped, and they did, think what we might do today with less destructive lesions, electrical stimulation and drug implants."[135]

To prove the necessity of their operations, promoters claim surgery is reserved for patients who are desperate cases. As an example, they usually cite one case of extreme violence, compulsiveness, depression, etc. and claim that without psychosurgery the patient would have died, committed suicide, or wallowed in mental torture forever.

Obviously, there *are* people who are suicidal or living in private hells, and on first impulse it may seem reasonable to do *anything*—no matter how desperate—if it offers a promise of rescue.

However, a first impulse is a poor guide when deciding if someone should have their brain tissue destroyed. Some thinking and reason should occur first.

First of all, even though psychosurgeons tell us they only perform on the most desperate cases, there is considerable doubt that this is true. "The claim is always made that it's the intervention of last resort," commented neuroscientist Stephan Chorover of the Massachusetts Institute of Technology in 1994. "I actually don't believe that's true in most cases."

At the time of Chorover's remarks, a two-hour cingulotomy cost $15,000 at Massachusetts General and doctors *are* working to make a living. How much this affects their decision to operate is hard to say.[136]

When we look at the remarks of the psychosurgeons themselves, we find they believe it should be used *earlier* than the "last resort." We have already noted the comments of neurosurgeon Knight on the subject. In 1992, his British comrade, surgeon Paul Bridges said, "Many psychiatrists believe psychosurgery would have *much* better results if they were done earlier in the course of illness." [137]

That same year, sociologist Andrew Scull of the University of California at San Diego predicted psychiatrists will seek to use drugs and surgery *more* to protect their "market share" and stay alive in the face of competing non-medical therapies. [138]

Secondly, when psychosurgeons speak of desperate cases, they specifically mean those people who have been treated *psychiatrically* to no avail. This is an extremely narrow view. As we have already demonstrated, psychiatrists have notoriously bad judgment on how to treat the human condition—and bad results. To label a person "hopeless" because psychiatrists have failed to help him seems absurd in light of what we know—that psychiatric treatment is so fruitless that statistically more people improve without it. In fact, it is normal to find a person in *worse* condition after extensive drug and shock treatment. To then declare such a person "hopeless" and compound his nightmare with irreversible brain surgery hardly seems rational.

It also does not seem reasonable to permanently alter someone's cerebral tissue simply because biological psychiatrists cannot think of a better solution. As we have seen, the field of psychosurgery has been studded with doctors regarded as insensitive by their peers. Who would knowingly put their mental future in the hands of such a person?

Thirdly, while there *may be* a rare few individuals who ask to have their mental torture stopped by psychosurgery, these individuals—being consulted only by psychiatrists—are denied any alternatives that could save them a lifetime of brain damage. And these few patients are used by the psychosurgery profession to provide a false front, so they can hold these patients out as justification for their acts, when in reality, as we have seen, they want to and do use psychosurgery as *less* than a last resort. While a handful of people *may* have had their demons temporarily quieted at a cost to themselves that they are often too mentally obliterated to grasp, an even greater number have not been helped—and must live with the consequences. This is neither just nor sensible.

Fourthly, while modern psychosurgeons claim their hospitals have established "screening committee" procedures to ensure only the most desperate will receive surgery, it should be obvious that the members of these committees are pro-surgery. Otherwise, no patients would be approved, a situation no hospital can tolerate.

And lastly, it should be clear that psychosurgery is, in fact, not a last resort. It cannot reasonably be called a resort at all. It has left a legacy of thousands of crippled minds in its wake. By permitting the psychiatric profession to continue to wield scalpels in the absence of understanding, we perpetuate false hope and potential mutilation for trusting souls whose only crime is believing in their doctors.

By barring this quick-fix with the knife, more humane alternatives would be forced to the fore.

The states of Oregon and South Dakota have banned psychosurgery. Lobotomy is illegal in Louisiana. Many other states have restricted these practices, e.g. the operations have stopped in California since regulations were tightened. All around the world the practice has become undesirable.

While psychosurgeons like to claim their surgeries are making a come-back, the truth is, as one of their members said, "The acceptance level has fallen to practically zero."[139] That seems sensible in a world that is seeking to rise out of the violence and barbarism of its past.

We would like to put forward the argument that it is time they were stopped altogether.

In closing, we have a request to honor. In exchange for his interview, John Barrella, the man who underwent three psychosurgeries, asked that we deliver a personal message from him:

"You know, I'm very angry that after all that was done to me, there's been no recognition. Not only for me. I was hurt. Fine. These people got away with it. Fine. But how many other people are going to suffer the same situation?... This is what people have to know—that these hospitals are still there. And yet they allow these things to happen.... These things are still happening."

CHAPTER VII

THE ALMIGHTY
PANACEA–DRUGS

"DREAM WITH ME FOR A MOMENT," WROTE RONALD SIEGEL, RESEARCH psychopharmacologist at UCLA's Department of Psychiatry and Biobehavioral Sciences, in 1990. "What would be wrong if we had perfectly safe drugs? I mean drugs that delivered the same effects as our most popular ones but never caused dependency, disease, dysfunction, or death. Imagine an alcohol-type drug that never caused addiction, liver disease, hangovers, driving under the influence, or workplace problems. Would you care for a cigarette that is as enjoyable as marijuana or tobacco but as harmless as clean air? How about a pain-killer as good as morphine but safer than aspirin; a stimulant more appealing than cocaine and less harmful than caffeine; a tranquilizer less addicting than Valium and more enjoyable than a martini; or a user-friendly hallucinogen that is as benign as a movie?"[1]

Why would we want this Drug Utopia? Because, according to Siegel, humans have a "fourth drive," like hunger, thirst, and sex, and that is the drive to take drugs, to be intoxicated. To indulge this drive is natural, Siegel says. A good thing.[2]

Whether natural or not, the fact, according to a 1993 report, is that more than 10 million Americans take tranquilizers each year.[3]

Enough orders are written annually for psychotropic drugs (these are drugs that exert an effect on the mind) to provide a prescription to nearly every man, woman, and child in the United States.[4]

And it is a trend that is steadily increasing. In fact, you might say, it is being heavily promoted by the "pushers" themselves. One study of patients' visits to psychiatrists' offices found, "One or more medications were ordered or provided in one-fourth of the 1975-76 visits, one-third of the 1980-81 visits, and almost half of the 1985 visits."[5]

The psychiatrist's dependency on the pill, indeed, the public's dependency, has become so widespread that the concept of getting "treatment" almost invariably implies medication.

In fact, if we consider psychiatry's current biochemical view of humanity, thought, and behavior, they would seem to have little reason *not* to prescribe drugs for any and all ills.

In spite of this modern trend, drugs have not always been the great panacea.

As recently as the 1950s and 1960s, the use of mind-altering chemicals in any form was considered a social taboo. Factually, that ethic is still quite popular today among a large segment of the population, but it has taken quite a beating.

Historically, the taking of any kind of psychotropic drugs has been suspect, their users relegated in public opinion as lost in a wasteland of degradation. Addicts, dopers, hopheads—there were few kind words for the men and women who had chosen to sell out reality for a quick ride down the road to euphoria.

"The illicit sale of (cocaine)…," said President Howard Taft in a speech before Congress in 1910, "and the habitual use of it temporarily raises the power of the criminal to a point where in resisting arrest there is no hesitation to murder. It is more appalling in its effect than any other habit-forming drug used in the United States."[6]

This view of drugs may seem ancient, but it came from centuries of mankind's experience with them. After enough eyewitness accounts of fathers, sisters, and acquaintances decaying, living the fate of the opium smoker, the morphine addict, the cocaine user—few needed further convincing.

However, that view stands in stark contrast to the psychiatric attitude toward drugs today.

A 1986 report in the *New England Journal of Medicine* gives us a rare view of exactly how enamored psychiatrists are with the use of mind-altering drugs. Of the doctors surveyed, it was discovered that not only were nearly half the psychiatrists *currently* taking self-prescribed psychotropic medication themselves, but, "psychiatrists had much higher rates for all types of [psychoactive drug] use at any time (83 percent)…than did other groups of physicians."[7]

Even the notable Dr. Freud had a well-known cocaine addiction, and it has been speculated that the roots of his theories may lie in the sexual stimulation that so prominently accompanies use of this drug. One doctor wrote, "In the early 1880s Freud made one of his earliest forays into psychiatry by attempting to cure another doctor who was addicted to morphine by giving him cocaine. He was warned correctly, but too late, that this could only result in a double addiction."[8]

Ronald Siegel was by no means the first to dream of a Drug Utopia. Back in 1981, psychiatrist Seymour Rosenblatt put forth his own euphoric view of the future. "Consider some of the possibilities," he wrote, "currently being promoted by serious scientists: In the next twenty years, it has been conjectured, we will be able to control people's feelings and emotions. Madness will go the way of smallpox, and mental institutions will become as rare as monasteries.

"Everyone will get a decent night's sleep. Senility will be arrested by a pill or an injection. Our memories will be extended beyond their present capacities, and both drug addiction and alcoholism will become things of the past.

"Sex offenders will be controlled by medication. Our system of penology will be in the purview of chemistry. Steel bars will be replaced by pharmacological agents, leaving criminals to roam free but restricted from harming people.

"We will have *jamais vu* ["never seen"] drugs that create feelings of novelty and *deja vu* ["already seen"] drugs to breed familiarity. Both boredom and anxiety will be alleviated, and our sex lives will be enhanced and intensified.

"Blood cells will be harnessed to become the psychiatrist's allies. They will become like beasts of burden, hauling drugs throughout our bodies. There will be no side effects, no nausea, no liver damage….

"Finally, we shall emerge into a drug-free society in which genetic engineering precludes mental illness. The substances produced by our biochemists will exactly match those endowed to us by nature."[9]

In his 1993 *Listening to Prozac*, psychiatrist Peter Kramer tells us drugs are no longer just for the infirm. Today they can serve a cosmetic use. "We can now see that the possibilities of *cosmetic* psychopharmacology extend far beyond the brightening of mood. Each of the *formes frustes* [an atypical form, as of a disease] of depressive temperament and personality should in principle be reachable through medication: a variety of individual traits will be treatable in people with otherwise unremarkable psychological histories.... As we have access to yet more specific drugs, our accuracy in targeting individual traits will improve."[10]

As always, psychiatry is projecting future developments to gain further government funding from politicians desperate for a solution to society's ailments—many of which were, as we have seen, created and exacerbated by psychiatry in the first place. Still, a world in which its practitioners "will be able to control people's feelings and emotions" is not necessarily the world most of us want. And to understand the true ramifications of this Drug Utopia they so enthusiastically promote we would do well to look first at where such efforts have taken us in the past.

THE ROAD TO EUPHORIA

Man has used psychotropic drugs of one form or another throughout history. However, since a great many of them were accompanied by well-recognized dangers, their applications never became widespread.

In the 1800s, with the advent of psychiatry, new compounds were developed but these were still used relatively sparingly. There were *bromides*, substances that depressed the central nervous system, providing a quieting effect, and then *barbiturates*, chemicals that acted as powerful sedating agents.

In the 1920s, newer barbiturates were synthesized and put to use. Then, in the 1930s, *amphetamines*—stimulants—came onto the market. The AMA reported that "no serious reactions have been reported," and even advised that persons could take the drug, "Benzedrine" or "bennies," under the strict supervision of a physician to capture "a sense of increased energy or capacity for work, or a feeling of exhilaration."[11] With claims such as

194

these, amphetamine abuse became a sporadic problem.

One of the most obvious drawbacks of the drug was that it was addictive. In a 1977 article co-authored with James Bakalar, psychiatrist Lester Grinspoon wrote, "Of all the myths surrounding the amphetamines that of their alleged nonaddictiveness is the most transparent, although when they were first introduced they were hailed as having little or no addictive potential. This is not surprising, as the medical establishment originally guaranteed as nonaddictive almost every drug now known to cause addiction.... Cases of addiction were reported almost immediately, but the drug industry was so successful in reinforcing and sustaining early medical enthusiasm that as late as 1958 C.D. Leake could categorically state that 'no clear case of addiction to amphetamine has been reported.'"[12] By the 1960s, of course, the problems were so widespread they could no longer be swept under the carpet. On the street, amphetamine addicts became known as "speed freaks" because of the bizarre and irrational behavior they exhibited.

In 1942, a new arrival came onto the psychopharmaceutical scene. Working out of a lab in Nazi-occupied Paris, researchers came upon a drug that was useful in the treatment of allergies. Further investigation into the drug revealed that similar compounds "produced a previously unknown type of central nervous system effect."[13] More development followed. In 1950, the French scientists found themselves closing in on a new compound that would meet their aim of "maximal behavioral disruption."[14]

Rats were first trained to climb a rope to reach food. When given one of the experimental drugs, on December 11, 1950, the rats became especially "confused and unable to decide whether or not to climb," the researchers stated.

Within a year, French psychiatrist C. Quarti tried this drug on herself. She would later write that one hour after taking the compound, "I began to have the impression that I was becoming weaker. That I was dying. It was very painful and agonizing." After another hour, "I felt incapable of being angry about anything...."[15]

This reaction must have been encouraging because psychiatrists decided to try the drug on a French mental patient.

By 1954 the new pill had reached the shores of America.

The scientific world called it *chlorpromazine*.

A U.S. drug company, Smith Kline and French, marketed it as Thorazine.

They must have marketed it very well, for in her 1974 *Chlorpromazine in Psychiatry*, Judith Swazey relates the avalanche that followed: "Within 8 months, Thorazine was given to an estimated 2 million patients. A stream of professional publications, now totaling over 14,000, began to describe the drug's 'revolutionary' impact on mental hospitals. The mass media hailed the new product as 'fantastic' and 'versatile,' as a 'miracle drug' that 'melts away anxiety.'...Chlorpromazine...and the other drugs which now began to appear in the psychiatrist's armamentarium created a new lexicon of terms—such as...'major' and 'minor' tranquilizers...and gave rise to the modern scientific discipline of psychopharmacology."[16]

Thorazine was the first in series of drugs called the *neuroleptics* ("nerve seizing"). So potent was its effect on psychiatric patients that it was promoted by one of the leading psychiatric researchers, Heinz E. Lehmann, as "a pharmacological substitute for lobotomy."[17]

Indeed, Dr. Peter Sterling wrote in 1979, "The blunting of conscious motivation, and the ability to solve problems under the influence of chlorpromazine [Thorazine] resembles nothing so much as the effects of frontal lobotomy.... A psychiatrist would be hard put to distinguish a lobotomized patient from one treated with chlorpromazine."[18]

But what mattered more to psychiatrists was that this new drug, the "chemical strait jacket," as it was sometimes called, put an end to so many custodial problems. Patients became docile. There were fewer outbreaks of violence. The patient was more cooperative and quiet. He would no longer act as "crazy." He would no longer cause trouble.

For hospital superintendents and staff, the housing and care of the mental patient became a far easier task. For psychiatrists, who felt rather impotent after such a long history of failure, this was a breakthrough, a demonstration to the world that they could at least change, even if not improve, human behavior.

As for the patient himself, however, Thorazine was not quite the "miracle drug" it had been promoted to be. One typical patient reported: "My tongue was so fuzzy, so thick, I could barely speak.... It was so hard to think, the effort was so great; more often than not I would fall into a stupor of not caring or I would go to sleep. In 8 years I did not read an entire book, or see a whole movie. I could not focus my blurred eyes to read and I always fell asleep at a film. People's voices came through filtered, strange. They could not penetrate my Thorazine fog; and I could not escape my drug prison. The drugs made me constipated as well as ravenously hungry. As a final misery they caused me to gain weight. For 8 years I took laxatives and suffered as I watched my body grow heavy and distorted. My hands shook so I could barely hold a pencil and I was afflicted with what Dr. Sternfeld lightly called 'dancing legs,' a Parkinsonian 'side-effect' of these chemicals."

As is often the case with psychotropics, the side effects required yet another drug to contain them. "For this I took a drug called Kemadrin, and if I missed a day or a dosage, my shoulder muscles would tighten into excruciatingly painful knots and my legs would go wildly out of control," said the patient.[19]

A *San Francisco Examiner* columnist tried what he called a day's dose—50 mg—of Thorazine to see what it would do. The writer, Bill Mandel, reported, "Simply put, Thorazine made me stupid. Because Thorazine and related drugs are called 'liquid lobotomy' in the mental health business, I'd expected a great gray cloud to descend over my faculties. There was no great gray cloud, just small but unsettling patches of fog.

"My mental gears slipped. I had no intellectual traction. It was difficult, for example, to remember simple words. I'd start to describe something and find myself unable to remember such terms as 'screwdriver' and 'volume.'"

It is noteworthy that a 1977 California study found 29 percent of patients in four state hospitals were being prescribed in excess of *800* mg. per day—16 times that taken by Mandel.[20]

The introduction of Thorazine marked one of the most significant social changes of the twentieth century.

The psychiatric community had shifted the centuries-old rule that one should not solve problems, or escape from life, with mind-altering drugs.

After drugging two million patients in eight months, it had given scientific reason why an exception should be made to the no drugs rule: it is okay to give psychotropic drugs to mental patients because they are mentally ill.

With considerable difficulty, the public tried to accept this medical rationale and go along with the tide of happy hospital administrators.

But the drug solution would follow the same pattern as mental hygiene, eugenics, and military screening. First it would be applied to the truly insane, then increasingly toward more minor disabilities and, finally, to the perfectly normal.

It did not take long. Drug companies saw the potential return and poured enormous amounts of money into research. In 1960, Librium—the tranquilizer—came onto the market.

Only six years had passed since Thorazine had been introduced to the market. But with Librium, psychiatrists now told a still-resistive public it was okay to take a pill, not just for insanity, but for nervousness and stress as well. Slowly the social mores shifted again to accommodate them. Resistance to this was, and still is, dismissed by psychiatric supporters as "irrational fear of addiction or a puritanical conviction."[21] (The psychiatric tendency to place negative labels on behavior or attitudes the profession does not agree with is again evident here; still, if "puritanical" is the worst they can come up with to describe self-reliance and integrity, so be it.)

In 1963 Valium—another tranquilizer—was introduced. The drug juggernaut continued to wear at public disagreement through ad campaigns, press reports, television, and the movies. Psychiatric medicines began to take on a respectability among wealthy and academic circles. And as time went on, pill popping became almost fashionable.

Valium became the most prescribed drug in medical history.[22]

Soon it became the top-selling drug in America. And it remained at the top of the drug hit parade until about 1984, by which time Valium's curses—addiction and side effects—were well known, and other drugs had come along to take the number one spot. Still, Valium rested in fourth place in the popularity poll among psychiatric and medical prescribers.[23]

The once high wall forbidding mind-influencing drugs into the body was now falling, brick after brick.

More psychotropic drugs flooded the marketplace in ever-increasing numbers and variety. By 1973—only 19 years after the introduction of Thorazine, about a third of Americans had taken some form of psychiatric drug.[24]

That year, authors Arnold Bernstein and Henry Lennard, writing in *Society*, warned an embattled public, "Drugs enter the human population through two gateways, one legal, the other illegal. Although public attention has been focused on the illegal use of psychoactive agents, by far the larger and more significant problem relates to legal use of such agents. Drugs enter the social body legally through two gateways. Moderately innocuous agents are sold over the counter in drugstores; the more potent and dangerous agents are prescribed by physicians. To a large extent, then, physicians stand between drugs and the public at large; and whether or not drugs are introduced into wide use will depend upon their willingness to employ them."[25]

Not physicians nor psychiatrists nor the public much heeded the warning. Drug use continued to mount.

In 1981, Xanax appeared on pharmacy shelves, a drug that would later be connected to violent episodes in some users.

Then came Prozac, which reached the market in late 1987. Touted as a miracle "mood brightener," sales hit $125 million in 1988 and $350 million in 1989. Despite 160 lawsuits brought against its manufacture over alleged violent or suicidal reactions, psychiatrists continued to prescribe the drug in record quantities. In 1993 the drug was widely promoted by Peter Kramer, monthly columnist for a publication called the *Psychiatric Times*, through his book *Listening to Prozac*.

That year the drug's sales hit $1.2 billion.[26]

THE PROBLEM WITH PSYCHIATRIC DRUGS

Down through the ages, there have, with good reason, been moral restrictions on the use of mind-influencing agents. While some may wish to regard such prohibitions as outdated superstitions or arbitrary religious dogma, the truth is that most moral codes have their roots in practical survival principles.

Most of our sexual mores, for example, are based on efforts to avoid unwanted pregnancy, disease, or the jealous inclinations of the human heart.

So it has been with psychotropic compounds. Centuries of living have shown such substances normally do more harm than good. They alter personality for the worse, they weaken the will, they deteriorate moral fiber. And commonly the man who has been changed by these chemicals is unaware of or stubbornly blind to his own decline.

Even surveys by pharmaceutical houses have found a great many people consider taking their tranquilizers to be immoral.[27]

It is not without reason that these substances have met with reproach in civilized societies.

But the psychiatrist's new drugs have added a twist to these time-tested beliefs. In the 1950s and 1960s, cloaked in the mantle of modern-day medicine, the psychiatrist has infused into the society the idea that these new potions were *somehow different*. These substances, he promoted, were not the same as substances from the past that did bad things. These were, in fact, classified as *medicines*.

We have heard this line of reasoning pushed so insistently and with such great fervor that the once-distinct line between good and bad substances has become perilously vague. Our certainty is shaken. Are these compounds truly different and somehow good for us?

To answer this we need to look at how mind-altering substances "work."

The body is an extremely complex biochemical machine, functioning constantly with a near-infinite number of chemical reactions and chemical flows occurring at any given moment.

The truly remarkable aspect to this is that these reactions and flows occur *in harmony and rhythmically one with another*. They happen in specific sequences, in certain quantities, and at exact rates of speed.

When a foreign substance such as a psychotropic drug is introduced into the body these flows and inner workings are disrupted.

The substance may, for example, cause the body to give a constant, excessive release of adrenalin. This gives the individual a feeling of euphoria, increased energy, or heightened alertness.

But it is not normal for the body to release adrenalin like this without cause. And a price must be paid. All the major and minor physiological activities that go into the manufacture and use of adrenalin have been called into play. They have stopped performing their routine function. Instead they have been speeded up, slowed down, dammed up, overwhelmed, denied critical metabolic substances—all manner of interference has been introduced into the normal operating patterns.

This is why psychiatric drugs produce side effects.

This is, in fact, why they produce any effect at all. They do not *heal* anything. They break into, in most cases, the routine, rhythmic flows and activities of the nervous system. Given a tranquilizer, the nerves and other body systems are *forced to do things they normally would not do*.

The human body, however, is unmatched in its ability to withstand and respond to such disruptions. The various systems fight back, trying to process the foreign chemical, and work diligently to counterbalance its effects on the body.

But the body can only take so much.

Quickly or slowly, the systems break down. After all, human physiology was not designed for the continuous manufacture of euphoric, tranquilizing, or anti-depressant sensations. Yet it is forced into this enterprise by psychoactive drugs.

Tissue damage may occur. Nerves stop functioning normally. Organs and hormonal systems go awry. This can be temporary. It can be partial, but long-lasting. It can be permanent.

Like a car run on rocket fuel, you may be able to get it to run a thousand miles an hour, but the tires, the engine, the internal parts, were never meant for this. The machine flies apart.

Bizarre things happen. Addiction. Exhaustion. Diminished sexual desire. Trembling. Nightmares.

These can be devastating. A classic example is *tardive dyskinesia* (TD), a side effect of Thorazine and similar drugs. *Tardive* means late and *dyskinesia* means an impairment of the power of voluntary movement.[28] It is "late" because it occurs after the drug has been taken for a while. TD involves the involuntary movement of the lips, tongue, jaw, fingers, toes, and other body parts. It includes the "dancing legs" mentioned by the former patient quoted earlier.

At first psychiatrists tried to make nothing of this deformity, saying it was a small price to pay or that it would pass. However, the complaints would not go away.

In 1968 the chairman of a NIMH workshop, speaking of patients who had had long-term drug treatment, stated, "Many such cases [of TD] can be seen if one takes the trouble of walking through the wards of mental hospitals…. Twenty to twenty-five percent of the patients are afflicted by this disorder according to our observations; the disorder may last for many years or perhaps indefinitely in the more severe cases."

But time would tell an even more serious story. When, in 1993, we interviewed Dr. William Glazer, one of the world's foremost authorities on TD, he told us, "We just published a paper, the first time this information is out...where we estimated that your risk of getting it [TD after long-term use] is about 70 percent."

When asked what percentage of patients had *permanent* TD after long-term use, even after being taken off the medication, Dr. Glazer responded, "We did a study and found over 95 percent."

And what is the cure for TD? "Well, there is none. There are approaches we can try, but there really is no successful treatment."[29]

Psychiatrist Seymour Rosenblatt, in his book, *Beyond Valium*, gives us a close-up view of TD as it began to appear in the mental wards: "Then one day we noticed something peculiar. Some patients developed a strange, wormlike tongue movement. It was hardly noticeable—a twitch of the tongue tip—but you could see it when they held their mouths open. As the days passed by, the symptoms grew worse. Their lips began rotating in a chewing movement. Soon the whole mouth was thrusting and rolling, the tongue flicking out like the tongue of an anteater.

"What kind of strange behavior was this? It grew worse. It afflicted their arms and legs. They began to writhe slowly, purposelessly, a few of them developing a to-and-fro rocking motion.

"Little did we know it, but we were in the process of observing the first serious drawback of antipsychotics [medication].... It swept through the hospitals like an epidemic. One after another the patients were stricken. Soon we had almost 50 percent of our mental patients chewing and grimacing in a horrible grotesquerie.

"What was the cause? We didn't know. Families of the afflicted patients went running to the doctors. 'What have you done to poor Joe?' they demanded. 'He's writhing so badly, we can't stand the sight of him!'

"Well, what we had done was try to fool nature—and nature, as usual, was not cooperating.... The Thorazine, you see, was blocking the [nerve] receptors. The receptors were not getting their usual transmitter messages. They were being required to fire less often, and it was a state of lethargy they were not accustomed to.

"Nature does not adapt well to change. It finds new ways of behaving as it always did. So...the patient's body...simply instructed the receptors to become more sensitive. They began to fire on fewer transmitters, sending out ill-conceived impulses to various body parts. Worse than that, new receptors appeared. The...neurons grew abnormally sensitive.... The tragedy is that the damage is often permanent. The new receptors cannot be easily demolished. This, of course, leads to irreversible symptoms."[30]

To measure this in human terms, recall that two million people received Thorazine within eight months of its release in 1954. And Thorazine and similar drugs are still in use today.

Truthfully, however, all psychiatric drugs "work" the way Thorazine does. They attempt to coerce the body and nervous system to behave differently than their design.

So in spite of psychopharmacologist Ronald Siegel's "dream" about psychotropic drugs that will give us the highest highs and yet be as harmless as air—common sense tells us these drugs do not exist. Nor can they.

They can only parasitize the existing functions of the body. And the body is not made for such chemically-induced euphoria, calm, or sedation as psychiatric drugs create.

The well-documented history of *every* new psychotropic medication has been one of great fanfare for its "harmless" nature, only to be followed by mounting evidence of freak-show side effects and temporary or chronic physical and mental malfunctions.

A typical example was pointed out by psychiatrist Peter Kramer in *Listening to Prozac.* When a new breed of medication came onto the market, hopes were high. "Each new...antidepressant," he wrote, "as it was introduced, was said to have fewer side effects than [another type]. ...Some of these claims held up marginally. But most of the purported advantages evaporated as the drugs came into general use."[31]

Unfortunately, psychiatrists appear to have a poor track record at seeing the full impact of side effects. There may be a number of reasons for this.

First of all, most of them don't know what else to do for a patient, so are very disinclined to not use drugs.

Secondly, the prevailing reasoning of the psychiatric community is that, even though they have no idea what the long-term damage is or even the full scope of short-term effects, of the drugs they prescribe, they are willing to make the claim that these effects are less harmful or painful than the patient's current misery. This, of course, presupposes the fallacious notion that the patient has no safe alternative route out of his misery.

Thirdly, if the psychiatrist is following the above two guidelines, of course, one would think he would not *want* to recognize or acknowledge any bad effects from the drugs as it would unravel his entire *modus operandi*.

So we see odd phenomena such as psychiatrists telling their patients they *need* their medication, regardless of side effects, because they have something called a "biochemical imbalance." New York psychiatrist Ron Leifer told us in an interview, "There's no biochemical imbalance. When people come to me and they say, 'I have a biochemical imbalance,' I say, 'Show me your lab tests.' There are no lab tests. So what's the biochemical imbalance?"[32]

And we see new psychotropic drugs introduced into the marketplace as miracle cures, such as Prozac, only to find out, as in Prozac's case, that, like all drugs before it, among many other side effects it ultimately mutates bodily systems into doing the abnormal. A 1992 scientific paper published in *Cancer Research* revealed that Prozac and other anti-depressants "bind to growth-regulatory...receptors," stimulating malignant cancer growth in rats.[33]

The problem with taking psychiatric drugs would seem to be easily stated.

There are prices to pay.

THE FLASHBACK PHENOMENA

Recent medical research has shed even more light on the deleterious effects of psychotropic agents.

It has been known for years that certain types of drugs, including diazepam (Valium) have a tendency to leave residuals in the body, particularly in fat. Thus, those using such drugs do not rid themselves of the chemical when they stop taking it. Vestiges of the substance remain, unprocessed.

What has come to view in modern studies is that these residuals can enter the bloodstream at any time, causing the normal physical and mental manifestations of that drug.[34]

A similar phenomenon was noticed back in the '60s during the LSD craze—people going on "trips" months or years after taking the drug—and was referred to then as a *flashback*.

This, of course, may explain why people are occasionally prone to strange biochemical reactions out of the blue. They experience sudden light-headedness, cravings, mental confusion—any and all drug phenomena.

If their drug history includes ingestion of residual-leaving psychotropic medications, they are then at risk for all the effects and side effects so produced. Since flashbacks occur randomly, there is no prediction if these will occur in one's sleep, while one is driving, or during the heat of an argument.

It is simply one more price to pay.

TREATING SYMPTOMS

In a 1993 interview, psychiatrist Al Parides told us one of the key problems with psychiatric drugs is "there is an unrealistic reliance on the chemical rather than on a change of circumstances, rather than try to relate to their wife in a different way, or the children, or deal with the grief.... You see a lot of people who have anxiety that is explainable...they lost their job, or they're having trouble with their wife, or with their husband, and they get Valium, let's say. Again, this might bring some sort of relief, but it's like taking a drink to solve a problem—that's not going to solve the problem."[35]

In their 1973 article, *The American Way of Drugging*, authors Arnold Bernstein and Henry Lennard remark that the use of drugs may make it easier for others to manage or cope with the disturbed or disturbing individual, but they do not reach the sources of anxiety or misery. An often overlooked result of this is that, additionally, the use of drugs tends to reduce the ability of a group to cope with the distress of its members.[36]

In some cases, then, families and other groups are not forced to revise their own destructive behavior which may have caused the individual trouble. Nor are they called upon to develop means that truly do help the person. Such necessities are *apparently* (though not actually) made unnecessary through the masking of symptoms.

Since the human growth process *requires* the oftentimes long and painful process of trying, making mistakes, failing, and trying again, such growth is denied to the individual whose problems sit unresolved in an anaesthetized mind.

While psychotropic drugs may deaden the mental or emotional pain connected with living, in so doing they kill the drive that promotes the search for solutions and improvement.

In the long run, the quick fix leaves the person perpetually limited in his ability to deal with his problems and his life. He never advances.

In the insane the results would seem to be no different. As we have seen, the mind has a great degree of natural recuperative powers. Left alone and not "treated," people *normally* work their way out of their psychotic periods. Studies have shown that even the majority of those labeled "schizophrenic," commonly deemed "incurable" by the psychiatric profession, in fact improve dramatically with the passage of time when not given psychiatric treatment and when not forced to live in insane asylum conditions.[37]

Statistics visibly show this. Of the population aged 18 to 44, 1.12 percent have claimed to experience symptoms considered psychiatrically to be "schizophrenia." In the 45 to 65 age group the percentage drops to 0.6. Over 65 it becomes 0.1 percent.[38]

The simple truth seems to be that people change over time. Without psychiatric medications. This has been observed throughout history. In the 1800s, in asylums where people were given "moral treatment"—decent food, rest, light labor to occupy them—it was common to release much improved patients. Some would return, some would not.

When treated with drugs, however, this natural healing process is stultified or halted as the individual's wits are too frozen to unravel themselves from the turmoil they are in.

Psychiatrist Walter Afield commented, "What's happening in the training of psychiatrists and in the quality of a psychiatrist is that they have become drug pushers. They have got an array of drugs that they keep changing, adding, taking away, adjusting, with really no good rationale and have forgotten how to sit down and talk to patients as to what their problems are."[39]

OPENING PANDORA'S BOX

The phrase *side effect* would seem to be a misnomer.

Truthfully, side effects can sometimes be more pronounced than a drug's intended effects. And they are not something that occur "on the side." They are, in fact, the body's natural response to having a chemical disrupt its normal functioning. For example, some psychiatric drugs are given for depression because they have a "damping down" effect. They suppress the physical feelings associated with depression. However, in the process, they squelch a host of other things for which the drug is not targeted.

One study reported in 1986 told of a survey of patients who were taking anti-depressant medication. They were asked, before and after six weeks of treatment, to fill out a sexual function questionnaire that broke down the subject into seven items. Other groups did likewise, including a placebo group.

In five of the categories, the patients receiving *any* kind of treatment (not placebo) scored lower after six weeks. In every case, those taking medication showed greater impairment than those taking placebos. These categories included thinking about sex with interest or desire, enjoyment of sex and ability to achieve orgasm.[40]

Often, the patient may complain about a side effect, only to find it is the intended result. Thorazine routinely makes people feel foggy, distant, or apathetic, but as a neuroleptic ("nerve seizing") drug, that is what it is supposed to do.

Many patients are surprised at the unexpected effects of psychiatric drugs. They take them, as the doctor ordered, to alleviate their anxiety or something similar, only to experience an array of odd physical and mental reactions. The result may be minor, such as dryness of mouth or loss of appetite or it may be a full-blown psychotic fit, and sometimes even death.

And this is no alarmist or exaggerated statement. In 1978, a New York state medical examiner reported that 30 percent of all psychiatric patient deaths in Rockland County were due to asphyxiation because of failure of their gag reflex as a side effect of psychotropic medication. He said the victims "vomited into their lungs because certain nerves necessary to prevent this from happening had been deadened by tranquilizers." He added, "This is not unique to Rockland County. This is going on in every institution in the state of New York and everywhere in the country. These deaths are not from overdoses. The deaths are occurring at the therapeutic dosage level."[41]

To give the full picture of what a drug can do, we have selected as an example the drug known by the generic name of *fluoxetine* and sold under the name of Prozac. We chose it because it is a more modern drug, one that the public would expect to be an improvement over past medicines.

According to psychiatrist David L. Richman, one study of this drug reported mild and short-lasting effects in these percentages: nausea (25 percent), nervousness (21 percent), insomnia (19 percent), headache (17 percent), tremors (16 percent), anxiety (15 percent), drowsiness (14 percent), dry mouth (14 percent), excessive sweating (12 percent), and diarrhea (10 percent).[42]

The full list of side effects, as listed in *The PDR [Physician's Desk Reference] Family Guide to Prescription Drugs*, are as follows:

More common side effects may include: Abnormal dreams, agitation, anxiety, bronchitis, chills, diarrhea, dizziness, drowsiness and fatigue, hay fever, inability to fall or stay asleep, increased appetite, lack or loss of appetite, light-headedness, nausea, nervousness, sweating, tremors, weakness, weight loss, yawning.

Less common side effects may include: Abnormal ejaculation, abnormal gait, abnormal stoppage of menstrual flow, acne, amnesia, apathy, arthritis, asthma, belching, bone pain, breast cysts, breast pain, brief loss of consciousness, bursitis, chills and fever, conjunctivitis, convulsions, dark, tarry stool, difficulty in swallowing, dilation of pupils, dimness of vision, dry skin, ear pain, eye pain, exaggerated feeling of well-being, excessive bleeding, facial swelling due to fluid retention, fluid retention, hair loss, hallucinations, hangover effect, hiccups, high or low blood pressure, hives, hostility, impotence, increased sex drive, inflammation of the esophagus, inflammation of the gums, inflammation of the stomach lining, inflammation of the tongue, inflammation of the vagina, intolerance of light, involuntary movement, irrational ideas, irregular heartbeat, jaw or neck pain, lack of muscle coordination, low blood pressure upon standing, low blood sugar, migraine headache, mouth inflammation, neck pain and rigidity, nosebleed, ovarial disorders, paranoid reaction, pelvic pain, pneumonia, rapid breathing, rapid heartbeat, ringing in the ears, severe chest pain, skin inflammation, skin rash, thirst, twitching, uncoordinated movements, urinary disorders, vague feeling of bodily discomfort, vertigo, weight gain.

Rare side effects may include: Abortion, antisocial behavior, blood in urine, bloody diarrhea, bone disease, breast enlargement, cataracts, colitis, coma, deafness, decreased reflexes, dehydration, double vision, drooping of eyelids, duodenal ulcer, enlarged abdomen, enlargement of liver, enlargement or increased activity of thyroid gland, excess growth of coarse hair on face, chest, etc., excess uterine or vaginal hemorrhage, extreme muscle tension, eye bleeding, female milk production, fluid accumulation and swelling in the head, fluid buildup in larynx and lungs, gallstones, glaucoma, gout, heart attack, hepatitis, high blood sugar, hysteria, inability to control bowel movements, increased salivation, inflammation of eyes and eyelids, inflammation of fallopian tubes, inflammation of testes, inflammation of the gallbladder, inflammation of the small intestine, inflammation of tissue below skin, kidney disorders, lung inflammation, menstrual disorders, mouth sores, muscle inflammation or bleeding, muscle spasms, painful sexual intercourse for women, psoriasis, rashes, reddish or purplish spots on the skin, reduction of body temperature, rheumatoid arthritis, seborrhea, shingles, skin discoloration, skin inflammation and disorders, slowing of heart rate, slurred speech, spitting blood, stomach ulcer, stupor, suicidal thoughts, taste loss, temporary cessation of breathing, tingling sensation around the mouth, tongue discoloration and swelling, urinary tract disorders, vomiting blood, yellow eyes and skin.[43]

Obviously, this latest drug of psychiatric choice also bears with it a certain price.

One particular sector of the society which has experienced the full brunt of the effects of psychiatric drugs has been our elderly. Psychiatrists and other physicians have found that their use makes nursing home populations more manageable. A 1986 study of 2,000 pharmacies found that 76 percent of prescriptions written for nursing home residents over 65 were *tranquilizers*. Sixty percent of the prescriptions were for what are called major tranquilizers such as Thorazine.[44]

A study that same year reported that 63 percent of the elderly expressed "very unfavorable attitudes" towards using such medications.[45]

Drs. Meyer Glantz and Michael Backenheimer of the National Institute on Drug Abuse have stated, "This level of psychoactive drug prescribing is very highly disproportionate for this age group's representation in the population and very highly disproportionate for their reported prevalence of mental health problems."[46]

Paralleling this situation is the fact that 73,000 elderly die every year in the U.S. from adverse drug reactions, interactions and medication errors. This is 25 percent more Americans than died in the entirety of the Vietnam War.

Although numbers can give one a good grasp of the picture of the effects of psychotropic drugs, they do not measure the price in human terms.

Here are some first-hand accounts of life on psychiatric drugs.

HALDOL: Wilda Henry of Florida reported her eighty-three-year-old mother became "a vegetable" five weeks after taking Haldol. The drug left the woman babbling, drooling, shaking, and unable to control her bowel function.

MELLARIL: Anise Debose of Washington, D.C., said her seventy-six-year-old father entered a nursing home active, laughing, and talking. Four days later, after taking the psychiatric drug Mellaril and four other drugs, "He was restrained to a chair as rigid as a board when I saw him. His head was thrown back and his mouth was limply hanging down. Both eyes were closed. The impression all of us had was that he was dead."

XANAX: Jo Novak reported, "I felt like I was on fire. I didn't know where I was. I felt spacey, like I was in another world." Addicted to the drug, Novak claimed it was torturous trying to break free of its clutches. "It's a little pill," she said, "waiting to take your life away from you."

VALIUM: Debbie Gorman on the drug's addictive properties: "The more Valium you take, the more anxiety you feel and the more Valium you need just to get through the day. I tried to get off many times…it took me a long time to get through the weird head trips that Valium puts you through."

VALIUM: Entertainer Liza Minelli, after a 15-year dependence on the drug, stated, "Valium addiction is much harder to break than heroin addiction."

PROZAC: "I became violent toward my husband," reported Janet Sims. "I would be happy one minute, and the next minute I would be very angry, throwing dishes and glass items and other breakable things. I also attacked my husband with my fists and tried to scratch his face…. While on Prozac, my marriage fell apart…. While on Prozac I started to have obsessive suicidal thoughts. [I thought] that I should just destroy my body in any way I could."

HALCION: Novelist Cindy Ehrlich began taking this psychiatric drug to help her sleep. "When by four o'clock each day I was crying and waiting for flying saucers to land," she reported, "I never dreamed it might have something to do with the sleeping pill I'd taken the night before."

HALDOL: James Armstrong: "After…a week…on Haldol, I was unable to speak. No matter how hard I tried, I couldn't say anything out

WILHELM WUNDT—*From his experimental psychology laboratory at the University of Leipzig, in Germany, he forwarded his theories that man was an animal and that all thought was the result of chemical reactions in the brain. His numerous students spread these unproven theories around the world.*

EMIL KRAEPELIN—*One of Wundt's German students who became known as the "Father of Psychiatry." He saw mental symptoms as hereditary and supported the sterilization of certain "mentally ill" so these defective genes would not be passed on.*

ERNST RÜDIN—*German psychiatrist and a student of Kraepelin. A rabid eugenicist, his racial theories were the basis for selling Hitler on the workability of creating a pure Aryan race. He has been described as the "most evil man in Nazi Germany."*

ADOLF HITLER—*The infamous atrocities perpetrated by Hitler were inspired by the racial purity theories of psychiatrists such as Ernst Rüdin.*

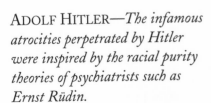

G. BROCK CHISHOLM—*Head military psychiatrist in Canada during World War II. He was the outspoken head of the World Health Organization and co-founder of the World Federation for Mental Health.*

J.R. REES—*Head military psychiatrist in England who was responsible for introducing psychiatry into the military there. He was director of the Tavistock Clinic in London and was the co-founder of the World Federation for Mental Health (WFMH).*

WILLIAM MENNINGER—*Menninger (on left) was highly influential in getting legislation passed that provided government funding to psychiatry. His historic 1963 meeting with President Kennedy at the White House came just before the passage of legislation which placed psychiatric clinics around the U.S.*

WINFRED OVERHOLSER—*Superintendent of St. Elizabeth's Hospital in Washington, D.C. Shown here (on right) with President Nixon at the opening of a new wing of the hospital. Overholser supervised the training of psychiatrists for duty during World War II. He also conducted experiments on soldiers at St. Elizabeth's for American intelligence during the war.*

ROBERT FELIX—*First head of the National Institute of Mental Health (NIMH)*
which he was instrumental in establishing. He was a key lobbyist for the psychiatric
industry and his efforts brought in untold millions of dollars of government funding
to NIMH, as he is shown demonstrating on this chart.

Below, at a 1946 meeting of the National Advisory Mental Health Council,
members discussed the mental health program of the nation. From left to right: Dr.
Thomas Paar, Surgeon General; Dr. E.A. Strecker, Professor of Psychiatry,
University of Pennsylvania; Dr. William Malamud, Professor of Psychiatry, Boston

University; Dr. Frank
Fremont–Smith,
Medical Director of
the Josiah Macy
Foundation, New York;
Dr. Robert H. Felix;
Dr. S. Allen Shallman,
Minneapolis,
Minnesota.

DANIEL BLAIN—*Long-time Medical Director of the American Psychiatric Association and influential lobbyist for psychiatry.*

CARL ROGERS—*Educational psychologist who introduced psychological programs into the schools. He later recanted when he observed that these programs not only did not work but were, in fact, destructive.*

LOUIS JOLYON ("JOLLY") WEST—*Psychiatrist who conducted experiments with LSD for the CIA and who later became head of the Neuropsychiatric Institute at the University of California Los Angeles.*

RADOVAN KARADZIC—*A psychiatrist who became head of the Bosnian Serbs, instigators of the war in ex-Yugoslavia. Karadzic was trained in the same racial purity policies as used to start the Holocaust. Karadzic instigated the concept of ethnic cleansing which resulted in concentration camps reminiscent of Nazi Germany. In July 1995, he was charged with genocide and crimes against humanity by a United Nations war crimes tribunal.*

loud and spoke only with the greatest difficulty.... It was as if my whole body were succumbing to a lethal poison."

NAVANE: A report on Robert Snider tells us that after nine months on the drug, he became a victim of tardive dyskinesia. The once handsome young man now grimaces and jerks in uncontrollable motions. With distorted, twisted limbs, he is mostly confined to a wheelchair. His face is a mass of tortured displays. His eyes clamp shut involuntarily. He cannot work. He cannot play with his four children.[47]

PROLIXIN: Wade Hudson, speaking before a Senate subcommittee in 1977, said, "The experience became sheer torture. Different muscles began twitching. My mouth was like very dry cotton no matter how much water I drank. My tongue became all swollen up. My entire body felt like it was being twisted up in contortions inside by some unseen wringer. And my mind became clouded up and slowed down—before I had been reasoning incorrectly, but at least I could reason. But most disturbing of all was that I feared that all of these excruciating experiences were in my mind, or caused by my mind—a sign of my supposed sickness."[48]

RITALIN: Mrs. Verne Watson was compelled by school officials to give the drug to her son to handle his "hyperactivity." "David would complain he didn't like the feel of his body when he took the pills," she said. "It took his appetite away and he would cry a lot. His dreams got so bad he couldn't even talk about them. He would get up in the night and walk the floor for hours. His body would shake and quiver something terrible." Finally one day, her son collapsed before school and told her, "I just can't take them anymore, they're torturing me."[49]

VALIUM: Ms. "W": "Whenever I woke up during the night I would take a ¼ or ½ pill of Valium to get back to sleep and finally I found myself taking Valium nightly. Over the last few years my heart had started to beat irregularly and I also started having anxiety attacks. I didn't know it at the time, but now I know that I was experiencing the effects of drug withdrawal from the Valium because my body was addicted to it and my body wasn't getting enough of it."[50]

MANUFACTURING INSANITY

On September 11, 1989, Joe was not doing well. He was restless and pacing. In his psychiatrist's words, he exhibited an "increased level of

211

agitation and anger." The psychiatrist wrote, "Plan—Discontinue Prozac which may be cause."

Three days later, carrying a gun, Joe walked into his former place of employment, a printing plant in Louisville, Kentucky, and opened fire on the people he used to work with.

When the shooting stopped, Joseph Wesbecker had gunned down 20 people. Eight of them died. The disturbed gunman then turned his weapon on himself.

High levels of Prozac were found in his bloodstream.[51]

According to the coroner's report, the drugs he had taken, Prozac and Lithium, may have been a contributing factor to the murder-suicide.[52]

Jacqui Miller, shot four times in the melee, was one of the last persons to see Wesbecker alive. "I looked up into the face of who was holding the rifle," she said. "He was completely gone. There was just nothing there of what makes a person a person. He was totally out of it."[53]

On the surface, the idea of tranquilizers or anti-depressants creating hostility and violence may not make sense. After all, they are supposed to make people calm and quiet. But the reality is that they can and do create this effect. The examples are numerous.

Authors Richard Shader and Alberto DiMascio wrote about a study done on Valium, known generically as *diazepam*, that demonstrated this phenomena. "Many of the patients receiving diazepam displayed a progressive development of dislikes or hates," they noted. "The patients themselves deliberately used the term 'hate.' This hatefulness first involved non-significant figures in the patients' environment, progressed from there to the involvement of key figures such as aides, nurses, and physicians, and went on to the involvement of important figures such as parents and spouses. The phenomenon was progressive and in some instances, culminated in overt acts of violence."[54]

In Peter Kramer's *Listening to Prozac*, he tells of a number of patients who showed disconcerting manifestations. "It was not possible to keep Lucy on Prozac," he wrote. "She reported an increase in her sense of undirected urgency. Overcome with cravings, she did not know what she craved. She had to do something, yet she did not know what. Case reports had emerged of Prozac's causing patients to experience suicidal ruminations, and I thought that Lucy's agitation resembled aspects of incidents in those reports."[55]

Another Prozac patient told him, "When I break up with a man, I have no bad feelings whatsoever, and I don't worry about whether I'm hurting him. Sometimes I wonder whether I haven't suffered a loss of moral sensibility."[56] Later he tells of another who experienced this "feeling...of the numbing of moral sensibility."[57]

A Canadian study was conducted on prisoners twenty years ago in response to "an apparent increase in acts of aggression by inmates when these inmates were on psychotropic drugs." Their observations were that any class of drugs containing antianxiety agents, when taken, showed a marked increase in the rate of aggressive incidents. They also observed that inmates were better able to control their aggression until they received psychotropic medication, whereupon the aggressive incident rate, in one group, for example, tripled.

The authors of the study, D.G. Workman and D.G. Cunningham concluded, "Perhaps antianxiety agents do not act to relieve anxiety and frustration but only to remove the anxiety and inhibitions about aggressive acts.

"Considering that certainly not all aggressive personalities are in prison, that frustrations also abound in society and that *diazepam* [Valium] is the most commonly prescribed drug in the United States with *chlordiazepoxide* [Librium] third, the implications of the combinations of anxiety agents and aggressiveness are astounding."[58]

Other psychiatric drugs have been implicated. A 1984 study published in the *American Journal of Psychiatry* found that 10 percent (8 out of 80) of the patients treated with *alprazolam* [Xanax] exhibited "extreme anger and hostile behavior" including two physical assaults, potentially dangerous behavior by two more, and verbal outbursts by the remainder. We are told, "'Mrs. A' erupted with screams on the fourth day of alprazolam treatment and held a steak knife to her mother's throat." Mrs. A had no history of such violence.[59]

A 1985 investigation into Xanax, also reported in the *American Journal of Psychiatry*, claimed that more than half (58 percent) of the treated patients experienced serious "dyscontrol," i.e. violence and loss of control compared with only eight percent who were given a placebo. Episodes included: "deep neck cuts," "transverse wrist cuts," "tried to break own arm," "threw chair at child," "arm and head banging," and "jumped in front

213

of car." Moreover, the findings showed that "the patient who threw a chair at her child had no history of physical violence toward the child, although she had frequently shouted at him. Similarly, the patient who cut her neck had no previous episodes of self-mutilation."[60]

A year later yet another study appeared in the same journal. This time an antidepressant, *amitriptyline* (Elavil), was found to be a source of belligerent behavior. "We noted a disturbing clinical worsening among some patients receiving amitriptyline," the article reported. "These patients appeared progressively more hostile, irritable, and behaviorally impulsive.... The increase in demanding behavior and assaultive acts was statistically significant.[61]

A similar drug, *imipramine* (Tofranil) was reviewed in 1965 in *Psychopharmacologia*. The analysis revealed what was called a significant increase in the expression of overt hostility outwards on the average for all subjects when they were on the imipramine.[62]

A 1986 article in the same journal was entitled, "Why Do Some Antidepressants Promote Suicide?"[63]

In an article published in 1980 in *Psychosomatics*, the authors tell of a study of children taking amitriptyline (Elavil). Some grew hysterical or hostile. One of the kids began "exhibiting excessive irritability and anger, pacing excessively and declaring that he was not afraid anymore, that he was 'not a chicken anymore.' He became openly defiant, belligerent, hostile, and argumentative."[64]

Another study, which appeared in the *Journal of Nervous and Mental Disease* in 1988 reports similar side effects from the drug *haloperidol* (Haldol). Many people with no history of violence before taking the drug "were significantly more violent" while on it.[65]

Psychiatrists often refer to such drug reactions as *akathisia*. Akathisia is a condition marked by restlessness, ranging from anxiety to inability to lie or sit quietly or to sleep. It is notably seen as a toxic reaction to phenothiazines, a drug group that includes Thorazine. In extreme cases of akathisia, homicidal violence can result.

Jerome L. Schulte, writing in the *American Journal of Forensic Psychiatry* in 1985, told of five such cases. One was a twenty-three-year-old man who was injected with Haldol in the admissions room of a psychiatric unit. Schulte tells what followed: "He then escaped from the emergency room and the authorities, ran several miles to a park, tried to get a policeman to help him, escaped again and totally disrobed. Within the next 45-minute period of time, he assaulted one woman who was walking her dog and attempted to rape her. When pulled off by the husband, he proceeded down the street, broke down the front door of a house where an 81-year-old lady was sleeping. He severely beat her with his fists, 'to a pulp,' by his own description, following which he found knives and stabbed her repeatedly, resulting in her death. Then, after being confronted in the street by a policeman who sprayed him with Mace, he returned through the house, exiting the back door where he ran into another woman with her child. He repeatedly stabbed the woman in front of the child, whereupon he moved onto the next person he encountered, a woman whom he severely assaulted and stabbed to the extent that an eye was lost and an opening into the anus was created resulting in major surgery and serious residual problems, including colostomy. He was then finally captured and subdued by eight policemen."[66]

Schulte also related a story of a man who, after taking haloperidol, killed his mother with a hammer. In 1988 in Tustin, California, Betty Hahn also killed her eighty-three-year-old mother by beating her in the head with a hammer. Hahn had received psychiatric treatment for depression and agoraphobia (fear of open spaces); she was taking Xanax prior to the murder.

Bizarre and senseless acts of violence such as these were extremely rare before 1960. Now they are frequent and increasing. And that rise seems to coincide with the influx of psychotropic drugs into widespread use.

In September of 1988, 19-year-old James Wilson entered an elementary school in Greenwood, South Carolina with a loaded .22-caliber rifle. He started shooting children, killing two and wounding seven others. For five years he had been taking psychiatric drugs, including Xanax and Valium. James Crossen, program director of the Chemical Dependency Recovery Unit at the Medical Center of North Hollywood, California, commented, "That that young man should have been on drugs all his life, since he was fourteen, is ghoulish. The drugs would be a major contributing factor in such a surprising and sudden act of violence, a major contributor."[67]

In April 1991, Hank Adams, a former San Diego County sheriff's deputy, shot his wife to death then killed himself, while his 17-year-old daughter looked on. He had no history of violence and people who knew him said the act was completely out of character for the mild-mannered, soft-spoken, ex-law enforcement officer. He was taking Prozac at the time of the incident.[68]

Mary Feurst was described by her husband Russell as a loving mother and spouse until she entered the mental health system. After extensive psychiatric treatment, including antidepressants, Mary said she was planning to kill their children. She was then institutionalized and treated with more medication. The husband said that the psychiatrists released Mary in June 1982, after what they felt was "significant recovery."

On July 22, 1982, Mary Feurst gunned down her own children with a .38-caliber revolver, shooting her 6-year-old son in the face and back and her 9-year-old daughter in the head. Both died.[69]

HOOKED: THE METHADONE STORY

"The history of the treatment of narcotic withdrawal," noted psychiatrist and methadone advocate Herbert Kleber in 1981, "is one, with a few exceptions, of finding treatments that are even more addictive or difficult to break than the one being treated, or else treatments that are far more dangerous for the individual undergoing withdrawal than the untreated withdrawal itself."[70]

In the 1800s a drug was introduced that was said to cure one of the most degraded human frailties of the time, opium addiction. The new substance was called *morphine*.

By 1870, physicians began to complain that morphine was more addictive than opium and presented greater problems than the original addiction.[71]

In 1898 a solution arrived. A new compound was offered to the market as a nonaddictive sleeping agent, as well as a treatment for morphine addiction. Experts of the day hailed it as the new cure. This fresh arrival was named *heroin*.

Within fifteen years, however, heroin's true nature became inescapable. Since it was even more potent than opium or morphine and could be diluted for greater profit, illicit dealers quickly embraced it as their product of choice.

The scourge of heroin addiction became a significant problem in western countries, accounting for a considerable percentage of their crime. With no solution available from the psychiatric community, the problem plagued leaders and law enforcement officials for well over a half century.

Coming out of Nazi Germany, however, was a new product named Dolophine, after Adolf Hitler. Following World War II, Dolophine was brought to the United States and used by psychiatrists to treat drug addicts. In America it was called methadone.

Promoted notably by psychiatrist Marie Nyswander, methadone was said to be a nonaddictive solution to the heroin problem. In 1963, Nyswander and psychiatrist Vincent Dole, both of the Rockefeller Institute, professed that methadone—now acknowledged as addictive—could "replace" heroin dependency, if necessary, for life.[72]

Unbelievably, on the basis of these claims, methadone maintenance became an accepted form of treatment for heroin addiction across the country. By the 1970s, such programs were treating more than 75,000 patients.

The drug's addictive qualities became legendary. Dr. Michael Smith of the Lincoln Detox Program in New York claimed, "Withdrawal from methadone is a long, drawn-out brutal experience. There is not a two-to-five-day crisis of vomiting and tremors, as with heroin. These and other frightening symptoms occur for weeks and usually months on end."[73]

The head of a methadone clinic in Ohio admitted that "less than 1 percent" of persons on methadone stop using it.[74]

In the mid-1970s, when Nyswander and Dole reviewed the effectiveness of their methadone program, they reported, "The great majority of heroin addicts remain on the streets, and the programs have lost their ability to attract them to treatment."[75]

A 1987 article in the *Journal of Psychoactive Drugs* stated, "Approximately half of those who were now paying for [methadone] maintenance reported resorting to crime to pay their clinic fees. As one client described the situation, 'The clinic has now become my dealer. I am now committing crimes to pay for an addictive drug [methadone]. It's really not much different than the street.'"[76]

Not much difference at all—because black market methadone was soon sold on the street.

That same year, in New York City alone, hundreds of people entered rehab programs because they had become hooked on illegally purchased methadone.[77]

In 1989, 60 percent of the 31,000 methadone patients in New York City were still active drug abusers, and the percentage was on the rise.[78]

Today psychiatrists are claiming they may have a solution to the methadone problem. It is another drug. This one is called *ibogaine*. An hallucinogen tested on prisoners as far back as 1955 by psychiatrist Harris Isbell, the drug has gained a following.[79] Since the drug is classified in the U.S. as a Class I (dangerous and of no medical value: LSD is Class I), currently treatment is only available in Holland under psychiatric care.

Once again, however, we see a cure that will probably turn out to be more lingering than the addiction. Numerous researchers have found that ibogaine kills cells in the cerebellum, up to 15 percent in a specific area.[80]

The lessons of heroin and methadone have been poorly learned by our mental health experts. Most drug addicts already feel they are in a netherworld from which there may be no return and, so far, these experts and their experimental cures have only led them deeper into it.

TO THE STREETS

Until the 1950s the social problem of drugs was relatively confined. Problems existed with heroin addiction in large cities, marijuana had a small following, some amphetamine abuse existed, but drugs were rarely mentioned as a broad-scale issue on the national agenda.

Things changed.

One of the turning points came in 1954 with the introduction of Thorazine. For the first time, a psychotropic drug was in wide use. And the psychiatric profession trumpeted this to the world as a good thing.

As we noted before, this event caused a shift, or at least an attempted shift, in social mores on the subject of mind-altering chemicals. Further shifts would follow as more psychiatric drugs were introduced.

Around the same time as the Thorazine deluge, another less visible drug was gaining steady popularity.

It was called LSD.

LSD—or *lysergic acid diethylamide*—was first synthesized in 1938 by Swiss chemist Albert Hoffman who was working for Sandoz Laboratories, while investigating the properties of *ergot*, a rye fungus. The compound was the twenty-fifth of a series he had concocted, so he labeled it LSD-25.[81]

Ergot has had a rather strange reputation, including being associated with a mass illness called St. Anthony's Fire. Medieval writings tell of villages and towns where nearly everyone went mad for several days. It is now believed they ingested bread unknowingly made from ergot-diseased rye flour.[82]

Hoffman's chemical was set aside after a series of unremarkable tests, and the chemist did not pick it up again until 1943. At that time he accidentally absorbed a minute dose through his fingertips.

Soon he felt "a remarkable but not unpleasant state of intoxication..." he wrote in his diary, "characterized by an intense stimulation of the imagination and an altered state of awareness of the world." He went on. "As I lay in a dazed condition with eyes closed there surged up from me a succession of fantastic, rapidly changing imagery of a striking reality and depth, alternating with a vivid, kaleidoscopic play of colors. This condition gradually passed off after about three hours."[83]

From there it soon moved into psychiatric ranks through the person of the son of Sandoz's president who happened to be psychiatrist Werner Stoll. He became the first person to investigate the psychological properties of the drug, publishing his findings in 1947, and claiming it could be helpful in the treatment of psychiatric patients.[84]

More psychiatrists followed suit, obtaining samples of the drug and testing them under all manner of circumstances. One popular application was to combine it with psychotherapy, thus allegedly bringing out things the patient might not ordinarily see—which is quite true, of course; people do not normally hallucinate or demonstrate psychotic symptoms.

It was not long before America's intelligence agency, the CIA, took an interest in LSD, backing experiments sometimes done on unsuspecting citizens. Martin A. Lee and Bruce Shlain, authors of *Acid Dreams*, tell us, "The CIA was particularly interested in psychiatric reports suggesting that LSD could break down familiar behavior patterns, for this raised the possibility of reprogramming or brainwashing."

The CIA recruited willing psychiatrists to help them explore the possibilities of "acid," as it became popularly known. One such psychiatrist was Dr. Ewen Cameron, former president of the American Psychiatric

Association, who tested LSD in combination with shock treatments to "depattern" the minds of paying patients. It is ironic that Cameron, who was a member of the Nuremberg tribunal hearing Nazi war atrocities, would later work for the CIA and violate the Nuremberg Code for medical ethics by sponsoring experiments on unwitting and unwilling subjects.[85]

Psychiatrist Louis Jolyon West engaged in research for the CIA's Operation MKULTRA, a program designed to develop chemical and biological agents during the Cold War.[86] Performing LSD research in the Department of Psychiatry at the University of Oklahoma, West was, as mentioned earlier, purportedly the first man in history to kill an elephant with the drug. West himself had taken acid the previous day.[87] After giving the animal a massive dose of LSD, it keeled over and remained in a motionless stupor. When West tried to revive the animal with a combination of drugs, it expired.[88]

Another contract worker for the CIA was psychiatrist Paul Hoch who popularized the theory that LSD was a *psychotomimetic* drug (mimicked psychosis). This idea prompted many of his colleagues to expand into LSD research, testing it on patients and looking for a connection between LSD and the chemical cause of psychosis. Despite an army of patients being subjected to the drug, no such connection was found.[89]

By the late 1950s, LSD had a solid following in the psychiatric community. It became virtually a buzzword in Hollywood circles as movie stars were given their first trips by their psychiatrists. Cary Grant was among those who promoted it after receiving the drug this way. Word of mouth was so intense, Lee and Shlain tell us "psychiatrists who practiced LSD therapy were inundated with inquiries."

In a 1964 paper, two NIMH researchers, one of whom was the chief of the NIMH Psychopharmacology Service Center, wrote, "To be sure, the therapeutic uses of these agents have been pioneered by psychiatrists in many instances.... With much of the published work, however, there is an implicit or explicit attitude that the self-knowledge...allegedly effected by these drugs may be of value or benefit to individuals who do not ordinarily consider themselves psychiatrically ill."[90]

These two scientists had hit upon what was obvious at the time. Psychiatrists had been promoting LSD consumption for what today would be considered recreational use.

The drug era had dawned.

Psychiatrist Roy Grinker, editor for the AMA's *Archives of General Psychiatry*, described in 1963 exactly how the psychiatrically-created transformation had occurred. He said originally the drug's effect on patients "interested many psychiatrists who administered the drug to themselves, and some, who became enamored with the mystical hallucinatory state, eventually in their 'mystique' became disqualified as competent investigators. Lay people 'bootlegged' the drug for its pleasurable effect, and a few writers published stories and books on the subject for the lay public. Motion picture actors extolled its benefits, and television psychiatrists enacted its curative powers.

"Now the deleterious effects are becoming more obvious.... Here again is the story of evil results from the ill-advised use of a potentially valuable drug, due to unjustified claims, indiscriminate and premature publicity, and a lack of proper professional controls."

But it was too late.

LSD-25 had spread across America and the world. Psychologist Timothy Leary, who tried his first psychedelics in 1960, long after LSD had entered social use via psychiatrists, joined the fray and preached the message to a young generation to "tune in, turn on, and drop out."

Flanked additionally by the early 1960's tranquilizer craze, a new philosophy crept into the American dream—and most were not quite sure how it had gotten there. They did not know who had brought LSD into popularity or who had plowed under traditional mores and created this notion that "self-exploration" through drugs was a good thing.

But they heard the calls to "turn on," to "mellow out," to not be so "uptight."

And some, particularly among the young, responded.

Marijuana, peyote, speed (amphetamines)—substances that had always been rejected by the bulk of the population—suddenly rode a meteoric rise to popularity.

The slang of the era took on a psychiatric cast. Talk of "getting my head together" and "finding myself" peppered the language of teenagers and college students who had no idea where these notions had originated.

Prescription psychiatric drugs in bountiful quantity found their way into the streets where the youth of America dubbed them "reds," "blues," "greenies"—catchy nicknames that belied the potency these pills had when they hit young blood streams.

It did not take long before the "deleterious effects," as Grinker called them, of this new drug era became manifest. Overdoses, bad trips, "burned out" brains, a plummet in sexual values and personal responsibility—the drug revolution racked nations and families across the world.

While governments and social leaders pushed hard on an anti-drug message to counteract the counterculture, the psychiatric community was being supplied with record-level funding and pushed psychiatric drug use into the public so heavily that tranquilizers became the top-selling medications in America.

As the years passed, the public gasped as it watched the unthinkable— the ever-deepening encroachment of drugs from college campuses into high schools and, finally, into grade school playgrounds.

Drugs found their way into places no one thought they could ever go. A 1986 *Los Angeles Times* article details a nine-year addiction to Placydil, a powerful sleeping agent, that was suffered by William H. Rehnquist from 1972 to 1981. Rehnquist, of course, was later appointed as Chief Justice to the Supreme Court. Doctors reported the jurist experienced "disturbances in mental clarity" and "distorted" perceptions of reality when he was weaned from the drug.

In a similar vein, during the presidency of George Bush, it was discovered the president was taking Halcion, a tranquilizer and sleep-inducing agent. It is rumored that Bush only discontinued taking the drug when dangerous side effects were alleged in the press.

Today drug abuse litters our streets. Yet the psychiatric promotion of drugs as a solution holds strong.

In his 1993 *Listening to Prozac*, a popular book that rode the best-seller lists, psychiatrist Peter Kramer pushed the drug for "cosmetic" use. He tells us he has given the drug to patients who really were not seriously disturbed. "Alternatively, we can say that they are normal people," he writes, "and that if they ask for Prozac they are requesting, according to our point of view, legitimate enhancement, legalized cocaine, or a neurochemical nose job. If I am right, we are entering an era in which medication can be used to enhance the functioning of the normal mind."[91]

There is no question as to whether the psychiatric profession wants to remove drugs from our society. It doesn't.

Seeing where these mental healers have taken us brings to mind the words of psychiatrist Walter Afield.

In looking over his profession, he told us, "People my age and older, who are very senior, who have been through this whole thing say, "Dear God, what have we done?"[92]

PART THREE:

PSYCHIATRY
AND
SOCIETY

CHAPTER VIII

PSYCHIATRY, JUSTICE AND CRIME

THEY HAVE, UNFORTUNATELY, BECOME COMMON STORIES. A 17-year-old Reseda, California, high school student is shot in the hallway by another youth who thought he gave him a "funny look."

A 13-year-old girl in Texas beats another girl and holds her down while a number of boys rape her.

Newsweek announces that "Between 1987 and 1991...the number of teenagers arrested for murder around the country increased by an astounding 85 percent, according to the Department of Justice."[1]

And so it goes: murder, rape, assault, robbery. Nor is it just kids, although this concept of conscienceless young monsters makes good media copy and is widely reported. In fact, the heaviest rates of imprisonment affect men aged twenty to forty.[2] In 1960, there were 160.9 violent crimes per 100,000 inhabitants; in 1992, there were 757.5.[3] Which is why the Justice Department makes dour predictions like, "83 percent of all Americans would be victims of violent crimes at least once in their lives."[4]

Media hype aside, there is undoubtedly an epidemic of violent crime in the United States. And figures are escalating in other countries as well. In Germany, drug offenses have multiplied ten times in ten years. In Canada, the 1988 statistic of violent crime was 340 percent of the 1965 figure.[5]

In the U.S., state and federal prisons held 883,656 inmates in 1992. And this population increased by seven percent in 1993. This is 2.9 times as many people in prison as in 1980.[6] Meanwhile, a fearful populace feels that the forces of law and order are fighting a losing battle and, as a result, 16.5 million of those who haven't yet given up belong to neighborhood crime-watch programs, while others are moving out of the cities to enclaves in the suburbs.[7]

We are living in an increasingly lawless society.

Law. Justice. They are the underpinnings of a civilized society. When they come undone, we have a barbarism.

Yet law and justice have been under fierce assault for the past four decades—and not only by criminals.

AND JUSTICE FOR WHOM?

When Virginia trial lawyer T. Brooke Howard took on a used-car salesman for a client there was no question about the man's guilt. His client had abducted a 30-year-old woman, held her hostage for almost half a day, and sexually assaulted her—repeatedly. But Howard (the father of one of the now-infamous Lorena Bobbitt's lawyers, Blain Howard, and a man who attained near-legendary status for the theatricality of his presentations) was undaunted. He felt he could fulfill his obligations to his client.

And Howard did just that. He stood before the jury and argued that the nine-hour ordeal suffered by the woman, the repeated rapes, the terror she experienced, were not at all the fault of his client. The actions of the man had not been willful at all. In fact, he couldn't help himself. No, Howard maintained, the salesman was also a victim. These barbarities were the tragic consequence of an "irresistible impulse" suffered by the rapist.

The used-car salesman was acquitted.[8]

Irresistible impulse. Post Traumatic Stress Syndrome. Diminished capacity. Black Rage Syndrome. Urban Stress Syndrome. Battered Wife Syndrome...

If you want to raise the hackles on just about any law-abiding citizen's neck, ask him what he thinks about today's insanity defense.

The use of "not responsible by reason of insanity" has become so pervasive in our courts that L.A. County Deputy District Attorney Dino Fulgoni said in 1981, "Seldom does a serious criminal case filter through the courts of California without the appointment of at least two psychiatrists to determine whether the defense of diminished capacity is a viable possibility."[9]

Earlier, in a 1980 article in *Prosecutor's Brief*, Fulgoni categorized the diminished capacity law as a set of haphazardly inconsistent standards which compound injustice by introducing vagueness and ambiguity into the law.[10]

Still, if it is contained in the law, naturally, attorneys will use it for their clients.

In the case of "diminished capacity," the use became so outrageous, the California legislature banned it in criminal cases in 1982.[11] Elsewhere it lives on.

Psychiatrist Lee Coleman has pointed out, "A lawyer is liable to be branded incompetent if he doesn't introduce psychiatric testimony."[12]

And, of course, the entire gist of psychiatric testimony is that the criminal is not responsible for committing the crime.

Which creates a dilemma.

PERSONAL RESPONSIBILITY

All civilized societies, to preserve order, have a system of laws and penalties.

Without such a system there is chaos. The very definition of *anarchy*, in fact, is, "the complete absence of government and law."[13]

The entire foundation of this concept is that *the citizen is personally responsible for his actions*.

In the interests of compassion and common sense, legal scholars through the ages have found the rare, rare exception to this rule, such as the three-year-old who starts a fire or the obvious lunatic who does harm to person or property.

Few in a civilized society have begrudged leniency for those involved in these extreme circumstances.

But when these exceptions become less rare, when they become, in fact, common, the man in the street is less tolerant. He feels his natural sense of compassion has been betrayed. After all, *he* has to deal with the day-to-day restrictions the law places on his actions. Perhaps he would love to avoid his taxes, let his emotions run wild, or partake of forbidden fruit. But he doesn't. For the good of all or for fear of the law or both, he exercises *restraint*.

Humanity is beset by a menagerie of impulses, drives, desires, and whims, which if not controlled, can result in harm of some kind.

Laws did not come about because of man's high reasoning capabilities.

They exist because he also sometimes has an inclination to be savage and self-indulgent. They are there because he has impulses—avaricious, vengeful, sexual, and otherwise—which are not logical, fair, or civilized, and which *commonly* diminish his capacity to reason.

But reason he must or civilization is doomed.

Which is why underlying the totality of our legal structure is the doctrine that man has a free will to choose or not choose *restraint*.

If he does not choose restraint, the remainder who *do* exercise self-control insist he pay the penalty so he and his like will not so readily give in to their urges in the future and damage the well-being of others.

Thus present and future order is ensured.

How then do we rectify this with the psychiatric concept so succinctly stated by legal scholar James Marshall in his book *Intentions and the Law*? "What a man proposes when in the clutches of his unconscious," he wrote, "gives him no more freedom of choice of action than if he were disarmed before another man with a loaded gun."[14]

RIGHT AND WRONG

The idea of an insanity defense goes back to ancient times. The biblical Hebrews, for one, decreed that neither children nor the insane should be held criminally responsible for their acts.

In the sixth century A.D. the Code of Justinian also held that the mentally unsound and the young were to be given lenience.

Until the 1800s, the question of sanity was judged, not by mental experts, but by those meting out justice. And there does not seem to have been much dispute over the concept, because in general practice it was applied to those who were truly and obviously insane.

However, in 1843 things changed.

In England a Glasgow man named Daniel M'Naghten, who believed the Pope and British Prime Minister Robert Peel were conspiring against him, sought out Peel to kill him. When M'Naghten came upon Peel's secretary, he believed the man to be Peel and shot him dead.

M'Naghten was acquitted on grounds of insanity.

The incident created an uproar in England. Fearing the ruling would set a precedent, making it easier to excuse criminal behavior, Parliament passed a measure which became known as the "right-wrong" test:

"It must be clearly proved that, at the time of committing the act, the party accused was laboring under such a defect of reason from disease of the mind, as not to know the nature and quality of the act he was doing, or if he did know it, that he did not know he was doing what was wrong." [15]

The *M'Naghten Rule*, as it is called, altered the face of jurisprudence. Before this, people found guilty by reason of insanity usually spent the remainder of their days in an asylum. But here was a statement that *even if the wrongdoer was not an obvious lunatic*, as long as he could prove he was not sane at the time of committing the act, he could be found not guilty.

The acceptance of this concept into the judicial process was a stark change from traditional justice. When we look at events that may have precipitated this new view, we find that, in the preceding half century, the psychiatric view of the criminal was being propagated in intellectual, medical and, no doubt, legal circles.

Benjamin Rush, for example, wrote his *Medical Inquiries and Observations upon the Diseases of the Mind* in 1812. He believed crime to be a curable disease. Viewing murder and theft as symptoms of this disease, he sought to have the perpetrators transferred from the control of policemen to that of psychiatrists. [16]

Again, it should be noted that prior to the birth of psychiatry in the 1800s, the insanity plea was not a source of social turmoil. Afterwards, however, the picture changed.

The *M'Naghten Rule* was adopted in the United States and was used by the vast majority of states until the 1960s. Problems followed at its heels almost immediately.

The following statement could well have been made in 1973. But it wasn't. In 1873 the managers of the New York State Lunatic Asylum warned the legislature, "...this matter of the testimony of experts, especially in cases of alleged insanity, has gone to such an extravagance that it has really become of late years a profitable profession to be an expert witness, at the command of any party and ready for any party, for a sufficient and often exorbitant fee." [17]

Had we heeded that warning, the entire face of the justice system could be different today.

Even celebrated nineteenth century humorist Mark Twain noted, "Insanity is certainly on the increase in the world, and crime is dying out.... Formerly if you killed a man, it was possible that you were insane—but now if you...kill a man it is *evidence* that you are a lunatic."[18]

And psychiatrist Karl Menninger (not one to downplay the potential role of psychiatry in society) said of the *M'Naghten Rule*: "The psychiatrists of the day did not (sufficiently) dispute this pontifical "decision" and some have gone along with it ever since, despite its absurdity. It requires an incalculable degree of presumption to say whether *another* individual "knows" right from wrong, especially when few of us could truly say (except in utter naivete or ignorance) what our own degree of expertise is in this distinction."[19]

Yet in spite of this lack of expertise, by the turn of the twentieth century, the concept of "temporary insanity" had its roots sunk deep into Western law. Psychiatrists in the courtroom became an accepted, if still ridiculed, facet of legal drama.

With the inception of the aggressive mental hygiene movement in 1909, psychiatric involvement with the justice system took on an entirely new dimension. Hygienists saw the criminal and juvenile delinquent as simply maladjusted and misunderstood, matters that proper hygiene could overcome. And they worked diligently to push this message, promoting to officials and public alike that psychiatrists, with their greater compassion for the tortured criminal personality should have a stronger hand in courtroom proceedings.

By 1915, William Healy's psychoanalytic discussion of the roots of delinquency *The Individual Delinquent*, appeared on the stands.

Three years later, court psychiatrist and eugenicist Erwin Stranky made his judicial aspirations for psychiatry known in the *General Magazine for Psychiatry*:

"Therefore the forensic activity of the psychiatrist can become a good part of applied psychiatry in the noblest sense of the word, by helping diplomatically to restrain and to dominate the human mind in the sense of race hygiene and protection of the society. Then—almost automatically—our profession will get its proper part of this domination....

"[The psychiatrist] will continuously educate judges, plaintiffs and defenders to such a degree, that actually he becomes, gently and slowly, the leading element of the trial; then he will fill charges, defense and verdict, with his ideas, having the outstanding high goal in mind, to direct all and everything into the port of the higher man-breeding where the medico is the safest pilot (guide). In this way the psychiatrist in the courtroom can fulfill a great deal of his mission as educator of man, if he only wants to , 'wants' in the sense of a medical imperialism which is the imperialism of culture...."[20]

The year 1924 marked the beginning of a new plan of attack for psychiatry's intervention into the legal field. It began with one of the most sensational courtroom dramas of the era, the Leopold and Loeb trial in Chicago.

The case involved two young men from affluent families. Both were charged with planning and carrying out the senseless killing of a younger companion, an act nearly unheard of in those times.

Karl Menninger, who was an APA member at the time, recalled what happened. "Partly just because the crime seemed so senseless, and partly because the families could afford to pay for their services, many prominent American psychiatrists were brought into the limelight of the trial to explain the state of mind of the offenders. These colleagues were arraigned against one another; the opinions sworn to by some were flatly contradicted and denied by others. This awkward and inconclusive exhibition gave rise to widespread public comment....

"Psychiatrists of the old school were kept waiting by the prosecution to refute and dispute these 'radical' psychiatrists speaking for the defense. Reputable, scholarly, dignified, friendly colleagues were soon swept up in the same old courtroom spectacle previously described—calling one another liars and fools in public and apologizing to one another in private (not literally, of course, but quite definitely), swearing to the truth of answers to questions which they probably did not understand, and confusing the judges, the jury, and the public by interpretations of 'facts' reported on the basis of utterly incongruous philosophies."[21]

So sensational and entertaining was the subject of psychiatric testimony that the *Chicago Tribune* offered Sigmund Freud, then in his declining years, $25,000 to come to America to "psychoanalyze" Leopold and Loeb. Freud declined.[22]

According to Menninger, APA president and mental hygienist William A. White testified at the trial that the boys' murderous behavior was the "product of impulses contrary to their conscious ideals but expressive of certain strange unconscious strivings that, for reasons not clear, overwhelmed their control."[23]

We have in White's declaration a very early, but clear, statement of the "irresistible impulse" concept.

Menninger relates, "That the veniality and corruptibility of psychiatrists seemed to be taken for granted was a grievous concern to many....[Dr. White] seized the opportunity to appoint a committee to study these public exhibitions of legal ignorance and medical confusion."[24]

The committee included not only White, but among others, Lawson G. Lowrey, director of the mental hygiene movement's Child Guidance Institute in New York City, former medical director of the National Committee for Mental Hygiene, Dr. Thomas Salmon, and the then-current director of the Committee for Mental Hygiene, Dr. Frankwood E. Williams.

The committee's final recommendations, approved unanimously by the APA in 1927, had little to do with reforming the "public exhibitions of legal ignorance and medical confusion" which had prompted its formation.

In fact, the final resolution called for vastly more psychiatric participation in the trial process, and simply made no mention of the embarrassing courtroom follies which already existed.

And, during this time, to cast further doubt on the real motives of the APA, the APA committee's chairman had given speeches for several years at the American Bar Association's annual meeting, urging a closer marriage between psychiatry and the legal profession. Utilizing the support he had gained, in 1929 he succeeded in getting the ABA to form a committee on the same APA resolution to increase psychiatric participation in legal matters.

The final wording was as follows:

"The committee from the Section on Criminal Law of the American Bar Association, after a conference with the committee from the American Psychiatric Association, recommends to its own association that it advocate:

"1. That there be available to every criminal and juvenile court a psychiatric service to assist the court in the disposition of offenders.

"2. That no criminal be sentenced for any felony in any case in which the judge has any discretion as to the sentence until there be filed as a part of the record a psychiatric report.

"3. That there be a psychiatric service available to each penal and correctional institution.

"4. That there be a psychiatric report on every prisoner convicted of a felony before he is released.

"5. That there be established in every state a complete system of administrative transfer and parole and that there be no decision for or against any parole or any transfer from one institution to another without a psychiatric report."[25]

In spite of its desires, at that time the APA was not able to implement its plan, its membership opinion being too splintered, and public and political opposition too great, for them to forward such an encroachment into the courts.

But if nothing else, the APA had made its intentions known and had made inroads into the ABA, laying the groundwork for the gradual infusion of its ideologies into the legal profession.

1929 also marked another advance. Only five years after William A. White's elucidation of the "irresistible impulse" concept in Chicago, the Court of Appeals for the District of Columbia adopted it as an acceptable legal doctrine, calling it an impulse that could "override the reason and judgment and obliterate the sense of right and wrong."[26]

Despite this further expansive interpretation of *M'Naghten*, organized psychiatry still found the courts resistive to its grander designs. On June 18, 1940, John Rawlings Rees delivered an historic speech in which he clearly made this point to the Annual Meeting of the National Council for Mental Hygiene. Rees had been longtime Medical Director of the famed Tavistock Clinic in England, military advisors to the British government. In his talk, "Strategic Planning for Mental Health," Colonel Rees said, "We have made a useful attack upon a number of professions. The two easiest of them naturally are the teaching profession and the Church: The two most difficult are law and medicine."[27]

In 1949, the California Supreme Court became the first to espouse the concept of "diminished capacity," carrying *M'Naghten* to further extremes.

One legal text explains this concept provides a way to mitigate the penalty by "introducing psychiatric testimony to show the defendant's mental condition at the time of the crime was not such as to be able to formulate the required intent."[28]

A century after the famous English ruling, the insanity defense had ballooned to include rationalizations of impulses and temporary loss of reason, excuses which had been unacceptable in the halls of justice for thousands of years. And to appreciate the folly of this, we must return to Karl Menninger's own comment just a few pages earlier regarding the "presumption" involved in judging whether another individual "knows" right from wrong and the "utter naivete or ignorance" involved in such a judgment.

Another historic ruling on the insanity plea came in 1954. It began with the 1951 case of Monte Durham, a 23-year-old man with a long criminal and psychiatric history. Durham was found guilty of housebreaking, despite his insistence that he was not guilty by reason of insanity.

Three years later the case came before Judge David Bazelon, in the U.S. District Court of Appeals in Washington, D.C. Bazelon overruled the lower court's decision and ordered a new trial because in his view, the trial court did not correctly apply existing rules governing the burden of proof on the defense of insanity.

In making the ruling, Bazelon declared, "An accused is not criminally responsible if his unlawful act was the product of mental disease or mental defect. A person could, in other words, know his behavior was wrong yet still be driven to it by mental disorder."[29]

With the sweep of a pen, Judge Bazelon had removed the right-wrong definition of insanity. In its stead was *no definition at all.* Questions of "diminished capacity" or "irresistible impulse"—things a lay person could at least struggle to evaluate—no longer mattered. The criteria now was only whether he had a mental illness or a mental defect, a matter which could be legally adjudicated only by psychiatrists.

The door had fully opened for psychiatry.

A 1956 issue of *Mental Hygiene* proudly announced to the profession, "Henceforth a testifying psychiatrist will not be required to sit idly by and watch an individual whom he knows to be anti-social because of mental illness go to prison instead of to a hospital for treatment merely because the accused knew what he was doing and knew that it was wrong."[30]

Abe Fortas, the court-appointed defense counsel in *Durham vs. United States*, who went on to become an Associate Justice of the Supreme Court, wrote in 1957, "What, then, is the basic significance of the Durham case? It is, I suggest, that the law has recognized modern psychiatry.... Its importance is not due to the new standard that it established for adjudication the defense of insanity. 'Durham' is not a charter of liberty for the insane. Rather...its importance is that it is a charter, a bill of rights, for psychiatry and an offer of limited partnership between criminal law and psychiatry."[31]

It was not by accident that it was Bazelon who opened the courtroom doors with the invitation for which psychiatrists had so long awaited. Robert Robinson, director of APA public relations for thirty years, remembered, "Interestingly, the good judge had had a satisfying experience with his own psychoanalysis and was favorably disposed toward the profession at the time. Now it would be possible for psychiatrists to tell the juries in court proceedings what they really knew about how a person came to behave as he did and to help the jury assess whether such behavior was the product of a mental disorder.

"It does not matter here that the judge soon became disenchanted with the performance of psychiatrists in the court room under *Durham* rule procedures. At that moment it seemed that a new day had arrived in forensic psychiatry."[32]

What Robinson did not mention was that Fortas too was "favorably disposed" toward the psychiatric profession. Exceedingly so. Hence his warm welcome to the "limited partnership" between criminal law and psychiatry. By then, he had been well connected to leading psychiatric figures for at least a decade. In 1946, when G. Brock Chisholm delivered a speech titled "The Reestablishment of Peacetime Society, The Responsibility of Psychiatry." He was introduced with glowing comments about his insight into the needs of future man by the then Undersecretary of the Interior— Abe Fortas.

The speech was delivered at the "William Alanson White Psychiatric Foundation" seminar. White was Superintendent of St. Elizabeth's Hospital in Washington and, through his foundation, had founded the Washington School of Psychiatry. Fortas was a trustee of the foundation in 1948, up until 1972, and was also a trustee for the school when he was a Supreme Court Judge. He was a consistent and active and very influential supporter of the psychiatric agenda.[33]

There is evidence, in fact, that psychiatrists practically wrote the *Durham* decision. Cited in Bazelon's ruling was a report written by the Group for the Advancement of Psychiatry (GAP) only two months earlier, calling for the "abolition of the M'Naghten Rules" in trade for greater psychiatric involvement.[34]

For some psychiatrists, Bazelon's ruling did not go far enough. In 1961, "diminished capacity" proponent psychiatrist Bernard Diamond urged his fellows to do what was necessary to occupy the witness stand—even when "mental disorder" was not an issue.

"I concede," he wrote, "that this whole business of lack of mental capacity to premeditate, to have malice or to entertain intent is a kind of sophistry which must not be allowed to remain an end in itself. Right now we must utilize these legal technicalities to gain entrance into the trial court.... The next step after Gorshen [a 1957 trial at which Diamond testified] is to expand the principle of limited or diminished responsibility of the mentally-ill offender to include all definitions."[35]

Four years later, Diamond, perhaps as exasperated as others, was no longer so supportive of his profession's courtroom aspirations. In the *Michigan Law Review* he wrote, "The psychiatric expert is apt not to be a very wise man, but rather a possessor of technical knowledge of some depth, but little breadth. He seldom comprehends or is sympathetic to the legal process.... The result is a pseudo-scientific veneer for the psychiatrist and his testimony, behind which the lack of wisdom and lack of legal comprehension are concealed."[36]

An example of the judicial chaos *Durham* created appeared in a 1962 article in *Northwestern University Law Review*, written by psychiatrist Alfred Baur. His hospital received a patient before trial for a three-month observation period. Three consultants, including Baur, concluded the patient had "no mental disorder."

The court then appointed two private psychiatrists to examine the man. One declared him to be schizophrenic, paranoid type, the other said he was in a paranoid state. Come the trial, two hospital psychiatrists testified they had found no mental disease. The two court-appointed psychiatrists testified to the opposite.

The prosecution then put a fifth psychiatrist on the stand and he, after explaining he had heard the testimony and read the reports of the other four, claimed he could find no basis for a mental disorder which would diminish the defendant's responsibility.

Baur tells us, "The jury thereupon found the man 'not guilty by reason of insanity' and 'still insane' and committed him to the hospital which had just testified it had found him without mental disorder."[37]

Needless to say, the problems created by *Durham* were multitudinous. Not only did the decision allow psychiatrists to excuse the most heinous crimes, but it also allowed them, by declaring defendants insane, to keep some locked up in psychiatric facilities indefinitely.

A 1966 article in *Wisconsin Law Review* reported, "Some legal experts have argued that the *Durham* rule is so concerned with the interests of psychiatry that it neglects the humanitarian needs of potential offenders and can result in serious abridgement of civil liberties."[38]

The writer, Dr. Seymour Halleck, Chief Psychiatric Consultant to the Wisconsin Division of Corrections, goes on to say, "In addition to criticisms of the theoretical basis of psychiatric testimony and the deficiencies of any legal test of criminal responsibility, it must be noted that many practical inconsistencies and injustices can arise through psychiatric involvement in the courtroom.... Effective utilization of the plea of criminal insanity implies that psychiatrists will come to eventual agreement on a workable definition of terms such as psychosis or mental illness. The writer contends that is unlikely."[39]

By 1970 another phenomenon had worked its way into the picture, giving even greater impact to the psychiatric legal invasion created by *Durham* and similar legal decisions.

Up to this point, a verdict of "not guilty by reason of insanity" may have kept someone out of prison, but the defendant also risked the high likelihood of ending up in a state mental hospital for indefinite duration.

However, starting in the mid-1960s Community Mental Health Centers came on the scene (see Chapter 4), and along with them a new practice to send patients home with their medication, in lieu of incarceration. For the criminal offender this meant a shorter stay in less sordid surroundings. One study of 55 murderers found "not guilty by reason of insanity" and placed in mental institutions between 1965-1976 found their average time served in the hospital to be 500 days.[40]

The insanity plea had become a very attractive alternative to prison.

Further interpretation and re-interpretation of the law ensued at the urging of psychiatrists in the legal arena, following a path of less and less expectation of responsibility from the individual.

This 1984 APA Task Force Report shows their progress: "Many states, however, specifically include, as mitigating circumstances, proof that the defendant had an 'extreme mental or emotional disturbance' or that his or her capacity to understand the wrongfulness of the conduct or to conform to the law was impaired, even if this impairment was not substantial enough to constitute insanity. This is a relatively new form of 'diminished responsibility' related to the defendant's mental state at the time of the crime. Psychiatric testimony is obviously relevant to the existence or absence of this mitigating consideration."[41]

The ancient doctrine of compassion for the lunatic had become twisted beyond recognition.

A case in point was the New York trial of 15-year-old April Dell'Olio, who on October 20, 1992 stabbed a 17-year-old 22 times. *Freedom* magazine reports the girl was acquitted of murder by reason of insanity, thus spared a prison sentence. However, two psychiatrists at the trial testified April did not pose a danger to society, so the girl was released with no incarceration whatsoever.

Presiding Judge Kevin Dowd said the insanity defense laws had forced him to treat the killing "with the psychiatric equivalent that April had had a 'bad hair day' on October 20, 1992."[42]

"VERY LOW RELIABILITY"

There is another aspect of psychiatric intrusion into the courtrooms, what might be called The Expert Witness Syndrome. Even in rigid sciences, expert witnesses can be a source of confusion to those who are attempting to sort right from wrong. However, in the psychiatric and psychological fields when the "experts" are talking about motives, states of mind and other behavioral factors confusion reigns supreme.

Professor Michael E. Tigar of the University of Texas noted that, for a fee, large numbers of "experts" will be happy to conjure up virtually any testimony. He pointed out that while these experts claim their testimony is based on fact, it can be, and in reality often is, fanciful and exaggerated."[43] Courts tend to overlook the fact that psychiatric incantations are merely theory—opinion masquerading as fact.

Anthony Oliver, an authority on psychiatric testimony, likens such experts to prostitutes. "Manipulation of the jury is the name of the game," he said.[44] This blunt assessment, of course, refers to the further complication of the fact that a paid witness has been hired to present testimony favorable to whomever is paying him.

In addition to pronouncements in the courts about the mental states of defendants, psychiatrists have also attempted to carve out even more territory for their services by claiming they can predict the future dangerousness of criminals. This gained some acceptance in legal circles for a while, but then studies were undertaken to determine the validity of these psychiatric claims.

The results were not impressive.

In his book *Mental Patients, Psychiatry, and the Law*, attorney Bruce Ennis reports on a well-known New York study of 989 people. All of them had been declared by psychiatrists to be so dangerous they would have to be kept in maximum security hospitals run by the Department of Corrections. However, a U.S. Supreme Court decision resulted in all of them being placed in routine civil hospitals instead. A year later, a review of the patients found a fifth of them had been discharged to the community and over half had agreed to remain as voluntary patients.

During the year, only seven of the 989 committed or threatened any act that was sufficiently dangerous to require movement to a maximum security hospital. Ennis concluded logically enough, "They are wrong more often than they are right."[45]

An exhaustive examination of the subject in *Rutgers Law Review* concluded, "The data just presented constitute the most definitive evidence available on the lack of expertise and accuracy of psychiatric prediction of dangerousness. The findings of this study taken together with the other works reviewed in this paper would appear to represent clear and convincing evidence of the inability of psychiatrists or anyone else to predict dangerousness accurately.... It in fact appears that psychiatrists cannot even predict accurately enough to be more often right than they are wrong. Thus, any attempt to commit an individual solely on the basis of

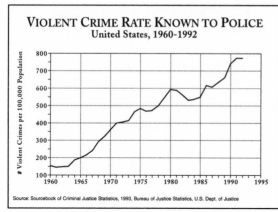

VIOLENT CRIME RATE KNOWN TO POLICE
United States, 1960-1992

Source: Sourcebook of Criminal Justice Statistics, 1993, Bureau of Justice Statistics, U.S. Dept. of Justice

dangerousness would be futile if psychiatric testimony were subjected to any of these three [aforementioned] standards of proof."[46]

The situation became so embarrassing—and legally troublesome—for the American Psychiatric Association that in 1979 it filed a brief *amicus curea* ("friend of the court brief") in a U.S. Supreme Court case admitting "such predictions are fundamentally of very low reliability, and that psychiatric testimony and expertise are irrelevant to such predictions...."[47]

Irrelevant perhaps, but in practice psychiatrists continue today to pass judgment daily on the potential states of mind and dangerousness of others, confining and incarcerating based on a judgment capability even their own professional organization considers to be without merit.

THE CREATION OF CRIME

"The indiscriminate, 'nonjudgmental' approach, of dubious value with neurotics, amounts to a frank condoning of crime when applied to offenders and threatens to undermine and eradicate social and moral attitudes. This is the more serious, since this psychiatric-social work approach combines with the 'permissive' or 'progressive' upbringing of the home and school and a very lax enforcement of justice by the police and the courts."[48]

The statement was made in 1962 by psychiatrist Melitta Schmideberg, president of the Association for the Psychiatric Treatment of Offenders.

If that's what she thought of conditions in

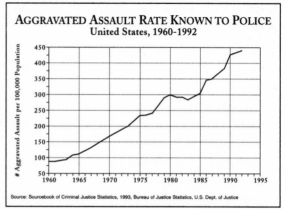

AGGRAVATED ASSAULT RATE KNOWN TO POLICE
United States, 1960-1992

Source: Sourcebook of Criminal Justice Statistics, 1993, Bureau of Justice Statistics, U.S. Dept. of Justice

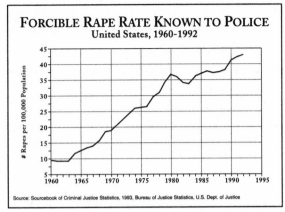

FORCIBLE RAPE RATE KNOWN TO POLICE
United States, 1960-1992

Source: Sourcebook of Criminal Justice Statistics, 1993, Bureau of Justice Statistics, U.S. Dept. of Justice

1962, what would Dr. Schmideberg think of our schools, courts, and homes of today?

She is identifying an ideological force, one with which she is quite familiar, which she says has spread into the courts, the schools, and the society at large.

And she is clearly stating that this force has consequences.

THE SEEPING EFFECTS

In 150 years we have dwindled from excusing the truly insane to excusing the temporarily insane, to excusing an irresistible impulse, to excusing a diminished capacity, to excusing extreme emotional disturbance.

As these concepts of declining personal responsibility have been gradually introduced into our courtrooms over the years, a greater and greater number of non-insane individuals have been able to utilize the insanity defense to escape societal censure for their crimes.

Needless to say, this has not escaped the attention of the man in the street. And he does not like this. However, with the growing presence of psychiatrists in the courtroom, official sanction continues to be given to their pronouncements on the mental states of man.

Dr. Thomas Szasz wrote in his book, *Insanity, The Idea and its Consequences*, "I am convinced that psychiatric explanations and interventions are fatally flawed and that, deep in their hearts, most people think so too." [49]

It would seem that most people do. Even at the time

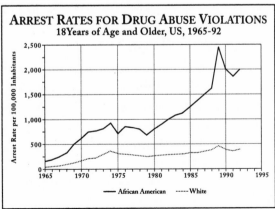

ARREST RATES FOR DRUG ABUSE VIOLATIONS
18 Years of Age and Older, US, 1965-92

— African American ······ White

of the *M'Naghten* ruling, the public was outraged. In fact, the press of today takes great delight in covering "irresistible impulse" cases and their like because they know it will stir up so much upset among their readers.

However, as time goes on, with continuous pressure from the psychiatric community to increase its role in society, we see the odd syndrome of yesterday stepping into the lingo of today. On talk shows the shortcomings of ex-soldiers are explained away by Vietnam Stress Syndrome. Children killing children in the ghettos are presented as victims of Urban Stress Syndrome.

This has a seepage factor into the public consciousness. There are those who will be glad to have their failures explained away by matters beyond their control. And there are those who, when life gets difficult, will remember these invitations to avoid the high road and blame a stressful past, diminished capacity, or an irresistible impulse.

Children are taught this. "Psychological Counselors" of all types spread the concept.

Even law professionals begin to believe it. In commenting in 1994 on the steep increase of juvenile involvement in serious crimes, Florida State University criminology professor Thomas Blomberg explained it as, "People have different ways of coping."[50]

As we have seen with the saturation of psychiatric thought into the educational system, it can become so commonplace that few question it any longer.

One can lose sight of how he came to think that way.

The only reminders available are continuously rising crime statistics and a steady stream of reports about the decline of values in modern day society.

CRIME FROM THE SCHOOLS

As we saw in the last chapter, psychiatric influences have brought about a marked decline in literacy, morality, and moral standards in our schools.

Commensurate with this has been a steady climb in street crime. And the connection is plain.

A survey in 1991 found the largest age group of accused murderers that year were between the ages of 15 and 19.

From 1987 to 1991 the number of youths under 18 arrested for murder had nearly doubled.[51]

Between 1988 and 1992 the number of juvenile arrests for serious crime rose 68 percent. Aggravated assault arrests were up 80 percent.[52]

As Adam Walinsky points out in *The Atlantic Monthly* of July 1995 ["The Crisis of Public Order."] regarding ghetto children, "The children born in 1965 reached their fifteenth year in 1980, and 1980 and 1981 set new records for criminal violence in the United States, as teenage and young adult blacks ripped at the fabric of life in the black inner city."[53]

Walinsky points a finger at the breakdown of the family unit, the fact that in 1965 the national rate of illegitimacy among blacks was 26 percent, and that by 1990 two thirds of black children were born to single mothers. But that is only a part of the picture. If our children are being taught there is no right and wrong, only opinion; if they are being told continuously to follow their feelings instead of their intellect; if they are being instructed overtly or subtly that alleviating stress is more important than self-discipline, it seems only reasonable that the outgrowth would be anti-social activities—crime.

When we interviewed Danny O. Black, former director of juvenile court and chief probation officer for Butler County in Greenville, Alabama, he said, "This idea of self-esteem, if you just tell a child he's good, and he's well, he's fine, does not produce anything, nor does it increase the child's self-esteem. Children begin to feel that no matter what they do, that it's okay. They're losing the concept of right and wrong. A lot of these psychiatric programs they do don't even address the issue of right and wrong anymore."

Illiteracy may be an even greater contributing factor to the increased lawlessness we see today. Black called illiteracy "one of the major causes of the rise of crime and delinquency." He claimed that teaching children to read would "reduce a lot of the problems with children trying to get out of school and running into mandatory attendance laws. And then getting sent to juvenile court, which, in turn, sends them to a psychiatric program. And the kids come back from there on psychiatric drugs or having learned from the other kids up there how to manipulate and use the system."[54]

Studies have made it clear that incarcerated juvenile offenders are crippled by illiteracy. According to author Michael S. Brunner in his book *Retarding America*, "90 percent of the adjudicated delinquents tested in a study conducted by the State of Colorado's Division of Youth Services were diagnosed as having learning problems." And he claims that the student who is not taught to read is "inevitably destined for programmed retardation." His point is that children are not held back from learning to read because of low IQ, but that not learning to read lowers IQ Furthermore, he mentions that a number of researchers have questioned the validity of premises underlying "learning disabilities," particularly the neurological basis of such. Rather, he says, it is the instructional methods themselves.[55]

When children can't read they are shut off from the fruits of an education. They are shut off from job applications, from reading directions and, if they can get a job, from work advancement. Additionally, this inability stigmatizes them as failures in their own eyes.

They are left to feel separate from and less capable than those who take literacy for granted. And, of course, who will they seek out as friends, people like themselves or those who make them feel uncomfortable?

Imagine trying to figure out how to succeed in life when you don't know how to read and don't believe you can learn.

Illiteracy breeds hopelessness and crime.

CRIME FROM DRUGS

As we saw in Chapter VII, the psychiatric contribution of mind-altering drugs to the world has not only affected patients but has mushroomed into a street epidemic unlike anything this century has seen.

In his 1983 *Encyclopedia of Mass Murder*, Colin Wilson reports, "We call a crime motiveless if it seems to do no one any good. Before 1960 such crimes were rare, and the few that occurred belong to the end of the decade."[56]

In the 1988 book *Mass Murder*, author Michael Newton confirms, "Indeed, statistics do appear to indicate an escalation in the number of random, senseless murders."[57] And this is further supported by Walinsky in his *Atlantic Monthly* article which quotes the Federal Bureau of Investigation's 1993 annual report on crime as estimating that 53 percent of all homicides are being committed by strangers.[58]

Los Angeles County District Attorney Gil Garcetti remarked upon the same phenomena in 1994, but he focuses on the young. "It's incredible," he said, "the ability of the very young to commit the most horrendous crimes imaginable and not have a second thought about it. This was unthinkable 20 years ago."[59]

Logic would seem to dictate that we not ignore the coincidence that the onset of this rise in senseless crime occurred right after the introduction of massive drug use in our mental hospitals (mid-'50s), which within a decade had translated into an outbreak of drug use in the streets.

Date-coincident has also been the educational decline and the dramatic increase in mental health funding.

The effect of psychiatric drugs on increased societal violence has been well documented. A 1975 study of psychiatric drug use among prisoners "found that violent, aggressive incidents occurred significantly more frequently in inmates who were on psychotropic medications than when the inmates were not on psychotropic drugs."

In the study, antianxiety agents caused an increase in aggressive behavior, ranging from 280 to nearly 500 percent while other psychotropic drugs doubled aggressive incidents.[60]

Additionally, research has consistently shown that patient arrests began to exceed those among the general population after the introduction of drugs. Prior to the widespread use of psychotropic medication, mental patients committed less crime than the public at large.

The 1984 text *Mental Health and Criminal Justice* notes studies done in 1965, 1966, 1967, 1976, 1977 and 1978 (2) *all* show patient arrest rates in excess of the general public. All studies done before drug use—1922, 1938, 1945 and 1954 show a patient crime rate below that of the public at large.[61]

Certainly the highest impact of psychiatric medicines on crime has been from the dramatic spread of psychotropic drugs for recreational use and abuse. The amount of lawlessness from this one source is so obvious to one and all that it hardly requires description.

A study released in 1989 showed that more than half those arrested for serious crimes in 14 major cities, and who volunteered for drug testing, were found to be drug users. In Philadelphia the figure was 82 percent.[62]

Robbery, assaults and prostitution to support habits; drug-deadened consciences carrying out tortures, ritual murders, adolescent killings—it is a depth of savagery practically unheard of before drugs.

"Youngsters used to shoot each other in the body. Then in the head," commented Washington, D.C. Judge Susan Winfield in 1994. "Now they shoot each other in the face."[63]

And the drug problem with its attendant ills is not going away. Even LSD has made a comeback. Use by high school seniors rose 50 percent between 1985 and 1993.[64]

Yet in the face of this chaos, the 1980 *Comprehensive Textbook of Psychiatry* tells us, "Taken no more than two or three times per week, cocaine creates no serious problems."[65]

So great has been the effect of psychiatric drugs on our culture that if the single problem of mind altering drug abuse could be removed from our society tomorrow, few would disagree that the transformation would herald a Renaissance.

THE PERPETUATION OF CRIME

In 1994, the United States achieved the dubious distinction of reaching the 1,000,000 mark in convict population in its state and federal prisons.[66]

For every 100,000 in population, America has 455 people in jail. This is four times the rate of Canada and China and ten times the rate of Ireland and Japan.[67]

And the inmate population is on the rise. In Washington state, for example, while the general population increased by 18 percent, the prison population went up 86 percent.[68]

Since the days of the mental hygiene movement, prisoners have been targeted by the psychiatric profession, which has found them to be mis-understood, genetically inferior, repressed, or cerebrally unsound— depending on which psychiatrist was doing the evaluating.

Since there was little financial gain to be had, however, prison psychiatry was meagerly practiced in the first half of the century.

Dr. Schmideberg remarked in 1962, "Though there are over fifteen thousand psychiatrists...treatment facilities for non-paying patients are almost non-existent.... Probably all over the country, only several hundred offenders, at most, receive any adequate psychiatric treatment."[69]

As a carryover from the mental hygiene days, juvenile counseling and treatment programs existed which claimed to reduce the likelihood of *recidivism,* the phenomenon of ex-offenders committing crimes again and ending up back in confinement. However, evaluations of these were begin-ning to show they were not the cure-all they had been promoted to be:

1. A 1963 study of young males showed those treated with psychotherapy did no better than others, but they did have a significantly higher parole violation rate.[70]

2. A 1961 study on the use of tranquilizers on young disturbed girls show them to have a higher parole suspension rate than non-treated girls.[71]

3. A 1961 comparison of 16- to 18-year-old male parolees treated with group psychotherapy to those given standard parole supervision showed the treated subjects did significantly worse on psychological tests than controls who actually improved on them.[72]

4. One 1963 survey of 15- to 17-year-old males treated with psychotherapy at two schools found no difference in how well they adjusted to the institutions compared to untreated boys except that at one school the treated boys were assigned to the disciplinary unit significantly more.[73]

5. In reviewing these and many other studies, authors Lipton Douglas, Robert Martinson and Judith Wilks, in their 1975 *The Effectiveness of Correctional Treatment*, stated:

a) "From an overall perspective, no clearly positive or negative general statement can be made as to the effectiveness of individual psychotherapy in reducing recidivism.[74] b) "In the studies [of group counseling] for which recidivism data is also available, there were no significant differences between the recidivism rates of treated and untreated subjects."[75]

An extensive 1971 examination of a typical California Department of Corrections counseling program in operation at a medium-security prison in that state showed similar results. In summarizing their findings, the authors of the study commented, "The data we have just presented do not confirm the expectations expressed by many persons at the outset of this study."[76]

What they discovered was that within three years, 78 percent of the male parolees they examined, who had received counseling had either "minor problems" with the law, "major problems," or were reimprisoned. Fifty-one percent alone were returned to prison.

The counseling had no significant effect on keeping the men out of trouble with the law or out of prison.

It is perhaps noteworthy that this counseling program was constructed in large measure on the teachings of psychologist Carl Rogers, who in his 1961 *On Becoming a Person*, confessed, "When I look back at the results of my past teaching, the real results seem the same—either damage was done, or nothing significant occurred. This is frankly troubling."[77]

With the advent of greater mental health funding in the 1960s and 1970s, came a dramatic increase in psychiatry's presence in the penal system.

From 1968 to 1975, for example, the Law Enforcement Assistance Administration (LEAA) spent upward of $6 billion on programs to curb America's lawlessness, including 537 research projects dealing with human modification.

As we have seen in previous chapters, psychiatric services have a proclivity to appear whenever federal funds are approved. And during this period, a whole catalogue of psychiatric solution's to crime came on the scene. We should note however, that in spite the $6 billion spent during those years, or perhaps because of it, violent crime rose 50 percent.[78]

All politicians should be asked why we keep giving these failures more money.

One popular psychiatric approach to dealing with prisoners was *behavior modification* programs. Using what was referred to as *aversion therapy*, these applied incentives such as pain, fear, shocks, etc. to get the individual to alter his conduct.

In a 1975 statement, the director of NIMH, Bertram Brown, wrote: "The Federal Government continues to support and encourage research and demonstrations that test new behavior modification techniques, that seek to refine existing ones and apply them to new clinical populations and new settings, and that promote the dissemination of techniques that have been positively evaluated.[79]

Dr. Brown also tells us that low-level electric shock "has been highly effective in ameliorating severe behavioral problems. When properly used, the shocks are very brief. Shock used this way causes no lingering pain or tissue damage and can be administered with precise control."[80]

One project was carried out at Atascadero State Hospital, a California maximum security prison that houses sex offenders and the criminally insane. Researchers experimented with the use of a muscle relaxant used in surgery called succinylcholine. In specific intravenous doses the drug relaxes the body's entire muscular system with an onset beginning in the first 30 to 40 seconds.

The heart slows and respiration ceases. The patient, however, remains conscious.

While the inmate gasps for air, the prison psychiatrist begins his "negative reinforcement," scolding the man, warning him to mend his ways or face more of this modification in the future.

This, of course, is no different from the early "brainwashing" experiments of the 1950s, at the height of the Cold War.

In a similar experiment at the California Medical Facility at Vacaville, twenty-five percent of the 64 prisoners tested likened it to dying.

The chief psychiatrist at Vacaville, Dr. Arthur G. Nugent commented, "The prison grapevine works fast and even the toughest have come to fear and hate the drug. I don't blame them—I wouldn't have the treatment myself for the world."[81]

The Atascadero researchers concluded, "Succinylcholine offers an easily controlled, quickening, fear-producing experience during which the sensorium is intact and the patient rendered susceptible to suggestion."[82]

In Iowa, prisoners found guilty of "not getting up on time, of giving cigarettes against orders...for talking, for swearing, or for lying" were subjected to injections of a drug that brought about uncontrollable vomiting for 15 minutes to an hour.[83]

All of this "therapy" sounds remarkably like what used to be called, in less civilized times, torture.

Even children have not been spared. A school in Florida, operating under a Department of Defense contract sought to alter the behavior of troublesome children by shocking them, fitting electric dog-training collars on them, and in some cases the children were forced to spend the night in graves they had dug for themselves. According to allegations made before the Permanent Subcommittee on Investigations in July, 1974, part of this behavior modification program involved injecting urine into the blood of some of the more troublesome children.[84]

Writer Sharon Daiken describes her personal experience at an adolescent psychiatric facility in Georgia when she was 15: "At one point my 'therapy' called for me to be dragged outside by three grown women in subfreezing weather—I was barefoot and in flannel shirt and jeans (no coat)—and forced to dig a two-foot-deep hole in the frozen ground with my bare hands. Some of the resulting scars on my hands are still visible ...for being 'smart-mouthed,' I was locked in a 4 by 4 isolation cell for ten days, during which time I was allowed only two quick showers. This happened three times in the six months I was there."[85]

In evidence of the effectiveness of such *treatments*, serious juvenile crime escalated 1,600 percent during the twenty years leading up to 1978, according the National Council on Crime and Delinquency.[86]

In 1967, three Boston-based psychosurgeons—Vernon H. Mark, Frank R. Ervin, and William H. Sweet—suggested a violence center to study the role of brain malfunction in urban unrest. They claimed that poverty, unemployment, slum housing , and inadequate education were well known causes underlying riots of that time period, "but the obviousness of these causes may have blinded us to the more subtle role of other possible factors, including brain dysfunction in the rioters who engaged in arson, sniping and physical assault."

The trio received a half-million dollar grant from NIMH to explore their theories.

After reporting they had cured violence in a handful of patients by cutting selected parts of their brains, their findings were followed up to reveal serious flaws. The subject whom they had touted as their finest success, Thomas R., turned out to be a disaster in reality. The brain mutilation caused a deterioration in quality of life far in excess of any problems Thomas R. had before.[87]

The lesson was not learned. In 1972, psychiatrist Louis Jolyon West, director of the Neuropsychiatric Institute at the University of California at Los Angeles proposed his own "violence center" to be established with government funds on an abandoned missile base near the university.

In a letter to Dr. J. M. Stubblebine, director of California State Department of Health, West wrote, "Now by implanting tiny electrodes deep within the brain...[it] is even possible to record bioelectrical changes in the brain of freely moving subjects, through the use of remote monitoring techniques. They are not yet feasible for large-scale screening that might permit detection of a violent episode. A major task of the center should be to devise such a test."[88]

West's Orwellian vision also contained suggestions that the center's subjects include "hyperkinetic" children and those with "chromosomal abnormalities." In words quite reminiscent of his World War II German colleagues, he wrote, "A long-range study should be instituted to identify children who have this type of genetic abnormality, and to compare their development with that of children who have normal chromosomes. ...Such research has great implications, especially,...to overcome hereditary defects."[89]

After considerable public outcry and governmental inquiry, plans for the center were dropped.

When behavior modification programs began to run afoul of public opinion, the psychiatric community turned toward a less controversial method of handling prisoners: drugs.

Since psychiatric drugs had so saturated the society at large, it was a natural evolution to expand it into the prisons. This is in spite of the fact that it had already been well established in the past that psychiatric drugs do not really help convicts.

In *The Effectiveness of Correctional Treatment*, the authors point out, "Medical methods may be practical expedients for controlling behavior in the institution, but this should not be confused with 'curing' disruptive behavior."

They also noted that since drugs may affect only *symptoms*, "the utilization of drugs, because of their highly visible effect on inmate behavior may supplant attempts to change the organizational structures and treatment orientations of institutions. However, unless organizational structures and treatment orientations change, there may be little effect upon offenders' behavior when they return to the community."[90]

The authors conclude, after their extensive review, that there is no evidence to indicate the administration of drugs solve either individual or organizational problems which are the source of acting-out behavior.[91]

Yet a 1980's NIMH-sponsored study of 43 jails in 26 states found that *all* of them provided prisoners with psychotropic drugs, distributing them via professional staff or correctional officers. They found "in general, jails tended to equate...treatment with psychotropic medications." The study also found in places the same "Rogerian" (Carl Rogers) counseling being offered as occurred in San Quentin.[92]

The researchers concluded, "Overall then, the jails that were studied emphasized services that focused on the behavior management of the inmate within the jail and not on longer-term mental health treatment concerns as they might benefit the inmate during incarceration or upon return to the community."[93]

Given the broad application of psychiatric medications and the fact that drugs are used for disciplinary reasons as well,[94] we can see their use is not only widespread *among* prisons and jails but within them as well.

So pervasive has psychiatric intervention become in the penal system that a 1979 study of jails found that 24 percent to 75 percent of the prisoners were referred for psychiatric evaluation.[95]

Our incarcerated youth are not spared any more than their adult counterparts. Psychotropic medication, given to children of all ages, is a staple of modern-day juvenile institutions.

For a great many of these prisoners, adding the mind-deadening and conscience-stultifying effects of drugs to the already difficult task of rehabilitation will be the straw that breaks the camel's back. Instead of climbing out of their criminality, they will dwindle still deeper.

The facts are clear. When psychiatry entered the penal system, it did so with the promise that it would end crime. And it has been paid millions upon millions of dollars to do just that. The exact opposite has happened. Recidivism hovers around 80 percent. The concept of rehabilitation is no longer even discussed. Instead, we are building more prisons. In 1951, New York City, for example, had 244 murders. Now it has nearly 2,000 murders each year.

Crime has won the day.

And we have in these psychiatric activities nothing approaching a cure, only the perpetuation of crime.

A COST TOO HIGH

A free society cannot exist in the absence of the concept of *individual responsibility*.

Indeed, the more this standard has declined in our own culture, the greater our liberties have waned.

There was a time when people complained they could no longer walk the streets at night because of the rise in crime.

Now they lock their doors and still do not feel safe.

Any ideology that beckons us down a path of undue leniency for the wrongdoer puts the rest of us at risk. History's graveyards are filled with people who were understanding and tolerant to the point of no return.

And yet as a matter of compassion—and self-preservation of the society—we cannot let the criminal be abused and driven into even lower states of degradation by those we entrust with his care. That debased soul will likely walk the streets again, with far less a conscience than before.

We cannot do these things if we cherish our survival. Yet they *are* happening outside our doors, creating a world where injustice is common and crime breeds.

But this epidemic did not just happen.

There are causes.

And it would seem that chief among them is the invasion of psychiatric doctrines into our courts, our prisons, and our very codes of conduct.

CHAPTER IX

THE BREAKDOWN
OF EDUCATION

PERHAPS *NOTHING* RUNS SO DEEPLY IN OUR CULTURE AS OUR LOVE AND concern for our children. We willingly sacrifice for them, work unselfishly to provide and care for them. And we worry incessantly about them.

There was a time in the not-so-distant past when we looked forward to sending our children to school, with our hopes and dreams in full bloom. We imagined them becoming imbued with knowledge and skills. We foresaw them growing into fine, capable men and women, pursuing greater heights than perhaps we were able to reach.

But things are not this way anymore. There are guns in schools. Drugs. Rampant promiscuity. AIDS.

These days, sending children to school has become, for many parents, their worst fear. For the children themselves it has often become a battle for survival—a battle that has taken a heavy toll.

The suicide rate among children, teenagers and young adults has tripled since the early 1960s.[1] Illegitimate births to girls 15 to 19 years of age increased by 110 percent since 1963. Since the early 1960s, illegitimate births to girls under 15 years old increased 140 percent.[2]

It is no great secret that the *quality* of education has plummeted as well, particularly since the early 1960s. Nationwide Scholastic Aptitude Test verbal and math scores have been on a steep decline since 1963.[3]

257

In a speech to the California Library Association in 1970, university professor Karl Shapiro noted, "But what is really distressing is that this generation cannot and does not read. I am speaking of university students in what are supposed to be our best universities. Their illiteracy is staggering.... We are experiencing a literary breakdown which is unlike anything I know of in the history of American letters. It is something new and something to be reckoned with."[4]

Within 13 years the "something new" had avalanched, plunging academic standards into an abyss.

In 1983, in a report prepared at the request of the U.S. Secretary of Education, the National Commission on Excellence in Education stated, "If an unfriendly foreign power had attempted to impose on America the mediocre educational performance that exists today, we might well have viewed it as an act of war."

The commission concluded: "Our society and its educational institutions, seem to have lost sight of the basic purposes of schooling and of the high expectations and disciplined effort needed to attain them."[5]

What has happened to our schools? And *why* has it happened?

Without a decent education to offer our children, without a safe, positive place in which they can learn, most of our hopes for their futures vanish like smoke in the wind.

Is it a lack of funds as some claim? That doesn't seem so. In terms of real dollars—adjusted for inflation—total expenditure per pupil has quadrupled since 1950, with a corresponding decline in classroom achievement.[6]

Is it simply all due to a decline in "the society?" That doesn't ring true either. Plato said, "The direction in which education starts a man will determine his future life."[7] In other words, to a great degree, our educational systems have *created* this society. To then *blame* society for the school's shortcomings hardly seems logical.

Once again, we see here a phenomenon at work. *Something* has seeped into our once-stellar halls of learning, and this *something* seems to encourage lower standards and bring out the worst in our children.

ALL ROADS LEAD FROM WUNDT

At first, the notion that psychiatry has entrenched itself into our schools may seem odd. After all, there are no psychiatrists in the classroom.

258

Although there may be psychological counselors in the administration offices, these seem innocuous enough.

But things are not always as they appear. So it is with our classrooms.

At the turn of the twentieth century, academic achievement in the United States and elsewhere was excellent. High standards of classroom conduct were maintained. Students were well-versed in history, the arts, classic literature. The "three Rs—reading, 'riting, and 'rithmetic" were emphasized. Children were sent to school to learn—period.

In 1910, the literacy rate was so high it was predicted "the public schools will in a short time practically eliminate illiteracy."[8]

It hardly seemed in need of fixing. But change was coming.

Earlier, we discussed Wilhelm Wundt, the "Father of Psychology," who began his illustrious career in 1879. Convinced that man was an animal, a biochemical machine, Wundt presented this view to the world as scientific doctrine. His students later boasted "that psychology had at last become a science without a soul."[9]

Yet Wundt's impact on education around the world has been nothing short of astounding. Slowly but steadily, his views began to permeate our schools via two separate, but not so different, paths—psychology and psychiatry.

Psychology was first. Three key players who implemented Wundt's theories into American education were Edward Lee Thorndike, John Dewey, and James Earl Russell.

The trickle-down from Wundt looked like this:

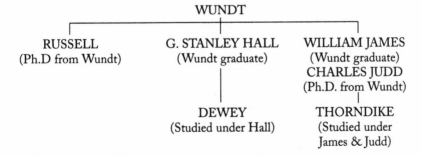

THORNDIKE

Thorndike performed some of the earliest experiments in "animal psychology." Entirely in keeping with Wundt's man-is-an-animal view, he investigated the mechanisms of learning by studying not humans, but chickens, rats, and cats as they worked their way around mazes he had devised. From these lessons came statements such as, "The best way with children may often be, in the pompous words of the animal trainer, 'to arrange everything in connection with the trick so that the animal will be compelled by the laws of his own nature to perform it.'"[10]

Thorndike's outpouring on the new subject of "educational psychology" was prodigious. He literally wrote the book. In fact, he published some 507 books, monographs and articles on the subject. Among these was *Educational Psychology*, published in 1903, and *The Principles of Teaching Based on Psychology*, published in 1906.[11]

His "principles of teaching" included such thoughts as this, from a book he co-authored: "Despite rapid progress in the right direction, the program of the average elementary school is too narrow and academic in character. Traditionally the elementary school has been primarily devoted to teaching the fundamental subjects, the three Rs, and closely related disciplines.... Artificial exercises, like drills on phonetics, multiplication tables, and formal writing movements, are used to a wasteful degree. Subjects such as arithmetic, language, and history include content that is intrinsically of little value. Nearly every subject is enlarged unwisely to satisfy the academic ideal of thoroughness."[12]

In contrast to the ideal of mastering one's environment and adjusting *it* to *oneself*—which was the popular view in the rugged, pioneering days of the nineteenth century and responsible for much of man's forward progress—Thorndike introduced a new idea: "Education is interested primarily in the general interrelation of man and his environment, in all the changes which make possible a better adjustment of human nature to its surroundings."[13] Suddenly man was no longer master, but servant of his environment, buffeted by the forces of nature, adjusting to fit in with them.

Further, with his Wundtian and animal psychology background, Thorndike did not see students as self-willed individuals, capable of choice and decision. He saw them as stimulus-response mechanisms. In his *The Principles of Teaching Based on Psychology*, he defined teaching as the art of giving and withholding stimuli with the result of producing or preventing certain responses. In this definition, the term stimulus is used widely for any event which influences a person, for a word spoken to him, a look, a sentence which he reads, the air he breathes, etc. The term response is used for any reaction made by him, a new thought, a feeling of interest, a bodily act, any mental or bodily condition resulting from the stimulus.

"The aim of the teacher," Thorndike said, "is to produce desirable and prevent undesirable changes in human beings by producing and preventing certain responses."[14]

It is a role that begins to sound more and more like that of the animal trainer.

DEWEY

John Dewey is known as the "Father of American Education." His goal, like Thorndike's, was to use the schooling process for something *other* than the simple transference of knowledge it has always pursued. "The school," he wrote in *My Pedagogic Creed*, "is primarily a social institution. Education being a social process, the school is simply that form of community life in which all those agencies are concentrated that will be most effective in bringing the child to share in the inherited resources of the race, and to use his own powers for social ends."[15]

As did Wundt, Dewey viewed children as animals requiring guidance, control and molding, but not particularly teaching. He claimed that to place the emphasis upon proficiency in teaching and discipline put the attention of the student teacher in the wrong place and tended to fix it in the wrong direction.[16]

He saw the purpose of education again not as a relay of data and skills to the student, but one of getting the individual to fit in. "The ultimate problem of all education is to coordinate the psychological and social factors.... The coordination demands...that the child be capable of expressing himself, but in such a way as to realize social ends."[17]

Here again we have the individual encouraged to adapt, this time to the social machine and its goals.

But Dewey also knew the public did not want his change and implementing it was a delicate problem. "Change must come gradually," he said. "To force it unduly would compromise its final success by favoring a violent reaction."[18]

THORNDIKE, DEWEY, AND RUSSELL

James Earl Russell received his Ph. D. from Wundt himself in 1894 and three years later became the head of the Department of Psychology at Columbia University's Teachers College in New York. That same year he was appointed its dean, a position he would hold for the next thirty years.

Not long after Russell's appointment, another psychologist suggested Russell add Thorndike to his staff at Teachers College. "Although the Dean found him 'dealing with the investigations of mice and monkeys,'" wrote the psychologist, "he came away 'satisfied that he was worth trying out on humans.'"[19]

Like Russell, Thorndike remained at Teachers College for thirty years.

Later John Dewey joined them.

Teachers College was now inundated with Wundtian thought, the new thought in teaching methods. However, only a small percentage of teachers went through its progressive doors, so the spread and use of psychology in schools was minimal.

Until 1902.

That year the school received a gift of $450,000 from oil tycoon John D. Rockefeller. Further endowments would ensue via the Rockefeller-founded and financed General Education Board. The stage was set for an upheaval that would hammer the foundations of American education unlike anything before it.

The goal of the Board was expressed in its *Occasional Letter No. 1*: "In our dreams we have limitless resources and the people yield themselves with perfect docility to our molding hands. The present education conventions fade from their minds, and unhampered by tradition, we work our own good will upon a grateful and responsive rural folk. We shall not try to make these people or any of their children into philosophers or men of learning , or men of science. We have not to raise up from among them authors, editors, poets or men of letters. We shall not search for embryo great artists, painters, musicians nor lawyers, doctors, preachers, politicians, statesmen, of whom we have ample supply.

"The task we set before ourselves is very simple as well as a very beautiful one, to train these people as we find them to a perfectly ideal life just where they are. So we will organize our children and teach them to do in a perfect way the things their fathers and mothers are doing in an imperfect way, in the homes, in the shops, and on the farm." [20]

Condescending? Paternalistic? Presumptuous? Arrogant? Regardless of the words used to describe it, this was the dream of a Brave New World in which every man would know his place and fulfill his destiny (a destiny decided by his betters). It was not the world of the American Dream which had moved this country on a path of progress the likes of which had never been seen before. If anything, it was the dream of an elite which had closed the doors behind it, barring further entrants. And it was a dream parroted years later by lobotomists Freeman and Watts with their, "It's better for [a patient] to have a simplified intellect capable of elementary acts than an intellect where there reigns disorders of subtle synthesis." Apparently, great minds think alike.

Needless to say, a condition of the funding was that Teachers College curricula align with the Rockefeller Board's objectives.

Secure in its finances now, the College's impact on American education soared.

One report glowed, "Only fifteen years after the move to 120th Street, Teachers College will meet the Rockefeller endowment terms and cover an entire city block crammed with seven buildings. Its facilities will operate from early morning to ten o'clock in the evening, for ten months of the year.... Its enrollment is to be exceeded in size by only ten universities in the entire United States; only Columbia, Harvard, and Chicago will have more students seeking advanced education in 1912 as, amazingly, Teachers College becomes the fourth largest graduate school in the nation." [21]

More Board funds poured in.

The consequences of all this to the nation's future did not go unnoticed. Speaking from the Senate floor in 1917, Senator Chamberlain of Oregon lashed out against this funding of "Progressive Education." Relaying the views of Bishop Warren A. Candler, Chancellor of Emory University in Atlanta, Georgia, he said, "With this financial power in its control, the general board is in position to do what no body in this country can at present even attempt. It can determine largely what institutions shall grow, and in some measure what shall stand still or decay.... Its power will be enormous. It seems as if it might be able to determine the character of American education.... We owe something to our ancestors, who founded and maintained our older institutions of learning. We have no right to bind up the offerings which they laid upon the altar of higher education in the enslaving conditions prescribed by the Rockefeller board for institutions to which it grants its humiliating doles."[22]

That same year Teachers College opened an experimental school in which to test and formulate its new educational methods. First called the Modern School, then the Lincoln School, it was the learning institution for four of five of the Rockefeller children. A biographer tells us, "Laurance [Rockefeller] gives startling confirmation as to 'Why Johnnie [sic] Can't Read.' He says that the Lincoln School did not teach him to read and write as he wishes he now could. Nelson [Rockefeller], today, admits that reading for him is a 'slow and tortuous process' that he does not enjoy doing but compels himself to do. This is significant evidence in the debate that has raged about modern educational techniques."[23]

Its failures notwithstanding, the curricula and methods developed at Lincoln School were presented as a showcase of the future of American education. Thousands of educators came to be enlightened.

By 1925, two of Dewey's disciples reported that more than 1,000 schools nationwide engaged in curriculum revision aligned with the new methods.[24]

The deluge had begun.

In 1928, Board grants to Teachers College were $2,000,000.[25]

The *degree* of penetration of Thorndike, Dewey, and Teachers College into the classroom—along with their ideas of molding the individual, teaching him not to master but adapt to his environment, and reducing academics—was probably best described in *A History of Teachers College Columbia University*: "The single most powerful educational force in the world is at 120th Street and Broadway in New York City. Your children's teachers go there for advanced training.... With 100,000 alumni, TC has managed to seat about one-third of the presidents and deans now [1953] in office at accredited U.S teacher training schools. Its graduates make up about 20 percent of all our public school teachers. Over a fourth of the superintendents of schools in the 168 U.S. cities with at least 50,000 population are TC-trained."[26]

FROM WUNDT TO MENTAL HYGIENE

The Progressive Educational movement by psychologists such as Dewey and Thorndike was not alone in its efforts to change the school systems of the early 1900s. Flanking it was a *separate* crusade to permeate the schools—and teachers—with *psychiatric* thought.

Separate, but not so very different.

In Chapter Three, we discussed the founding of the Mental Hygiene movement in 1909. The original organization was founded by ex-patient Clifford Beers, but only with the extensive help of William James. James, as you will recall was a Wundt graduate (and also mentor of Thorndike).

James was the man who first read Beers' autobiographical manuscript about his battle with mental problems. He encouraged Beers to publish and provided his backing so Beers could gain support in the medical and psychiatric community.

When the ex-patient founded the National Committee for Mental Hygiene, James served as one of the twelve founding members and forwarded a copy of Beers' book to John D. Rockefeller, requesting money for the cause.

Rockefeller gave millions.

The primary objective of the Committee was the *prevention* of mental illness. And one of its key targets was schools.

In a 1982 speech before the History of Education Society, the society's president Sol Cohen said, "Few intellectual and social movements of this century have had so deep and pervasive an influence on the theory and practice of American education as the mental hygiene movement."[27]

The hygienist's ideas on mental illness were that it was the result of improper personality development. If somehow one could reach into the personal lives of humanity and control the growth process of personality, it was reasoned, mental illness would be eliminated.

Regarding children, hygienists believed:

1. Childhood is the most important period in the development of personality.

2. Children are very susceptible to "personality disorders."

3. The school is the ideal focal point for detecting, preventing, and fixing personality disorders.

4. The development of personality must take precedence over any other educational objective.[28]

5. Shyness, daydreaming, withdrawal, introversion, the "shut-in person-

265

ality" are psychiatric danger signals in children.

6. Stress is the chief precipitating cause of psychiatric symptoms and stress warps personality.[29]

Some people may recognize these as things "everybody" knows. They are not.

These were not common or broadly accepted beliefs before psychiatrists created them.

The mental hygiene movement had no proof that any of this was true or necessary. And there is no evidence they ever tested their methods to see if they actually helped people. Pervasive throughout the movement was the persistent attitude that the hygienists simply knew what was good for people and should, therefore, be permitted to impose their good judgment.

As they did with their ideas on the proper way to raise and educate children.

Today these ideas are so imbedded in the social fabric we may think of them as common sense because "everybody" knows them. They may be common but we should question calling them *sense* if they are creating the chaotic world in which we now live.

A good example of hygiene thought is the notion that children are so fragile we must not put academic expectations on them for fear of damaging them with the stress or ruining their "self-esteem" should they fail.

This is a blatant falsehood responsible for poor scholastic performance and lower quality lives around the world.

Yet it is presented as truth in the points above.

And it is a staple upon which modern schools operate.

The desire to manipulate the school came early in the mental hygiene movement. In 1918 psychiatrist and hygienist C.M. Campbell wrote that there is "no more hopeful avenue of approach to many of the...social problems of today than through the school."[30]

The director of the National Committee during the early years, Thomas Salmon, stated, "Psychiatrists...must be permitted to enter the schools."[31]

Before resigning in 1922, Salmon outlined the Committee's "Program for the Prevention of Delinquency." This plan was the genesis of not only child psychiatry and psychiatric social work, but created "child guidance clinics" (psychiatric counseling) around the globe and was the driving wedge for the entry of mental hygiene concepts into the schools.

The Commonwealth Fund, another Rockefeller organization, funded the program.

Its initial intention was to provide psychiatric intervention for "pre-delinquent" and "problem" children via the guidance clinics. After failing to make acceptable headway with these children, the hygienists, instead of concluding their ideas were wrong, deduced instead *they hadn't intervened soon enough.*[32]

Since they believed parents to be too ignorant of child personality development to be trusted to raise children adequately, the Committee launched a parent education campaign in the 1920s. Unfortunately, this had the drawback of voluntary participation. Parents could not be forced to accept, listen to, or practice the good advice of the Committee.

Thus there remained only one alternative: the schools.

"If we are going to prevent dependency, delinquency, insanity, and general inadequacy," wrote Ralph Truitt, the head of the Committee's Division of Child Guidance Clinics in 1927, "...the school should be the focus of our attack."[33]

And attack they did.

Three sources of stress, they claimed, had to be eliminated from the schools:

1. School failure.

2. A curriculum centered around academics.

3. Disciplinary procedures.

School failure was the chief villain, they said, leading to "feelings of inferiority," behavior problems like truancy or juvenile delinquency, withdrawal, an unsocial attitude, or a shut-in personality.[34]

The solution was clear. Eliminate the emphasis on academics. This, they reasoned, would rid the student of the stress of school failure.

The Committee did not offer any substitutes for academics, however. "Education has been...too much confined to teaching," wrote renowned psychiatrist and hygienist William Alanson White in 1927. "It needs to be developed as a scheme for assisting and guiding the developing personality."[35]

School discipline was another evil. Child misbehavior was "not a sin, but a symptom."[36]

Cohen remarks, "Hygienists called upon the teacher to pay less attention to the child's overt behavior and more attention to understanding the motives, 'more or less unconscious,' underlying behavior, and over which the child had little control and for which the child could not be held responsible."[37]

Hygienists called for the establishment of non-authoritarian classrooms to avoid the inherent stress which could be so damaging to child personality, forcing the child to hide his emotions and thus inhibiting his psychological growth.

The Committee's plan for getting teachers into the mental hygiene fold was to inundate public leaders with their principles via the written word. By 1928, they had distributed nearly 100,000 free copies of books and pamphlets with such titles as "Some Extra-Curricular Problems of the Classroom" and *The Problem Child in School*. The publications were not distributed randomly; they targeted social workers and psychologists as well as leading groups in child welfare and parent education.

To disseminate their ideas through these sectors was indeed successful.

Cohen tells us, "Gradually, through the profusion...of a vocabulary, of a nomenclature and language, certain hygienist ideas, the hygienist way of looking at things, the hygienist language of discourse, filtered into the consciousness of influential publics."[38]

Few things demonstrate this so well as the 1930 White House Conference on Child Health and Protection. The Conference, involving some 1200 experts, provided a national forum for mental hygiene principles and gave quasi-official approval of its tenets. Using the language of the movement, the Conference disseminated the gospel of the Committee as the latest in learned thought.

Some samples from the Conference report:

1. The question is not "what does the child learn in school but how does the child feel because of school?"

2. "Failure in school is a frequent source of children's problems."

3. If the school and child conflict, "these conflicts will disappear as the teacher interests herself less and less in what the child did and more and more in why he did it."

4. The school is "primarily an experiment in life adjustment for the child."

5. From the Conference's Children's Charter: "...for every child understanding and the guiding of his personality as his most precious right."[39]

A significant development at the 1930 Conference was the involvement of an important group of psychologists who now wanted to pick up the mental hygiene banner.

All were from Teachers College.

The 1930s marked the marriage of the purposes of the Progressive Education Association (PEA)—an organization that promoted these new psychologically-laced teaching ideas—and the Committee. The PEA, at its height during this period, worked strenuously to promote mental hygiene ideals in the schools. One PEA-sponsored group, the Commission on Secondary School Curriculum stated in its summary volume, "It cannot be too strongly stated that considerations of mental hygiene must come to pervade the whole atmosphere of the school."[40]

The Committee's principles had begun to appear in a trickle of educational texts in the late '20s, but a decade later the flow of books had reached high tide. Teachers were flooded with titles like *The Mental Hygiene of the School Child* (1934), *Mental Health Through Education* (1938), *Educating for Adjustment: The Classroom Applications of Mental Hygiene* (1936) and *Practical School Discipline from the Standpoint of Mental Hygiene* (1941).[41] And the deluge continued into the mid-1940s.

During this same period, mental hygiene principles began to appear in the publications of powerful educational organizations such as the National Education Association, the Educational Policies Commission, and the American Council on Education.

In 1950, the Committee faded from national view, combining with several organizations to become the National Association for Mental Health. (As mentioned in an earlier chapter the very name, "mental hygiene" had gained a few unpleasant connotations since the discovery of the Nazi concentration camps.)

But the momentum of infiltration of mental hygiene thought into American, indeed global, education had become a force of monumental proportions—a force that barrages parents and teachers to this very day.

At the Mid-Century White House Conference on Children and Youth in 1950, mental hygiene was in full swing. The Conference's slogan was "A Healthy Personality for Every Child."

269

"The school," the Conference said, "must assume the primary responsibility for the healthy development of the whole personality of each child."

Even without a Committee to push the mental hygiene principles, these educational "truths" have so insinuated themselves into the thinking patterns of educators they have by now nearly assumed the status of ancient lore.

The Conference gave a chilling prophesy of what we now see in our schools and what is yet to come: "The school, as a whole, has an opportunity and a responsibility to detect the physical and mental disabilities which have escaped parental or pre-school observations and which would prevent development of a healthy personality, and to initiate the necessary health services through the various agencies and resources of the community. ... All schools should move as rapidly as possible toward adequate guidance and counseling services *for all individuals at all age levels*. This should include I) Study and the understanding of the total personality as a basis for adaptation of the curriculum to individual needs for fullest physical, mental, emotional and spiritual development." (Emphasis added.)[42]

The Conference also decided to expand the meaning of a phrase that once was quite clear: "The group felt the term 'handicapped children' should be interpreted to include all children having a physical or mental limitation of any degree, from marginal to complete disability."[43]

And like the sweet smells from a bakery, offering promises but no substance, mental hygiene principles continued to saturate the porous bones of a now-decaying American educational system gone awry.

In 1962, the Joint Commission on Mental Illness and Health—a group commissioned by the U.S. government to make recommendations on future policy—wrote, "The school is the one place where all youth congregate and where it is thus feasible to detect, if not treat, [mental] illness. Many informed people, therefore, view the nation's schools as the most suitable single place to begin reducing this burden. Their goal is to improve the health of the 'next generation'—children now in school...."[44]

The great irony of the 1962 report is that, unlike earlier commissions and conferences, this one was seeing a tide of public opinion that had turned sour. Periodicals and the press were filled with attacks on schools, they wrote. A favorite target was the practice of making "life adjustment" and "a healthy personality for every child" educational goals at the expense of the three Rs.[45]

While trying to call it something else, psychiatrists continued to preach the gospel of mental hygiene, sounding uncannily like their predecessors half a century earlier: "Preventative measures, taken during the 'formative years' when the groundwork is laid for later disturbances, are said to be capable of forestalling trouble completely. If prevention has failed and actual illness begun, it is best treated when caught early. Even those emotional upsets that do not foreshadow serious psychiatric problems may justify treatment, because, in addition to humane considerations, they may keep a child from learning while in school."[46]

Acting on the 1962 recommendations, President Kennedy signed into law in 1963 the largest federal funding of mental health services in the nation's history up to that time.

Psychiatrists had, for the first time, access to school rooms and federal funds via programs for the all-embracive "handicapped children," as well as "seriously emotionally disturbed" children, and "other health impaired children who by reason thereof require special education."[47]

As a sign of the times, school prayer was outlawed by the U.S. Supreme Court in 1962.

It would be comforting to think the Supreme Court judges' decision was based on a full, conceptual grasp of the Constitution and its intent.

But weaved into the text of the Court's decision were not the words of the Founding Fathers, but the words of psychiatric hygienists: "When the power, prestige and financial support of government is placed behind a particular religious belief, the *indirect coercive pressure* upon religious minorities to conform to the prevailing officially approved religion is plain." (Emphasis added.)[48]

Three years later, to fully implement the inundation of psychiatry into the classroom, the Elementary and Secondary Education Act of 1965 provided for "comprehensive guidance and counseling, psychological, and social work services designed to enable and encourage persons to enter, remain in, or reenter educational programs."

The following statistics speak for themselves.

The mental hygiene movement and the progressive education movement of Dewey and Thorndike may no longer exist in name, but their beliefs and objectives live soundly and course through the very heart and into every minute capillary of our educational system.

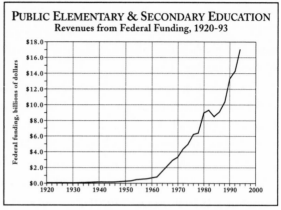

PUBLIC ELEMENTARY & SECONDARY EDUCATION
Revenues from Federal Funding, 1920-93

Their legacy continues under names such as "sensitivity training," "nondirective group discussion," "death education,"—but these are the same concepts and have the same intentions.

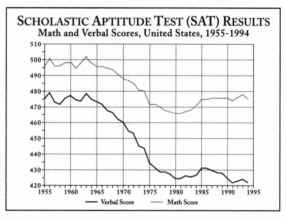

SCHOLASTIC APTITUDE TEST (SAT) RESULTS
Math and Verbal Scores, United States, 1955-1994

— Verbal Score   ······· Math Score

They see the child as an animal needing molding. He is someone who needs to be taught how to "feel" properly. And academics—well, academics are still too stressful.

THE GRIM RESULTS

"[Daddy] said: 'All children must look after their own upbringing.' Parents can only give good advice or put them on the right paths, but the final forming of a person's character lies in their own hands."
—Anne Frank, July 15, 1944
From *Anne Frank: The Diary of a Young Girl*[49]

It is almost astonishing that Anne Frank, a 15-year-old girl who spent the last months of her life hiding from the Nazis in an attic with her family, would have a fuller grasp of the human condition than the entirety of the mental hygiene movement and progressive educators of the past and present.

Her simple statement embodies the principles upon which successful, traditional education was constructed for centuries: Schools *teach*. They do not sculpt personalities.

Traditional education was aimed at the intellect.

Modern education, imbued with psychiatric thought, targets the emotions and feelings.

This has had serious consequences.

THE FALL OF ACADEMICS

Academics are those subjects that are not vocational or technical in nature. They include "the three Rs," history, literature, the arts.

In education, academics are the whetstone upon which intellect is honed.

As we have seen, there has been a tremendous push in the past century by psychologists and psychiatrists to water down or completely eliminate the school's emphasis on academics. Certainly, every effort has been made to stress to teachers how *unimportant* they are.

"The issue must be made clear," wrote Daniel Prescott in *Emotion and the Educative Process* in 1938, asking the rhetorical question, "Is it more important that children develop adjusted, integrated personalities, or that they fulfill some other traditional academic objectives?"[50]

Let us answer the question. Do academics have a place in the world, in our lives?

We could start with history, as an example.

In spite of Thorndike's assertion that history includes content that is "of little value," the subject itself has shown us that a population without a knowledge of history is like a mind without a memory.

They will never be able to truly judge the present or future because they have no past to compare it with.

They will not learn the ultimate lesson of history, that our acts, *all of our acts*, have consequences and these can reverberate into other people's lives and, indeed, into centuries long after the doer of the deed is gone (perhaps Wundt would be a good example).

With no awareness, let us say, of the Great Fire of London in 1666 and other such disasters, the building contractor of today thinks modern fire codes are "stupid." So he cuts corners to avoid what he thinks are pointless regulations. Catastrophe results.

Shoddy workmanship. Racial hatred. Economic chaos. All can and do result from a society that has no understanding of all that has gone before. It can not learn from humanity's mistakes, and so is doomed to repeat them.

And so we spend our own last breaths—and our children's—to learn the same lessons again.

Science is another academic subject. It covers the fields of electronics, biology, medicine, chemistry, physics and a host of others.

Without an elementary grounding in the sciences, we are creating people who are becoming more and more dependant on technological advances while becoming less and less aware of the basic information upon which these advances are based.

We end up with a population that does not understand the mechanics of disease, building structures, electricity, bodily functions, nutrition, plant growth—the list is endless.

Yet these are things that touch all our lives and our knowledge or ignorance of them can mean the difference, literally, between life and death.

As for the Arts, the fact that they are the open window into the human soul must immediately disqualify them from serious consideration as a subject worth the "stress" of study. After all, according to Wundtian thought, there is no human soul.

Yet without an awareness of the fine arts, man would seem spiritless indeed.

They stir our imaginations, they touch upon our intimate sense of beauty. They permit us to see all that is great and wonderful in ourselves and the world—as well those things undesirable.

A society nursed on TV and comic books and sheltered from the "stress" of the arts is one that has no inkling of the heavenly pinnacles of which humanity is capable.

And therefore, it does not strive for these heights, but sits in its doldrums, looking for meaning in the satisfaction of coarser appetites.

Finally, we could consider literature.

There is, perhaps, no faster or surer way to literacy and knowledge than a high quantity reading of literature of all manner and subject.

Such a grounding gives us a grasp of the great breadth of language available to us. It enlightens us about an endless number of people, places, ideas, events, cultures, practices, customs, occupations, technologies, and everything else godly, human, of this earth and beyond. And we ingest it at our own pace in our own thoughts, evaluating each fact and opinion so we may judge and conclude as we see fit.

To deny children the opportunity—factually, the necessity—of such an experience because we don't want to "pressure" them with reading requirements or "burden" them with difficult vocabularies is to deny them the only lasting legacy the human race has: its knowledge.

In looking at the world we live in today, we see a humanity utterly uneducated in the world's literature. They have no understanding of cultures and customs, and thus often see foreigners as not entirely human. They are oblivious to universal philosophical and religious tenets and stumble through life ignorant of how to evaluate right and wrong.

Knowledge promotes understanding.

It is only logical then to surmise that *denying* knowledge promotes blindness and bewilderment.

And *that* creates more social and human ills than any book can catalogue—*all* of which can be seen on the streets of today.

The result of these crusades against academics is that a populace which once cut its teeth on the works of Lincoln, Jefferson, Cicero, and Aristotle, now props itself in front of television sets, abysmally ignorant of its culture, its heritage, and the vast scope of human potential.

THE FALL OF LITERACY

Part and parcel with the decline of academics has been the demise of literacy in America and across the world.

The 1983 report of the National Commission on Excellence in Education, entitled *A Nation at Risk*, stated, "Business and military leaders complain that they are required to spend millions of dollars on costly remedial education and training programs in such basic skills as reading, writing, spelling and computation."[51]

The $14 million National Adult Literacy Survey of 1993 found that even though most adults in the survey had finished high school, 96 percent of them could not read, write, and figure well enough to go to college.[52]

Even more to the point, 25 percent "were plainly unable to read," period.[53]

In a 1989 speech, Albert Shanker, President of the American

Federation of Teachers, the nation's second-largest teachers union, said, "So the question is, how many of our 17- to 18-year-old youngsters…what percentage of those kids are able to *really* read something that's fairly difficult [such as a newspaper editorial]? What percentage of them can write a letter or an essay of 1, 2, 3, 4, 5 pages and do a good job? What percentage of them can solve a two-step math problem?

"Well, the answer is, depending upon whether you take reading, writing, math, or science, the percentage of those still in school at age 17 and about to graduate who are able to function at that top level is: 3, 4, 5, or 6 percent.

"*3, 4, 5, or 6 percent.*

"The percentage of those able to write that 1 or 2 paragraph letter with lots of errors in it is only 20 percent. In other words, 80 percent of those who have *not* dropped out cannot even write two paragraphs loaded with mistakes which have a single idea in it.

"*80 percent cannot!*"[54]

Shanker says that when prospective teachers are given a 6th grade math test, 30 to 40 percent get a failing score of below 65 percent.[55]

Things were not always this way.

In 1930, illiteracy rates in the U.S. were as follows:

1. 1.5 percent among native-born whites.
2. 9.9 percent among foreign-born whites.
3. 9.2 percent among urban blacks.
4. 16.3 percent among blacks in general

In 1935, a survey of the 375,000 men working in the Civilian Conservation Corps—a government-sponsored work project to provide employment—found an illiteracy rate of 1.9 percent. And this was among men primarily of low socio-economic status.

The only reason some people *were* illiterate was they simply hadn't gone to school.

By contrast, today the illiteracy rate among blacks is about 40 percent. For whites, it is 7 to 30 percent, the exact figure being unknown.[56]

The psychiatric contribution to illiteracy has not been just the lowering of standards. They actually altered the way children were taught to read.

The standard, workable way to teach reading in times past was the phonetics method. Children were taught the sounds of letters and thus learned to pronounce and spell any and all words.

But in the early 1900s, psychologist James Cattell, a Wundt graduate and faculty member of Teachers College, decided a different method should be used.

It was the "whole word" method and taught students to learn reading by learning to recognize each individual word. Phonetics were ignored.

This method was shotgunned far and wide into the nation's schools and remains to this day. Rudolph Flesch, author of the 1955 classic *Why Johnny Can't Read*, tells us, "It's a foolproof system, all right. Every grade school teacher in the country has to go to a teachers' college or school of education; every teachers' college gives at least one course on how to teach reading; every course on how to teach reading is based on a textbook; every one of those textbooks is written by a high priest of the word method. In the old days, it was impossible to keep a good teacher from following her own common sense and practical knowledge; today the phonic system of teaching reading is kept out of our schools as effectively as if we had a dictatorship with an all-powerful Ministry of Education."[57]

Evidencing the effect of the "whole word" method on reading skills are the 1991 reading scores of the San Diego Unified School District. In 1990, 51 percent of their students scored above the national median. In 1991, a year after they adopted the "whole word" method, only 25 percent of the students scored as well.[58]

Researcher and author Samuel Blumenfeld, one of the most knowledgeable historians of methods of teaching reading in America, shows the transformation in his book *The New Illiterates—And How You Can Keep Your Child From Becoming One*. He reviewed the well-known Dick and Jane "pre-primers," books designed to teach the "whole word" method. Each word was to be learned by sight, not phonetics.

Blumenfeld notes that in 1930 the Dick and Jane pre-primer taught 68 sight words in 39 pages of story text, with an illustration per page, a total of 565 words and a Teacher's Guidebook of 87 pages. In 1951 that same pre-primer had been expanded to 172 pages, divided into three separate pre-primers, with 184 illustrations, a total of 2,613 words, and a Guidebook of 182 pages to teach a sight vocabulary of only 58 words.

In 1930, he says, the word *look* was repeated eight times in the preprimer. In 1951 it is repeated 110 times. In 1930 the word *oh* was repeated 12 times, in 1951 138 times. In 1930 the word *see* was repeated 27 times, in 1951 176 times.

Blumenfeld asks, "How much more evidence was needed to prove that the method was a pedagogic failure?"[59]

When "Dick and Jane"—commonly used in the first grade—are compared with primers of traditional education at the turn of the century, we see stark differences. Whereas the 1951 "Dick and Jane" taught 58 words in 172 pages, the traditional first grade text, *McGuffey's Reader*, contained *64* words on a single page. The "guidebook" for the teacher was two pages at the beginning of the book instead of 182 pages.[60]

Needless to say, the consequences of all this on the individual, his family, and the nation have been staggering.

Not only have these people been denied the fruits of an academic curriculum as children, they are forever shut off from such knowledge for the rest of their lives.

Their hopes for advancement in the job market, for personal growth, for taking full control of their lives—these hopes fade into the horizon, out of reach for virtually all of those who cannot read or write.

The illiterate feel left out. There are things they cannot read and therefore do not understand. They often feel an antagonism toward that which they cannot comprehend. They often feel isolated, separated out from the rest of society.

They are left to solve life's problems with faulty information or none at all.

Crime, poverty, and failure result.

It is perhaps the greatest irony in education.

Psychiatric thought has told teachers to save children from "feelings of inadequacy" by letting them pass through school illiterate so they wouldn't feel like failures.

In the end, they have created a massive sector of the populace doomed, in fact, to a lifetime of failure.

THE FALL OF MORALS AND STANDARDS

Given the beliefs and practices that psychiatry and psychology have inculcated into our schools, it should come as no surprise that we have a moral crisis in our young people, our schools, indeed, in our whole society.

• 82 percent of schools polled in 1993 reported a rise in violence for the previous five years.

• A 1992 study found 14 percent of 12th graders had been threatened with a weapon at school.[61]

• A 1987 article by William Bennett reported that:

    a) More than half of 17-year-olds had had sex

    b) 400,000 teenage girls per year were having abortions

    c) More than 1,000,000 teenage girls per year were pregnant[62]

• A survey of 1,093 high school seniors showed:

    a) 66 percent would lie to achieve a business objective

    b) 67 percent would pad a business expense account

    c) 59 percent would be willing to negotiate an illegal deal worth $10,000,000, even at the risk of six months probation[63]

In the schools themselves, we find the following educational doctrines, laid in in years past, as we have seen, and perpetuated to this day:

1. Discipline causes stress, therefore, discipline is bad.

2. Stress causes mental disorders, therefore stress is bad.

3. If self-discipline causes stress, one should not be so hard on oneself.

4. Almost any activity is justifiable if it is done to reduce stress.

5. Almost any activity should be avoided if it creates stress.

6. Discipline reduces the child's right of autonomy (self-government). That is bad.

7. Bad behavior is not to be corrected, but understood.

8. The rights of the individual are greater than the rights of the group.

9. How you feel is more important than how you behave.

10. We are not *really* responsible for what we do.

11. There is no right and wrong, only opinion.

12. There are no philosophical or religious truths, only opinion.

When author Rita Kramer personally inspected 20 modern schools of education for her book *Ed School Follies*, she found their theories "tightly focused on feelings and hostile to standards and the idea of competition. Grades and marks are bad, too, since they characterize and divide children."[64]

Educator Alan Larson, former Secretary of the Oregon Federation of Independent Schools, told us, "This whole emphasis on *stress* in schools is based on the psychiatric principle that standards are bad, and they are bad because they produce stress. The only way that you can run up any stress is if you run into a standard that you are having trouble measuring up to. That is the producer of stress. Therefore the whole *stress* thing was just another little channel in this whole overall campaign to *get* at standards."[65]

It would appear that G. Brock Chisholm's dream of the "eventual eradication of the concept of right and wrong" is well under way.

Not only have the schools, via hygienist theory, created a breeding ground for the abandonment of self-discipline and morality, they have actively assaulted the values taught in the home.

In 1973, psychiatrist Chester M. Pierce, in an address to the Childhood International Education Seminar, claimed, "Every child in America entering school at the age of five is insane because he comes to school with certain allegiances to our founding fathers, toward our elected officials, toward his parents, toward a belief in a supernatural being, and toward the sovereignty of this nation as a separate entity. It's up to you as teachers to make all these sick children well—by creating the international child of the future."[66]

Testimony before the U.S. Department of Education in 1984 unfurled the story of one of many such efforts. This one was called Values Clarification.

Its program was outlined in a handbook for teachers and students. The book laid out 79 strategies and included a seven-step procedure which allowed the child to first "thaw out" previous values which had been instilled in him through his family, his home and his church. The student was instructed to set these values aside for the time being. During the second phase, the student could consider and select a new set of values which he felt was important to him. Phase three of the procedure instructed the child to refreeze his newly-chosen values; he was committed to making them a part of his lifestyle, to act on them.

Some sample questions and exercises:

1. How many of you think there are times when cheating is justified?

2. How many of you approve of premarital sex for boys?

3. How many of you approve of premarital sex for girls?

4. How many of you would approve of a marriage between homosexuals being sanctioned by a priest, minister or rabbi?

5. How many of you would approve of a young couple trying out a mar-

riage by living together for six months before actually getting married?

6. How many of you would approve of contract marriages in which the marriage could come up for renewal every few years?

7. Tell where you stand on the topic of masturbation.

8. To whom do you tell your doubts about religion?

9. "I would lie if_____."

Knowing the psychiatric fascination with sex, it is not unexpected that we find the above and other efforts aimed at incessantly infusing this topic into the classrooms. Books, classes, detailed films of nude masturbation, condom-fitting on cucumbers, having each girl say "penis" and each boy say "vagina" aloud in the classroom—the variety of methods have been endless.

Some school systems teach sex education from kindergarten to the twelfth grade. Given the fact that the sexual act and reproduction are *very* simple to teach and learn—most parents seem to be able to cover it within thirty minutes—one has to ask what possible purpose could be served by such a saturation with sex?

And the truth be told, since schools have begun concentrating so heavily on it, promiscuity, sexual disease, and teenage pregnancy have soared.

In 1988, California legislators were so alarmed by the incessant exposure and tacit promotion of sex in the classroom, they made it a law that the schools had to teach abstinence from sex as a viable alternative to the presumption of sexual activity so prominent in the schools.

The law's text stated, "...the California teen pregnancy rate has tripled in the last 15 years, and that the California abortion rate for teenagers is 64.8 percent higher than the national average. This is the same period in which sex education courses became a regular part of the public school curriculum."[67]

THE MYTH OF "SELF-ESTEEM"

Among the rubble of crumbling values is a buzz-phrase we hear continuously: self-esteem.

The rule is: we must promote and preserve the child's self-esteem.

Behind this is a complete miscomprehension of where true self-worth comes from, which is *actual accomplishment*.

Instead of pushing children toward genuine achievement so they *know* they are competent and capable and thus (correctly) esteem themselves, the psychiatric concept, as we have seen, is to *tell* the child he has accomplished whether he has or not. According to this view, he must be coddled and shielded from failure or any awareness of failure so his fragile sense of self can be preserved.

A 1993 *U.S. News and World Report* article called "A for effort. Or for showing up." tells us: "At Harvard in 1992, 91 percent of undergraduate grades were B- or higher. Stanford is top-heavy with As and Bs too; only about 6 percent of all grades are Cs. At Princeton, As rose from 33 percent of all grades to 40 percent in four years.... For whatever reason (and the feel-good self-esteem movement is surely one), marks have broken free of performance and become more and more unreal. They are designed to please, not to measure or to guide students about strengths and weaknesses."[68]

Educator Larson tells us, "Children who are told they made it when they didn't absolutely despise adults. They think they are total fools. And when their whole life is like that, they become apathetic about it, because the whole world is crazy. They feel bad about hiding the truth (that they *didn't* make it) and they withdraw from the area and it produces a complete disassociation of the kid from the subject of education because it is a lie. And kids know it underneath, kids know that the only thing that causes self-esteem is confidence and production."[69]

THE FALL OF OUR CHILDREN

Once psychiatrists found themselves able to step into the classrooms via the federal legislation of 1963 and 1965, educational psychiatry became an entire industry.

Funding for "special education" reached $1 billion in 1977.[70]

According to *U.S. News and World Report*, by 1994 the special education system had ballooned into more than a $30 billion-a-year activity, with the costs still climbing.[71]

In 1975 Congress passed the Education for All Handicapped Children Act of 1975. Tacked onto the end was the inclusion of "children with specific learning disabilities."[72]

And, naturally, as the funds increased, so did the number of children found to have "learning disabilities." From 1977 to 1992 the number of "learning disabled" children in the U.S. rose from 782,085 to 2,214,326.[73]

As serious as it sounds, the term *learning disabled* simply means that despite normal or above intelligence, the student—for some reason—cannot read.

However, the definition is so ambiguous that researchers at the University of Michigan found 85 percent of the students they tested, who had previously been identified as normal, would have been classified as learning disabled under one or another of the assessment systems for learning disabilities used by diagnosticians.

Despite the obvious stigma and denigration involved with labeling a child as learning disabled (something he obviously "is" for life), schools are actually encouraged to so brand them. Why? A 1989 *U.S. News and World Report* article tells us when students are classified "LD," they qualify for the supplementary federal funds earmarked for the handicapped.[74]

In spite of a vast input of funds into these programs, reports to Congress show that nearly seven out of ten special education students drop out, "age out"(reach their 22nd birthday), are expelled, or leave school with unearned diplomas. Perhaps one or two out of ten complete a standard high school curriculum of any kind.

Currently 26 percent of U.S. public school students are in special education classes. In other countries, just 1 to 3 percent are unable to learn in regular classes.[75]

So indoctrinated are teachers with the notion that there is something inherently wrong with slow-learning children that a 1981 nationwide Teachers Survey found teachers considered 57.7 percent of all students somehow defective and in need of special extracurricular help.[76]

This, of course, is taking the concept of irresponsibility to such a low it becomes betrayal. Teachers who no longer know how to teach claim the children are defective.

In a 1994 article in the *Right to Read Report*, Regna Lee Wood, a woman who began her teaching career shortly after WWII, commented, "These grim statistics show that 80 percent of the Special Education students were born seventy years too late. For virtually all of the 4 million with normal intelligence and no limiting physical disabilities could and would have learned to read in regular first- and second-grade phonics classes in the Twenties and early Thirties. Proof is in the scores on 17 million academic military tests taken by World War II registrants who could read at today's fifth-grade level."[77]

The psychiatric community, however, has not taken such a simple view of the problem. They see the child who fails to learn as sick.

French psychiatrist Robert Castel remarked on this in his 1982 book *The Psychiatric Society*. "It is common knowledge," he wrote, "that the American educational system is particularly inefficient in some areas. Perhaps this is why cause and effect are often reversed, and pupils are made responsible for the poor performance of the school system—a conspicuous example of blaming the victim. More than in other countries, there is in the United States a tendency to diagnose failure and maladjustment as effects of individual problems or maladies; psychological therapy and/or drugs are then prescribed as appropriate treatments."[78]

The nail in the coffin came when psychiatry listed an array of learning troubles as *mental disorders* in their diagnostic bible, the *DSM*. These include Arithmetic Learning Disorder, Developmental Expressive Writing Disorder, and Developmental Reading Disorder.

A sample description: "Developmental Reading Disorder...Reading achievement, as measured by a standardized, individually administered test, is markedly below the expected level, given the person's schooling and intellectual capacity (as determined by an individually administered IQ test)."[79]

Another diagnosis bandied about freely in educational circles is *dyslexia*. Eight percent of America's children are said to have this affliction, an alleged defect in the language center of the brain that prevents literacy in the early grades.[80]

No explanation is offered as to how past illiteracy rates could have been so low if 8 percent of the population had this disorder.

Pediatric neurologist Fred Baughman remarked in a 1993 article, "What parents and teachers are usually not told, however, is that over sixty years of research have failed to confirm that a defect of any sort exists in the brain of a child who has been labeled dyslexic. Sadly, maintaining this condition to be fact is doing incredible damage to these individuals and to the country."[81]

The most aggressive diagnostic labeling of children, however, came on the scene as ADD or Attention Deficit Disorder. Currently the *DSM IV* lists it as ADHD or Attention Deficit/Hyperactivity Disorder.

When we interviewed Baughman in 1995, he said, "On this ADHD thing, I have been a very busy clinician and a busy physician all these years, and I am someone who has some scientific credentials and have in my own practice discovered new diseases. I have been looking at all these children said by their schools, by psychiatrists and pediatricians to have all these diseases and I have been looking at them very carefully. Looking at the interaction of the school with that child, I don't find anything wrong with the child. I am finding something wrong with the schools."[82]

This psychiatric disorder is said to affect 40 percent of boys and 17 percent of girls.[83] Considering that 26 percent of public school children are in special education classes for the disabled—primarily *learning* disabled—this would mean that more than 50 percent of the nation's male children have mental disorders by psychiatric standards—just from ADHD and LD alone.

Its symptoms, as listed in the *DSM IV*, include:

1. Often does not seem to listen when spoken to directly.
2. Often has difficulty organizing tasks and activities.
3. Often loses things necessary for tasks or activities.
4. Is often easily distracted by extraneous stimuli.
5. Is often forgetful in daily activities.
6. Often fidgets with hands or feet or squirms in seat.
7. Is often "on the go" or often acts as if "driven by a motor."
8. Often talks excessively.
9. Often blurts out answers before questions have been completed.
10. Often has difficulty awaiting turn.[84]

While many may be amused by these extravagant statistics and the above catalogue of common childhood behavior, the reality is there is nothing funny about ADHD.

The standard treatment of choice is drugs.

The commonly used medication—stimulants such as Ritalin, Dexedrine, Cylert—tripled in production from 1990 to 1994.[85]

ADHD is said to account for ⅓ to ½ of all children mental health referrals.[86]

The most popular drug, Ritalin, is currently used by as many as one million U.S. children.[87] Ritalin is addictive and its withdrawal symptoms have included suicide. *The International Journal of the Addictions*, published in 1986, listed 105 different adverse reactions from this drug.

A 1975 study in the *Canadian Medical Association Journal* reported, "Findings suggest that children who take [Ritalin] even in moderate doses for several years may in some cases fail to grow at expected rates."[88]

The manufacturer of Ritalin, CIBA Pharmaceutical Company published the following warning in 1985:

"DRUG DEPENDENCE

Ritalin should be given cautiously to emotionally unstable patients, such as those with a history of drug dependence or alcoholism, because such patients may increase dosage on their own initiative.

"Chronically abusive use can lead to marked tolerance and physic dependence with varying degrees of abnormal behavior. Frank psychotic episodes can occur, especially with parental abuse. Careful supervision is required during drug withdrawal, since severe depression as well as the effects of chronic overactivity can be unmasked."[89]

Some cases in point:

1. On July 20, 1987, two parents found their 16-year-old son hanging from the ceiling of their garage. The noose was fashioned from a water skiing rope. He had been undergoing Ritalin withdrawal after nine years on the drug to treat his "hyperactivity."

2. In one high-profile Massachusetts case, teenaged Ritalin user Ron Matthews killed a fellow classmate with a baseball bat. He had been using the drug since the age of seven and was withdrawing from it when he exploded in 1986.

3. In 1993, another Massachusetts youth, Gerard McCra shot his parents and sister to death. He was 15 and had been on Ritalin since the age of six. In spite of the vivid 1986 warning about "frank psychotic episodes" (McCra was reportedly abused by his parents), a *Boston Globe* article on the story opened with, "There is no scientific evidence indicating that Ritalin causes or in any way triggers violence in children who take the commonly prescribed medication for hyperactivity, medical specialists said yesterday."[90]

It seems reasonable to assume that if drug treatment really *is* the right thing to do for the child, his school performance would improve.

The facts, however, show differently:

1 (*The Learning Mystique*, 1987): "…all the conclusions converged: 'stimulant drugs have little, if any impact on…long-term academic outcome.'"

2. (*American Journal of Orthopsychiatry*, 1976): "…we again find no support for the assumption that 'learning'—in any general sense—improves as a consequence of drug treatment."

3. (*Journal of Abnormal Child Psychology*, 1981): "The belief that long-term

drug intervention will continue to be of value or produce better outcome in hyperactive children has not been substantiated by this or other studies."

4. (*Journal of Learning Disabilities*, 1983): "The ideal dose for the suppression of conduct problems may actually impair cognitive performance or neutralize beneficial cognitive effects which, theoretically could negate any beneficial effect on academic achievement or even exacerbate the child's learning problems."

5. (*Journal of Applied Behavior Analysis*, 1975): "The present results suggest that continued use of Ritalin and possibly other drugs to control hyperactivity may result in compliant but academically incompetent students.... The control of hyperactivity by medication, while effective, may be too costly to the child, in that it may retard his academic and social growth, a human cost that schools and society can ill afford."

Educator Larson told us that in his personal experience with children who have been on Ritalin long periods, "...as near as I can tell, and this is completely unscientific, but by our work with them, they have got brain damage. The tragedy is deepened by the fact that the labeling of children with ADD is not because of a problem the kids have; it is because of a problem teachers who cannot tolerate active children have."[91]

Neurologist Baughman noted that perhaps the most repugnant aspect of all is that these children believe they have something wrong with their brains that makes it impossible for them to control themselves without using a pill. And the most important adults in their lives, their parents and teachers, believe this as well.[92]

Another approach to treating children, even normal children has been the psychological approach. Thomas K. Fagan, Professor and Coordinator of School Psychology Programs at Memphis State University, studies the growth in number of school psychologists and estimated their growth as follows in 1993:

1920	. . . . .200 psychologists in schools
1940	500
1950	1000
1960	3000
1970	5000
1980	10,000
1990	. . . . .22,000[93]

There is little surprise, then, to find that their influence has mushroomed in the past decade in the form of classes, "sensitivity training," "role playing," psychological testing, counseling, etc. Often entire classrooms of normal children are required to partake in these activities.

The intent of these programs is to get children to look within themselves, to place great emphasis on their feelings and emotions.

An example—one of a great many—is the "Stress Test" put out by the Center for Applied Research in Education in 1986.

Part of it is a list of about 80 items that may cause stress. The child is instructed: "On the checklist below, put a check mark on the line before those things that make you feel stress."

At the end of the list, he is told, "Count the number of things that make you feel stress. Is this number higher than you thought? Why or why not? Is this good or bad?"

Next come signs of stress. The child checks off items among over 40 symptoms like headaches, depressed, bored with life. He is then asked, "Looking at the chart, how often do you show or feel signs of stress? Is this good or bad? Is there anything you can do to help yourself? Do you think your relative is suffering from stress? If yes, what can you do to help?"

The child does a "stress inventory." He chooses from 40 different stressful situations, which apply to him. Each has a numerical value. At the bottom, it says, "My stress inventory is _____. *Remember!!* The higher the number, the *more* stress you're experiencing. Are you surprised with your total for your stress inventory? Why or why not? Is there anything you can do to *reduce* the stress you are under?"

If our children are being told they should avoid stress—and such things as marriage, the ladder of success, even fidelity and integrity cause stress—if they are being told they are incapable because of a bad brain which they can do nothing about, and if they hear these things from the mouths of their own mentors as absolute gospel, what kind of a future do these children have?

MORE OF THE SAME

Today a new Era of Educational Reform rises on the horizon. It is called Outcome-Based Education or OBE.

According to Ron Sunseri, author of the 1994 book *OBE*,

Understanding the Truth about Education Reform, this program, among other things:

"1. De-emphasizes academics and focuses on changing behavior, attitudes, and feelings.

2. Holds top achievers back from further learning by making them teach the slower students.

3. Performs psychological tests on your children.

4. Keeps your children from graduation if they disagree with the values taught in school."

It doesn't sound much like reform. In fact, it sounds familiar.

The eugenicist will probably tell us the trouble in our schools is because of a mingling of bad blood and the perpetuation of hereditary incompetence.

The psychiatrist may tell us it is because our children have disorders and need less stress and more treatment.

Most likely, the psychologist will tell us the school kids are simply responding to bad stimuli as all animals do.

Unfortunately, these pronunciamentos have not garnered us better, more capable children.

Indeed, if we look around us, we see quite the opposite.

But if we look honestly at the history of all this…

If we go back to where education was doing well and children thrived… and then come forward…

We can see where things went awry.

There are exact reasons for our educational decline.

Perhaps the only shining star in this tale of turmoil is that, knowing these reasons, we can do something about it.

And with that we may save not only our children, but an entire civilization.

CHAPTER X

THE DEPRIVATION OF HUMAN RIGHTS

AT THE HEIGHT OF WORLD WAR II, 16 MENTAL DEFECTIVES WERE placed in refrigerated cabinets to study the effect of frigid temperatures on mental disorders.

For each, his sole source of comfort was a mattress covered with sheets.

The temperature was dropped to as low as a sub-freezing 30 degrees Fahrenheit for periods lasting as long as 120 hours.

Body temperatures declined to as low as 81.8 degrees.

The observing scientists noted clinically, "The chief complications resulting from the treatment were skin injuries from ice and respiratory infections.... The respiratory infections were more serious and were responsible for the two deaths attributable to the treatment. Five patients...had bronchitis and bronchopneumonia following treatment. These patients with two exceptions recovered after varying periods, but prolonged mental retardation and physical decay bordering on cachexia [a general wasting of the body, as with chronic disease] occurred in the survivors....

"Two deaths occurred as a direct result of the treatment.... Both these patients suffered from mental illness of long standing which quite justified the risk associated with treatment. Another patient died two months after the treatment without apparent cause."

Several years later, the Nuremburg Tribunal denounced this type of human experimentation as a violation of "moral, ethical and legal concepts."[1]

However, the doctors in charge of the refrigeration research escaped retribution from the Tribunal, because they were never tried.

They were never tried because Nuremburg authorities were only hearing the crimes of European war criminals.

This experiment happened in Ohio.

It was, in fact, published in 1943, with no apparent censure, in the prestigious American psychiatric journal *Diseases of the Nervous System*.[2]

On the subject of human rights, psychiatry has often had a somewhat different view than the majority.

Much of this would seem to come from a common theme inherent in all psychiatric thought: the concept of *otherness*.

They hold that the mentally disturbed are something "other" than normal, that they are ill, hereditarily so. They see the lunatic as someone not quite human. He is genetically deformed. He will never be normal like "us." He is strange, something "other" than us.

Thus it is hard to assign him emotions, an intellect, a capacity to love and feel and hurt.

According to psychiatric tenets, there are those among us who are subhuman. Their chromosomes carry mental illness. They have unseen brain disorders. They have dyslexia, ADD, schizophrenia. And their numbers increase constantly. We must be careful that our children don't marry them. The psychiatrically-designated "ill" take on the cast of nameless foreigners.

In addition to the "ill" there are, of course, the weak, the inferior, those not endowed with the same quality of blood and intellectual substance as "us." They are the "learning disabled," the "mentally challenged," the "socially disadvantaged." They, too, are "other."

When a person becomes an "other," it becomes easier to take his rights away.

Without a flutter of conscience, we can put him in a refrigerated box and watch him shiver and degenerate for five days.

He is, after all, not one of "us" and not truly human.

It was because of philosophies and actions such as these that on April 12, 1989, the European Parliament met to formulate a "Declaration of Fundamental Rights and Freedoms."

Twenty-eight articles were listed.

Article 1 was: "Human dignity shall be inviolable."

Article 2 was: "Everyone shall have the right to life, liberty and security of person.

"No one shall be subjected to torture or to inhuman or degrading treatment or punishment."

As inalienable and universal as these rights are to most people, the psychiatric community, while claiming to endorse such a creed, has, in truth, actually practiced a slightly different faith along a slightly different path.

And, as you shall see, the ways in which human rights can be violated along this twisted path are many.

STRIPPED OF RIGHTS:
THE ORDEAL OF INVOLUNTARY COMMITMENT

On January 17, 1995, 54-year-old Chuck Volanti of Olympia, Washington, received a phone call he would never forget.

It was from a nursing home in Ohio.

"I don't know how to tell you this," the woman caller said, "but we have your mother here."

"Sure, you do," Chuck replied.

He knew it wasn't true. His mother had been dead nearly half a century.

When he was six he had seen his mother being driven away to the hospital. "That was the last time I ever saw her," he said. "Some time later, my dad said she was dead, she died in the hospital—and that was that."

Or so he thought.

Chuck's father remarried and sent his son to live with relatives.

Forty-eight years later, Chuck Volanti was thunderstruck by the news that his mother was still alive.

Equally shocking was the story of how she had vanished from his life without a trace.

In 1945, his mother, Mary, had filed unsuccessfully for divorce to end a physically abusive marriage.

The following year her husband Sam filed his own papers. He insisted Mary needed to be committed to a mental institution. Apparently basing their opinion largely on the husband's description of his wife's behavior, two doctors signed an affidavit claiming Mary showed symptoms of schizophrenia.

Ruling on the case, the judge voiced reservations about the doctors' testimony, but nevertheless ordered her committed. The woman was sent to Cleveland State Hospital.

Mary had been out of touch with her family so no one knew. When her sister Irene discovered the matter several years later, she was stunned. She knew her sister was not insane, but didn't know how to correct the situation. "I didn't have enough money for an attorney and couldn't fight it," she said.

So she visited regularly and watched her sister deteriorate as life in a mental institution took its toll. "If you were sent there and stayed there two days, you'd be nuts too," Irene remarked. "She wasn't crazy. But after a while, I think she just gave up."

In 1974 the mental hospital closed and Mary, now 52, was moved to a nursing home. The papers authorizing her transfer said simply, "Condition: Improved."[3]

It wasn't until January, 1995 that the nursing home traced Chuck Volanti and called to tell him his mother was still alive. And it wasn't until March that they were finally reunited.

As incredulous as it may seem, Mary's story is not isolated. Every year 1.5 to 2 million people are involuntarily committed to mental hospitals in America.[4]

The committed individual has, in truth, fewer rights than even a convicted criminal.

The normal and basic human rights we have come to expect, rights granted even to killers or terrorists, are denied people who have been labeled mentally disordered. The "burden of proof" for civil committal is largely based only on "probable cause," "reasonable grounds," or a "reason to believe" there is a danger to self or others.

By contrast, for any alleged criminal to be convicted of a crime and incarcerated, his illegal act has to be proven "beyond reasonable doubt."

"The fact that psychiatric imprisonment is called 'civil commitment'" said Thomas Szasz, "is, of course, simply part of the linguistic deception characteristic of the mental-health system. Since civil commitment results in the loss of liberty, and subjects the victim to health hazards at the hands of medical criminals whose ostensible healing function is legitimized by the state, it entails far greater deprivation of rights than does incarceration in prison, a penalty carefully circumscribed by constitutional guarantees and judicial safeguards."[5]

Laws vary by state in the U.S., but generally four procedures are used to incarcerate people against their will.

Under most U.S. state laws it has to be determined that persons are a danger to themselves or others or are "gravely disabled."

According to some laws, however, the practical realities are that if you are found walking down the street intoxicated or if you get into a violent altercation with your neighbor, either would be sufficient cause to pick you up and forcibly place you under psychiatric care.

The ways in which a person can be detained are:

1. *Emergency detention.* The fastest and easiest method of commitment. It is used most often because it circumvents the judicial process and therefore deprives the person of nearly all rights. It is "the predominant commitment route in many states, especially in major cities," according to a 1984 survey of 20 states' laws and it is "often used even when no emergency actually exists." Community psychiatrists or mental health practitioners, hospital officials and peace officers only need write a statement with alleged facts showing why a person should be admitted.[6]

According to California statistics, emergency detention orders account for 60 percent of involuntary admissions. The admission usually is considered a "short-term" detention—a "72-hour hold." However, this can involve three days of drug treatment—perhaps with potent tranquilizers—against the wishes of the patient. Additionally, if the person was conveyed to the hospital by police, as is often the case, the admission particulars become a part of the permanent record against him or her.

Another frequent use of this emergency detention route is to "convert" voluntary patients to involuntary ones. Any person who voluntarily signs into a psychiatric facility may find he feels abused, gets no benefit from the treatment, or wishes to return home. If family members or doctors feel differently, "conversion" allows the victim to be rapidly switched to the involuntarily detained category. There have been cases, for example, where a patient consented to electroshock and decided after a few treatments he wanted no part of it, only to be told he was too confused by the treatment to make such a decision. That this contradicts the previously touted "beneficial" aspects of the treatment is beside the point.

2. *Semi-judicial commitment* differs from emergency commitment only in

that it does not require immediate capture and detention of the individual. A psychiatrist examines a person and certifies, in writing, that hospitalization is required. A judge then reviews the paperwork for authenticity and signs the authorization for involuntary detainment. The individual is not present at this transaction and, therefore, has no right to defend him or herself.

3. *Judicial commitment* requires court jurisdiction prior to commitment. Legal documents must be filed alleging the person should be involuntarily hospitalized. Judicial commitments are more adversarial than the first two methods. Some states give victims the right to an attorney. Though the outcome may be decided by a judge, it rarely involves a jury.

4. *Conservatorship or Guardianship* laws allow the legal guardian or conservator of someone found to be incompetent to commit that person at will, without any judicial approval or review. This presumes greatly that an earlier court procedure accurately diagnosed the victim as incompetent.

In most states, "any person with knowledge of the facts or with reliable information may file a petition for a non-emergency judicial commitment."[7]

One of the key allegations against the person facing commitment is that he is dangerous to himself or to others. However, as noted previously, even the APA has admitted to the Supreme Court that psychiatrists are no more "qualified than the general public to predict future violent behavior."[8] (It should be pointed out that the APA declaration was made defensively to defuse a lawsuit. In 1969, a family sued a therapist who had not warned them of the danger posed by his patient. Their daughter was murdered.)

Despite this clear awareness that they are no more expert than the man in the street, psychiatrists continue to hire themselves out daily to attest to the potential dangerousness of thousands of individuals. Given the psychiatric track record, as already noted, of being more wrong than right in this arena, this means that more than half of the patients—at a minimum, hundreds of thousands—are unjustly incarcerated and deprived of liberties on this single basis.

Leonard Frank of San Francisco was one such person. In the 1960s he learned firsthand what involuntary commitment was all about. "I troubled other people with my conduct," he told us, "with my beliefs and my ideas, in the things that I said and my lifestyle. The people that I troubled were the people of my own family. I had never gotten into any difficulty with the authorities, I had never been charged with any criminal activity nor had been a nuisance.

"They, my family, just couldn't deal with the kind of person I had become. I had felt that I had gone through a spiritual experience, a transformative experience, and that I had grown tremendously from the person that I had been previously, and they felt that that was really a personality change and regarded it as a totally negative thing."

So Leonard was committed.

And, as related in an earlier chapter, against his will he was given 50 insulin shock treatments and 35 electroshock treatments. He was detained in three different hospitals for a period of nine months. And his life was devastated.[9]

Although insulin shock is no longer in use, could something similar happen today?

In a word, yes.

After a national survey of psychiatric examinations in civil and criminal cases, researchers found that while the alleged mental patient's rights may appear to be granted on paper, these will routinely be abridged unless an attorney is present to defend those rights.[10]

Some states give a person the right to legal counsel, but not all. Regardless, the likely scenario is that they may be forced to pay for an attorney to defend themselves against incarceration and psychiatric treatment they don't want and which, incidentally, their insurance may have to pay for.

While in *criminal* matters one has the right to remain silent, during psychiatric examination, one's silence could be—and often is—diagnosed as being withdrawn, resistive or suffering a "Noncompliance With Treatment" disorder. Whatever is said, however, can and will be used against the individual. At last check, only two states, Wisconsin and Illinois, actually require that a respondent be notified of the right to remain silent during a mental health examination.

If the information (by the person with "knowledge" or the psychiatrist) used to commit the individual is false or the diagnosis turns out to be wrong or if the person is given treatment that physically damages him (e.g. heavy medications or shock), no psychiatrist will be held liable. He only needs to show that he acted according to statutory requirements and liability cannot be challenged. The burden of proving negligence rests with the victim.

Many states do not even require the victim be notified of his or her rights. Where they do, there are no uniform stipulations of how, by whom and—notably vague—how soon after commitment. Many don't require notification be given in understandable (non-legal, non-medical) language.

And even with the laws that *are* on the books to protect individual liberties, psychiatrist Lee Coleman claims, "All groups of professionals in the mental health system—judges, attorneys, psychiatrists, administrators, social workers, psychiatric nurses and technicians—often ignore the law because they consider the legal limitations merely a formality that need not hinder their work. They see themselves as answering to a higher authority, one that requires the patient to receive treatment no matter what."

Coleman speaks from experience. "I was party to this lawlessness," he admits, referring to his experience in a San Francisco crisis intervention unit. He has since refused to be part of involuntary commitment proceedings.[11]

Then there is the unseen—but powerfully manipulative—side to involuntary commitment: its use as a coercive tool. Coleman claims that for every person committed there are several others who sign themselves in under the threat of being incarcerated against their will.[12] Through such leverage, the individual often resigns himself to a bewildered acceptance of drugs, shock, loss of liberty—any and all "necessities" deemed by his family or psychiatric caretakers.

Such concessions are commonly demanded during a period when the individual is confused, disturbed, or overwhelmed—what would seem to be the worst time possible to be pressuring someone to sign his freedoms away or agree to mind-altering treatment.

As was the case with Mary Volanti, psychiatric detainment can end up being a life sentence. The committal process can keep a person indefinitely in the hospital, or he may be conditionally released under conservatorship orders. Conservators serve as guardians for persons deemed "mentally incompetent." In California alone, for 1990-1991, there were 22,268 "conservatorship" orders. The subjects are required to accept any treatment that is meted out to them.

The process of involuntary commitment has evolved over the years as a solution to a social problem.

It has been used to not only put away the person who is a threat to public security but also the person who behaves peculiarly or lives his life in unconventional ways. And, of course, as with Mrs. Volanti and many others, it has been used by a spouse who simply wants to get rid of his partner. All it takes is a gullible or complicitous psychiatrist. Unfortunately, as we show, these are not all people with the highest ethical or moral standards.

To be sure there are people in our world who are prone to violent outbursts or do anything and everything imaginable that is disruptive to family and public order. But the traditional handling has been to put such people where they will no longer bother anyone. This is a *policing* function, and of course, must be done in some form and under certain circumstances if we are to live in peace.

However, over the past two centuries, psychiatry has gradually altered this to become a *medical* or *therapeutic* function, i.e. the individual so policed must now be treated.

This is *not* a traditional legal concept.

It is a psychiatric one.

And it has gradually clouded the police function so much that today one commonly hears someone "should be committed" simply because he is odd. He "needs treatment."

The law has become so backwards that the 1966 U.S. Court of Appeals in the District of Columbia declared an involuntary patient has a right to treatment, based on the notion "that if an inmate is being kept in a mental institution against his will, he must be given proper medical [including psychiatric] treatment or else the inmate can obtain his release at will in spite of the existence or severity of his mental illness."[13]

In short, the court declared an involuntary patient cannot simply be left alone to gather his thoughts. He *must* be treated.

Again, the source of this idea is psychiatric.

It is generally propounded by the profession as an act of human kindness: it is cruel to leave the demented or disturbed in their current tormented state.

However, such a claim is premised on the assertion that they have helpful treatments to begin with, a supposition which is debatable at best. In fact, as pointed out, psychiatric treatment can often create violence or mental states of incompetence—which would give cause for further incarceration.

Also, this act of kindness is being perpetrated on someone who clearly does not wish it, who may well have rationally considered he does not want to be drugged or shocked because such treatments are dangerous and harmful to his state of mind. And involuntary treatment is just that: involuntary. Yet he can and will be subjected to forced drugging, at a minimum—and all the ensuing consequences—regardless of his own desires to keep his thought processes as they are.

While no doubt involuntary commitment has been used to corral destructive raving lunatics, it has also been and continues to be amply utilized to incarcerate the individual who does not "get his mind right" and go along with parents, school officials, law officers, or perhaps the county psychiatrist.

A 1994 *Los Angeles Times* article tells the story of a thin 20-year-old homeless woman named Tressa who liked to sit on a certain park bench in New York. She wore five layers of clothing. "The holes in her jeans were stuffed with cardboard. Her shoes were wrapped in silver duct tape.

"She had occupied the same bench every day, all day, for the last five months. A psychiatrist and a nurse, members of an outreach organization called Project Help, were trying one last time to persuade her to enter the Bellevue Hospital Center psychiatric ward voluntarily.

"Eyes wide with fear, Tressa refused, as she had for five months. 'There's a time and place for everything,' she told them. 'Even though I'm just sitting here, I certainly hope I'm not drifting from reality. I have a strong belief in God. He has always let me know when the right moment comes.'

"Within hours...invoking special authority recently granted to health professionals, a Project Help psychiatrist took Tressa to Bellevue, despite her pleas to be left alone in the tiny triangle park where she felt safe."[14]

Psychiatric intervention is essentially a dictate that certain individuals do not have a right to their mental views and must be compelled to think otherwise.

If psychiatrists did not believe this, their use would be strictly limited to controlling not thought but illegal and disruptive behavior, which is a police function, not a medical one.

In his book, *Psychiatric Slavery*, Szasz says, "When people do not know 'what else' to do with, say, a lethargic, withdrawn adolescent, a petty criminal, an exhibitionist, or a difficult grandparent—our society tells them, in effect, to put the 'offender' in a mental hospital. To overcome this, we shall have to create an increasing number of humane and rational alternatives to involuntary mental hospitalization. Old-age homes, workshops, temporary homes for indigent persons whose family ties have been disintegrated, progressive prison communities—these and many other facilities will be needed to assume the tasks now entrusted to mental hospitals."[15]

As to the dangerous person, Szasz points out in *The Therapeutic State*, "...in American law, dangerousness is not supposed to be an abstract psychological condition attributed to a person; instead, it is supposed to be an inference drawn from the fact that a person has committed a violent act that is illegal, has been charged with it, tried for it, and found guilty of it. In which case, he should be punished, not 'treated'—in a jail, not in a hospital."[16]

Indeed, we must deal with and morally assist the violently insane, the suicidal, the socially destructive.

However, the moment we enter the psychiatric idea that such an individual must have his mind involuntarily treated "for his own good," we have begun—in no small measure—to strip away his liberties. And we have, in effect, become "thought police."

For who among us wants to let another decide how his mind should be manipulated "for his own good."

"I have sworn upon the altar of God," wrote Thomas Jefferson in 1800, "eternal hostility against every form of tyranny over the mind of man."[17]

Unfortunately, when it involves psychiatry, involuntary treatment is only one such form of tyranny.

When Treatment Turns to Rape

"Barbara Noel felt herself floating toward consciousness. It was Friday, Sept. 21, 1984, and she was in her psychiatrist's office in Chicago, waking from a dose of sodium amytal, a barbiturate he had been giving her in order to help her explore her subconscious. This morning, though, instead of awakening dreamily by herself, she says she felt a weight on top of her. A man was breathing heavily onto her shoulder. Still sedated, Noel moaned and stirred. The breathing stopped, and the body on top of her carefully lifted away. Pretending to sleep, Noel opened her eyes a crack. She could make out a person standing at a sink with his back to her. He was bald, with a tan back and stark white buttocks. Noel's heart stopped. The man, she says, was Dr. Jules Masserman, her psychiatrist of 18 years."[18]

Jules Masserman was the 1979 president of the American Psychiatric

301

Association. Although denying the charges made against him, he paid malpractice settlements to Noel and three other women and signed an agreement to never again practice therapy in the United States.[19]

Some 2400 years ago the Hippocratic Oath was fashioned to decree, "Whatever houses I may visit, I will come for the benefit of the sick, remaining free of all intentional injustice, of all mischief and in *particular* of sexual relations with both female and male persons, be they free or slaves." (Emphasis added.)

The relationship between doctor and patient has always held a sacred trust. One aspect involves confidentiality, for the patient often reveals personal and intimate matters to the physician.

The bond of the therapeutic counselor has been equally deemed sacrosanct. The seeker of help ofttimes bares his or her soul completely to such an advisor, exposing weaknesses, placing himself or herself unquestioningly in his hands.

At times like these the patient has an inherent right to assume his or her vulnerability will not be exploited.

There is the right to assume one's confidentiality will not be betrayed.

There is the right to assume information revealed will not be used to extort, rob, or exact some other advantage.

There is the right to assume that in moments of turmoil, weakness or loneliness, frail passions will not be seduced.

There is the right to assume that one will not be used for the counselor's personal gratification in the name of therapy.

There is the right to assume one's physical being will not be molested.

And there is the right not to be raped.

Unfortunately, these very human rights have not always been observed by members of the psychiatric profession. On the contrary, instances of violations seem to spring into the media with abundant, and perhaps increasing, regularity.

Though it has become the subject of much discussion, it has shown no sign of diminishing.

In *Sexual Intimacy Between Therapists and Patients*, Kenneth Pope and Jacqueline Bouhoutsos list 10 common scenarios that summarize situations of therapist-client sex:

1. *Role Trading:* Therapist becomes the "patient" and the wants and

needs of the therapist become the focus.

2. *Sex Therapy:* Therapist fraudulently presents therapist-patient sexual intimacy as a valid treatment for sexual or other kinds of difficulties.

3. *As If...:* Therapist treats patient's attraction to him as something separate from the therapeutic situation, therefore not bound by its rules.

4. *Svengali:* Therapist creates and exploits an exaggerated dependence on the part of the patient.

5. *Drugs:* Therapist uses cocaine, alcohol, or other drugs as part of the seduction.

6. *Rape:* Therapist uses physical force, threats, and/or intimidation.

7. *True Love:* Therapist uses rationalizations that attempt to discount the clinical/professional nature of the relationship with its attendant responsibilities.

8. *It Just Got Out of Hand:* Therapist fails to treat the emotional close-ness that develops in therapy with sufficient attention, care, and respect.

9. *Time Out:* Therapist fails to acknowledge and take account of the fact that the therapeutic relationship does not cease to exist between scheduled sessions or outside the therapist's office.

10. *Hold Me:* Therapist exploits patient's desire for nonerotic physical contact and possible confusion between erotic and nonerotic contact.[20]

Pope and Bouhoutsos, both psychologists who have studied the problem of therapist-patient sex extensively and have counseled its victims, give us a fictitious example of psychiatric rape from category six above. Though it is a hypothetical situation, it is based on their experiences of accounts by actual victims:

"Karen is a 14-year-old victim of incest. Dr. Louis, a hypnotherapist, is treating her for the incest trauma. He makes her lie on his couch and attempts to put her in a deep trance. She is so nervous that she is unable to concentrate on what he is saying. She does not trust him, does not want to be seeing him, and lies on the couch, her face covered by her hands, crying.

"He says it looks as if she needs reassurance, and he lies down next to her. He tells her she has nothing to be afraid of, that he will protect her and comfort her. He presses himself against her and, before she can scream, puts his hand over her mouth. He holds her so that she can neither cry nor move. He rapes her.

"When he is finished he tells her it never happened, that she is crazy and imagined the whole thing. He tells her that if she tries to tell anyone that no one will believe her. Everyone will believe that she is psychotic and needs to be put away in a hospital. If she tries to tell anyone, they will know that she was just making up stories about the incest, so they will either return her to her father or put her in jail. No matter where they put her, he will still be in charge of her treatment and they will always believe a famous hypnotherapist rather than a hysterical little girl who is always making up fantastic stories that show what a dirty mind she has. He may even tell them that she tried to seduce him and told him that she had made up the stories about the incest because she had been unable to seduce her father. He told her that if she tried to tell anyone what she had imagined had happened, that he would prescribe drugs that would make her a vegetable and might operate on her brain. If he felt like it, he might arrange for her to die. As she got dressed to leave, he slapped her to stop her from crying. He told her not to be late for their next appointment."[21]

Pope and Bouhoutsos also point out that Masters and Johnson, the well-known researchers in human sexuality, have claimed that therapists who use their power to engage in sexual intimacies with patients should be charged with rape. "In this sense," we are told, "all sexual intimacy within the context of a therapeutic relationship constitutes a form of rape."[22]

Dr. Gary Shoener concurs, pointing out the view is the same in the courts of his state. He runs a Walk-in Center in Minnesota that services women who have been abused by their therapists. "Consent is no defense," he stated. "So even if it looks like the patient had a romance with the therapist, if it happened during the course of the professional relationship, it is a felony...statutory rape.... It means that if you prove it happened, you don't have to prove anything else."[23]

As an indication of how difficult such encounters are on patients, a 1983 study by Bouhoutsos of 559 women found that 90 percent suffered ill effects from sexual involvement with their therapist. One percent committed suicide.[24]

In an earlier chapter, we noted a 1986 study that found that 6.4 percent of psychiatrists had committed such psychiatric *rape*, as Masters and Johnson call it. However, the authors of the report state, "We assume that our data can provide only conservative estimates of the prevalence of psychiatrist-patient sexual contact. Some offenders are undoubtedly so concerned about confidentiality, despite assurances of anonymity, that they would never return a questionnaire of this nature."[25]

Other estimates put the figures much higher.[26]

Psychiatrist Nannette Gartrell, a member of the APA Committee on Women claimed in 1986 that many women patients in increasing numbers were not only filing complaints with the APA Ethics Committee, but also malpractice complaints against psychiatrists for sexual abuse.

"It became clear," she said, "that this was a problem which potentially was affecting large numbers of women patients throughout the country and undoubtedly larger numbers than we were even hearing about."[27]

And the complaints continued to pour in. Six years later APA president Lawrence Hartmann told the association, "For posterity's sake, I would like to record that perhaps never in the history of the American Psychiatric Association has an APA president been called upon to spend so much of his time considering psychiatrist-patient sexual contact as this year."[28]

Despite a dramatic rise in complaints, a 1987 study shows that though 65 percent of psychiatrists hear of such sexual abuse through their clients, only 8 percent report them. This in spite of the fact that psychiatric rape not only violates professional codes but in some states is strictly illegal.[29]

Perhaps one damper that prevents complaints from being filed is the APA's own unwillingness to deal with the matter. In commenting on one case in which a female APA member filed a complaint against her own psychiatrist, Gartrell said, "In her perception the structure works to the perpetrator's benefit. The matter took 3 years and 11 months to be resolved. During this time she stated that she was pressured by her residency training director to stop the complaint even after the Ethics Committee had voted to censure her former therapist. She concluded, 'I would never refer a patient of mine to the Ethics Committee because the process was so traumatic to me, and because ultimately I was not believed or the abuse was seen as insignificant, worthy of one year suspension. I just keep wondering who the Ethics Committee believes if not a fellow psychiatrist in good standing, at a good residency.'"[30]

A 1984 Wisconsin Task Force into psychiatric sexual abuse reported, "Quiet crimes, such as abuse by [psychiatrists] are, much like incest, accompanied by so much embarrassment and disbelief that public avoidance and denial continue to be the primary response to revelations."

It is noteworthy that Masters and Johnson mince no words in calling psychiatrist-client sex rape. Yet the culprit professions, psychology and psychiatry, seem to soften the blow considerably through their euphemisms for the same subject. Pope and Bouhoutsos refer to it as "sexual intimacy" and the *American Journal of Psychiatry* calls it "psychiatrist-patient sexual contact."[31]

This may speak volumes as to how seriously these professions actually view these encounters. And it may go a long way towards explaining why they have had so little success in their apparent efforts to police the ranks.

Like other "nonjudgmental" and "values neutral" phrasing that psychiatry seems to enjoy, "psychiatrist-patient sexual contact" says nothing of the damage this activity inflicts or even whether it is good or bad.

If the psychiatric community were, indeed, to refer to it as rape, as Masters and Johnson call it, this would considerably enhance their avowed mission to bring about change.

Should we be surprised to find such a closet full of sexual abuse in this profession?

Perhaps not. As we saw, they (and their spouses) rank number one among physicians who have trouble with extramarital affairs.

They have long preached the foolishness and stressfulness of morality.

Their primary philosophy is that they are mere bodies ruled by biochemistry and, therefore, like all other humans, who are rife with irresistible impulses and diminished capacities, there are times when they cannot help themselves.

The majority of the profession are atheists and agnostics, thus have no religious standards to answer to.

Its leaders—as we have seen with Menninger, Freud, Harry Stack Sullivan—have frequently and consistently demonstrated personal sexual misconduct and/or the promotion of it to others. A 1990 *U.S. News and World Report* article comments, "Many practitioners, among them some of Freud's disciples—even married former patients or conducted lengthy affairs with them in full public view."[32]

Given such a track record, are we to be shocked to hear the profession's members can't seem to bring their passions under control?

And perhaps more to the point, should we be baffled that the psychiatric community seems to be so ineffectual at putting discipline into its own?

As to what the leaders of the profession are doing about it, the truth is, in 1988 a study by Kenneth Pope reveals a higher incidence of sexual abuse among prominent practitioners—tenured professors and chairmen of ethics committees—than among the rank and file.[33]

So resigned was one 50-year-old psychiatrist to his colleagues' disreputable behavior that when asked about mandatory reporting of psychiatric sexual assault, he responded, "It would add another PR nail in our professional image's coffin."[34]

There is also another reason why the APA is reluctant to take a firm stance against sexual abuse within the ranks. If mandatory reporting or such were to go in, the number of exposed psychiatrists would leap. And so would the cost of malpractice insurance.

One former APA president and current Harvard law professor commented, "We should all realize that there is a serious conflict of interest between the APA's professional concerns for the victims of sexual exploitation in therapy and its financial concerns when the association's economic interests are at serious risk."[35]

The association's failure to keep its house in order has compelled state legislatures—fifteen as of 1995—to pass laws outlawing psychiatric sexual misconduct, making it punishable by fines and/or imprisonment. In California, for example, a victim has cause to recover damages from a therapist if the sexual involvement takes place within two years after psychotherapy ends. This legal trend is rising. In 1990 only five states had such laws.[36]

Thomas Szasz, commenting bluntly on his profession's penchant for sexual misconduct, said, "This is intellectual bankruptcy compounded by moral paralysis. The assertion that sexual contact...may be therapeutic for the patient is self-serving and stupid. Using it to justify such sexual contacts is illogical and immoral."[37]

The following are a small sampling of recent cases of psychiatric sexual abuse: The first two case histories are from interviews; names have been withheld to protect those assaulted:

• A Utah woman who began seeing a psychiatrist in the late 1970s noted that over the years he made sexual comments to her and let it be known he wanted to have a sexual relationship with her. After the woman's marriage broke up, the psychiatrist began to ask her out, insisting that since she was no longer his patient, there was no impropriety. However, he *was* prescribing her a highly addictive drug. One night the psychiatrist asked the woman to come to his then-deserted office for a meeting. When the woman got there, the psychiatrist raped her. After this point, the sexual assaults continued, with the woman relenting. She was addicted to the drugs he prescribed to her and he had implied that he would cut her off if she didn't cooperate. In 1990, the woman finally stopped seeing him and later reported him to Utah's licensing board. The psychiatrist has since lost his license.

• In 1993, a young Florida policewoman went undercover to investigate a Florida psychiatrist suspected of abusing prescription drugs. Much to her dismay, after the psychiatrist thought he had successfully hypnotized her, he tried to pull off her clothes and rape her. Fortunately, fellow officers were nearby. The psychiatrist was arrested. He was subsequently investigated for sexually assaulting and abusing other female patients, while they were under hypnosis. The psychiatrist was 71 years old at the time of the incident.

• In June 1991, Canadian psychiatrist James Tyhurst was sentenced to four years in prison for sexual assaults on four psychiatric patients who said he led them to believe they must enter master-slave relationships as a condition of therapy. He was a professor emeritus at the University of British Columbia. Tyhurst's defense was complete denial that the incidents of nudity, whippings and sexual acts, as described by four women complainants, ever took place.[38]

• In March 1988, an Australian behavioral science student at Melbourne University assaulted and sexually penetrated a seven-year-old girl and videotaped the rape. When it came time to face criminal charges, James Spencer claimed the interlude was actually "psychological research." Psychiatrist Neville Yeomans of Sydney came to Spencer's defense by insisting that child rape is acceptable in certain psychiatric situations and contending that the child in the video appeared to be "enjoying" it. Taping such a sexual assault against a seven-year-old, he said, would be an acceptable psychiatric practice if made by psychiatric research workers under "proper" direction and protocol. The judge did not agree. Spencer was sent to prison for five years.[39]

• In April 1988, Louis J. Poetter, founder and director of the Anneewakee psychiatric center for adolescents in Douglasville, Georgia, pleaded guilty to nineteen counts of sodomizing young boys brought to the center for treatment and was sentenced to eight years in prison and twelve years probation. According to testimony of workers at the center, Poetter encouraged sex between staff and children as "good for the boys," and himself engaged in frequent homosexual relations with the young-sters. Nearly two years later, a $35 million settlement—believed to be the largest in Georgia's history—was reached in eight lawsuits arising from the scandal.[40]

• Another psychiatrist, Markham Berry of Atlanta, molested children for more than half a century, according to a government source involved in the investigation. In July 1986, Berry pleaded guilty to sexually abusing six boys who were sent to him for help, one of whom reported that Berry had molested him from the time he was seven until he reached puberty. Another of the children, sent to Berry for hyperactivity when he was eight, was undressed and molested during every visit over a three-year period. The boy had kept quiet for fear his father would be angry with his mother for having sent him to a psychiatrist in the first place.[41]

• In June 1994, New Jersey psychiatrist, Dr. John W. Schermer, Jr. was fined $60,000 by the State Administrative Law Judge for sexual abuse of a patient. His license was permanently revoked and he was ordered to pay two patients $10,500 and to refund monies to patients who had paid for therapy with him.

• A Riverside, California, psychiatrist, Dr. Paul Lowinger was charged with 16 counts of grand theft, fraud and "inappropriate sexual activity" with patients and for prescribing drugs without legitimate medical pur-pose. The "psychotherapy" that Lowinger billed Medi-Cal for consisted almost entirely of having sex with the patient. The patient, Francine Rahn, was awarded $7.1 million in August 1994.

• In 1989, Dr. Paul A. Walters, psychiatrist in charge of student health at Stanford University, Massachusetts and former head of Harvard University's Health Services' Mental Health Division, was forced to resign after allegations that he had "frequent sex" with a female patient. The patient, who had been the victim of sexual abuse as a child, was awarded more than $200,000 in an out-of-court settlement. She said Walters had used her to perform oral sex on him, "sometimes as often as two out of three psychiatric analysis sessions per week."

• In 1975, a New York jury convicted psychiatrist Renatus Hartogs of malpractice, awarding $350,000 in damages to Julie Roy, a secretary at *Esquire* magazine whom Hartogs had seduced while she was his patient.

• In 1990, Robert Ferguson, a psychologist, was sentenced to two years jail in Colorado for having sex with a female patient.

• In Utah, in 1992, Donald Persson, a psychologist, pleaded guilty to state child sex-abuse charges and federal charges of transporting child pornography.

• In 1992, psychiatrist Margaret Bean-Bayog faced not only medical malpractice charges but a massive civil suit by the family of Harvard College medical school student Paul Lozano, who committed suicide after treatment with the Boston doctor. Charges alleged that Bean-Bayog used therapeutic techniques to carry out a lurid and bizarre relationship with Lozano which included sending him notes complimenting him for "phenomenal sex." Lozano killed himself after Bean-Bayog ended her relationship with him. The psychiatrist resigned her medical license before a public hearing was held. She made an out-of-court settlement of $1 million to Lozano's family.

• Early in 1992, John Hamilton, deputy medical director of the APA stepped down from office and had his license suspended for only a year—after having sexual relations with a patient who, in turn, filed a complaint. Ironically, Hamilton wrote and edited the APA peer review manual.

• In 1991, Orange County, California, psychiatrist James Harrington White, was charged with and convicted of the forced sodomy of a male patient. White was also found to have drugged young men, then videotaped himself having sex with them. The psychiatrist was also alleged to have sodomized his adopted son for years, drugged him, forced him to dress as a female, and to have given him hormones to make him look feminine. To guarantee the boy's cooperation and his silence, the doctor is said to have administered sodium pentothal and ECT with hypnosis. Even when the young man finally left home and married, his psychiatrist "father" continued the sexual abuse, ultimately castrating the young man when he discovered the man's wife was pregnant. At this point the man broke free of the psychiatrist. Several years went by and the son only came forward with the story and evidence of the abuses after the psychiatrist was arrested for sexually abusing another young man whom he had also adopted.[42]

Dennis Bauer, the Senior Deputy District Attorney for Orange County wrote, "I have been a prosecutor for 12 years and have specialized in Sexual Assaults and Child Abuse prosecutions for the past four years. Even for my background the history behind Dr. White's case is bizarre. Dr. White's view of life is perhaps more twisted than anyone he ever attempted to treat, or manipulate, as a psychiatrist."[43] White was sentenced to prison for almost seven years.[44]

THE DOCTRINE OF INFERIOR BLOOD

In 1851, Samuel A. Cartwright, a prominent Louisiana physician published an essay entitled "Report on the diseases and physical peculiarities of the Negro race" in the *New Orleans Surgical Journal*. In it, he claimed to have discovered two forms of what modern psychiatrists would call a "personality disorder."

The first was "Drapetomania." Taken from *drapetes*, a runaway slave, and mania, meaning mad or crazy, this disease, according to Cartwright, caused blacks to have an uncontrollable urge to run away from their masters. The treatment for this illness was "whipping the devil out of them."[45]

The second disorder Cartwright dubbed "Dyaesthesia Aethiopis." Like a number of psychiatric illnesses, this one affected both mind and body. Symptoms included disobedience, answering disrespectfully and refusing to work. The cure was to put the slave to some kind of hard labor, which apparently sent "vitalized blood to the brain to give liberty to the mind."[46]

Earlier than this, Benjamin Rush, the Father of American Psychiatry, had found an even worse affliction among the Negro race. After seeing a slave named Henry Moss develop white blotches on his skin until, several years later, he was mostly white, Rush concluded Moss had an illness and was only now recovering.

Rush, as mentioned in an earlier chapter, called this ailment "negritude." At a special meeting of the American Philosophical Society on July 14, 1797, the good doctor read a paper entitled "Observations intended to favor a supposition that the black Color (as it is called) of the Negroes is derived from the LEPROSY." The black man's thick lips, flat nose, and woolly hair, he claimed, were classic phenomena in leper colonies.[47]

The notion that the Negro and other races were inferior maintained a strong following among the psychiatric community. For one thing, their "man-is-an-animal" view provided strong scientific legitimacy to the eugenics movement that took root in the late 1800s.

Leading experts on the mind had no reservations making dogmatic pronouncements about the "inferior Negro race."

Psychiatrist John E. Lind of St. Elizabeth's Hospital in Washington, D.C., wrote in the *Psychoanalytic Review* in 1920, "The precocity of the children, the early onset of puberty, the failure to grasp subjective ideas, the strong sexual and herd instincts with the few inhibitors, the simple dream life, the easy reversion to savagery when deprived of the restraining influence of the whites…all these and many other things betray the savage heart beneath the civilized exterior." [48]

Their disdain was not just limited to the black man. A typical comment was by Madison Grant, an active member of the Immigration Restriction League and eugenics societies in 1916: "Sterilization should be applied to an ever widening circle of social discards, beginning always with the criminal, the diseased and the insane, and extending gradually to types which may be called weaklings rather than defectives, and perhaps ultimately to worthless race types." [49]

Any evidence that disproved these racist theories was hastily ridiculed or even squelched. The discovery of the disease *pellagra* was a typical example.

For centuries, pellagra, which affects the immune system and lowers one's resistance to infection, was misdiagnosed variously as leprosy, scurvy, and syphilis. This became a political issue when the high rate of disease-caused absenteeism among the poor-white field hands impacted the textile mills. The U.S. Public Health Service put their field investigator for infectious diseases, Joseph Goldberger, onto the problem. In 1914, Goldberger found the cause, cure, and way to prevent pellagra.

He observed that the disease was common in asylums but did not occur among the rich or moderately well-off, except from noneconomic causes such as alcoholism. Poor and institutionalized people—living mostly on corn, which is high in starch and sugar content—lacked the more expensive meats and dairy products that are the main source of vitamin B. From this and other research, Goldberger deduced that pellagra was caused by a dietary deficiency of niacin and B complex vitamins, and he proved unequivocally that adding to the diet foods rich in these nutrients cured and prevented the disease.

Goldberger's discoveries were not eagerly accepted. They were fought strenuously by eugenic-minded psychologists, who insisted pellagra was an infectious disease caused by inferior genes, and therefore incurable. Charles Davenport, the director of the Eugenics Record Office in Cold Spring Harbor, New York, in fact, published an extensive medical report on pellagra that deliberately covered up Goldberger's findings.

In 1920, Davenport wrote an article for the American Psychological Association's bulletin that successfully discouraged any action from being taken to ease the suffering of pellagra victims.

As a result, even though the cure was known and easily obtained, the death rate from the disease increased nearly eight times between Goldberger's discovery in 1914 and his death in 1928.[50]

After scientifically asserting their theories of racial mental inferiority, psychiatrists and psychologists then set off to prove their doctrines through the development of what they called *intelligence quotient* or IQ.

According to them, native intelligence was measurable through certain tests. In 1913 psychologist Henry H. Goddard, protégé of Wundt graduate G. Stanley Hall, translated such tests developed in France and gave them to immigrants arriving at New York City's Ellis Island.

His results shocked the world. He found 83 percent of the Jews, 80 percent of the Hungarians, 79 percent of the Italians, and 87 percent of the Russians to be "feeble-minded."

Goddard's calculations ignored the fact that the tests included such inquiries as "What is Crisco?" and "Who is Christy Matthewson?"—questions entirely unsuitable for individuals not yet familiar with American life.[51]

However, he felt the test's findings were "wonderfully accurate," measuring an inherited, unchangeable capacity for intelligence. Results were even condoned for use as the deciding factor in whether a person should be involuntarily committed to a state institution for the feeble minded.[52]

When Iowa researcher J.E. Wallin used Goddard's methods to test successful businessmen and wealthy farmers in his boyhood town, all of them "proved to be morons and dangerous feeble-minded imbeciles by the standards of the Goddard tests."

Another study by investigator Mary Campbell found that the mayor and other leading officials of Chicago tested out as morons.

313

Even though these findings were presented to the American Psychological Association in 1915, Goddard's theories prevailed. He helped write tests for the U.S. Army that were interpreted to mean that many Americans were "not able to be educated." Perhaps even more distressing, the exams were used to prove that Jew and other non-Anglo-Saxon immigrants were mentally inferior. This permitted Congress, through the U.S. Immigration Act of 1924, to restrict further immigration of genetically inferior groups to small token quotas. Shamefully, the legislation ultimately denied sanctuary to millions of Jews and others who were trapped in Europe when the Nazi party came to power in 1933.

Needless to say, if the Irish, Italians, and Jews—Caucasians—were targeted for exclusion, the colored races hardly had a prayer.

In fact, when American eugenics advocate Dr. Paul Popenoe published his findings, "Intelligence and Race—a Review of the Results of the Army Intelligence Tests—the Negro in 1918," he propounded the theory that the amount of IQ in blacks was determined by the amount of white blood they had. The lighter the man's skin, Popenoe concluded, the smarter he was.

"The Negroes' low mental estate is irremediable.... The Negro is mentally, therefore, eugenically, inferior to the white race. All treatment of the Negro...must take into account this fundamental fact," he stated.[53]

By the 1950s ideas of racial inferiority were accepted knowledge in Western culture. "Everybody knew" that one's Irish temper, Scottish stinginess, or Negro laziness was in the blood.

This was more of the psychiatric philosophy of otherness. Like mental patients, non-Anglo peoples were portrayed as being a different breed of man, not altogether as human as the sentient, upright-walking scientists making these observations.

In the 1950s, black prisoners in New Orleans were used for psychosurgery experiments which involved implanting electrodes into the brain. The experiments were conducted by psychiatrist Robert Heath from Tulane University and Dr. Harry Bailey of Chelmsford fame. Bailey boasted in a lecture to nurses 20 years later that it was "cheaper to use niggers than cats because they were everywhere and cheap experimental animals."[54]

Heath had also been funded by the CIA to carry out drug experiments which included LSD and a drug called bulbocapnine, which in large doses produced "catatonia and stupor." Heath tested the drug on black prisoners at the Louisiana State Penitentiary. According to one memo, the CIA sought information as to whether the drug could cause "loss of speech, loss of sensitivity to pain, loss of memory, loss of will power and an increase in toxicity in persons *with a weak type of central nervous system.*" (Emphasis added.)

At the National Institute of Mental Health Addiction Research Center in Kentucky in the mid-1950s, drug-addicted African Americans were given LSD in another experiment. An even more unfortunate seven of them were kept hallucinating for 77 consecutive days. At this same center, healthy black men were still being used as test subjects almost 10 years later, this time for an experimental drug, BZ—which was supposedly 100 times more powerful than LSD.

In 1960, the chairman of the psychology department at Columbia University (home of Teachers College) and former president of the American Psychological Association, Henry E. Garrett, poured more fuel onto the racism fires with a pamphlet called *Breeding Down*. The average black IQ is 80, maintained Garrett, while the average white IQ is 100. Thus an interracial marriage, he warned, produces children with IQs of 90.

"It is that 10 percent differential that spells the difference between a spire and a mud hut," he declared. "Ten percent—or less—is the margin of civilization's 'profit'; it is the difference between a cultured society and savagery." [55]

In 1969, the diatribe continued. Arthur R. Jensen, a psychology professor at the University of California in Berkeley, received recognition for his article on heredity and intelligence, published in the *Harvard Educational Review*.

"'In the actual race of life,'" he wrote, "'which is not to get ahead, but to get ahead of somebody, the chief determining factor is heredity.' So said Edward L. Thorndike in 1905. Since then, the preponderance of evidence has proved him right.

"On the average, Negroes test about one standard deviation (15 IQ points) below the average of the white population in IQ," Jensen wrote.

In 1971, psychiatrist Ernst Rodin, head of the neurology department of the Lafayette Clinic in Detroit, advocated in a speech to fellow psychiatrists that "medical technology" be applied to solve the riots in Detroit's black ghetto. The methods Rodin was referring to were psychosurgery and castration. He said children with low IQs may become violent if treated as "equals," and suggested psychosurgery as a way to make them "more placid." Rodin called for "dumb young males who riot" to be castrated in much the same way as oxen:

"Farmers have known for ages immemorial that you can't do a blasted thing with a bull except fight or kill and eat him; the castrated ox will pull his plow; try to ride a young stallion and you will gladly settle for a gelding or a mare. It is also well known that human eunuchs, although at times quite scheming entrepreneurs, are not given to physical violence. Our scientific age tends to disregard this wisdom of the past."[56]

Around this same period, psychiatrist Louis Jolyon "Jolly" West was making his plans for a "violence center" in California to be used for the study of how to control urban violence. According to West, "The major known correlates of violence are sex (male), age (youthful), ethnicity (black), and urbanicity."[57]

Today this psychiatric trend continues to see something inherently wrong in the black race. A 1993 *U.S. News and World Report* article reveals that in 39 states blacks are overrepresented in special education programs. These are programs where most of the children are labeled with psychiatrically-determined "learning disabilities." (The article tells of a man who was similarly "diagnosed" as mentally retarded for 15 years. He is now dean of education at a Michigan university.)

Significantly, the figures show black students are most likely to be overrepresented in special education classes when they are students in predominantly white school districts.

The article concludes, "These findings tend to support arguments by critics of the special education system who attribute the over-representation of African-American students in the system to cultural bias in testing and placement procedures—not to any inherently high level of disability."[58]

SCIENTIFIC RACISM BECOMES LAW

Perhaps nowhere in the world in the Twentieth Century has the separation of races been so pronounced as in South Africa. How is it possible, many wonder, that a nation would adopt a policy so overtly discriminatory to the black race—in their own native land?

It indeed looks puzzling until we discover that the architect of apartheid, a man who became South Africa's prime minister, was also a psychologist.

In 1924 Dr. Hendrik Verwoerd earned his doctorate in psychology and went on to become a lecturer on the subject at Capetown's Stellenbosch University.

Two years later, he furthered his studies in psychology at universities in Hamburg, Leipzig and Berlin in Germany. At the time, of course, these institutions were immersed in the philosophy of eugenics, laced with the seeds of Nazi concepts of Aryan superiority.[59]

In *Final Solutions: Biology, Prejudice and Genocide*, Richard A. Lerner says these views characterized the black man as "slothful, unintelligent, though motorically and physically capable people, who live in crime, poverty, and generally socially deteriorated conditions, and do so because of their genetically based limited mental capacities."[60]

So in 1948, apartheid—separate development—was born as law in South Africa, bearing a striking resemblance, in word and spirit, to the German racial purity laws banning cohabitation of Aryans and non-Aryans.

Verwoerd used his scientific facade to lend a credibility to policies of "separate development" and "separate freedoms." In debating to Parliament over the education of blacks, he claimed, "Racial relations cannot improve if the result of Native education is the creation of frustrated people who, as a result of the education they received, have expectations in life which circumstances in South Africa do not allow to be fulfilled immediately, when it creates people trained for professions not open to them...."

Laws were passed in the 1950s allowing blacks to live or travel only in certain parts of the country, and requiring a "pass" for excursions outside these prescribed areas. Blacks caught breaking the "pass laws" were arrested by the police, and thousands were processed through the government into private psychiatric institutions.

Between 1960 and 1965 the number of African patients in private psychiatric institutions increased by 500 percent. And the patients were exploited as a large and cheap labor force for the benefit of numerous individuals and companies that had holdings in the institutions. Black "mental patients" were contracted out to local factories for "industrial therapy."

317

Their only pay consisted of token rewards like candy or tobacco they had grown themselves. The psychiatric business reaped large profits from both this enforced labor pool and directly from the South African government for their psychiatric "treatment."

The psychiatric institutions themselves were generally barren, bleak concrete buildings with cement or dirt floors. Barbed wire encircled the compounds. Most patients slept on the floors, and most were forced to go without such items as toilet paper, sheets, blankets, and adequate bathing and toilet facilities. Some latrines consisted of "squat" toilets running down the middle of the sleeping quarters.

With no properly equipped medical facilities in the institutions and few, if any, doctors to care for the patients when they needed help, no real treatment was administered. Instead, powerful psychiatric drugs, mostly tranquilizers, were dispensed in large volume and given daily to keep patients under control.[61]

Up to 10,000 Africans at a time were incarcerated.

Electroshock treatment was given without anaesthetic, an action that, as we have seen, is not only horrifying to the recipient, but results in broken vertebrae in a high number of cases.

According to the chief government psychiatrist, Dr. J.P. Henning, anaesthetic was denied because, "It's simply too expensive, too slow and too risky. Blacks appear to be more susceptible to the effects of anesthetics and because we treat more Blacks than Whites, we would have to double our staff if we used anesthetics."[62]

Black patients died from easily treatable illness such as pneumonia or respiratory diseases. Communal burials were allegedly performed.

The bodies of those patients who died and whose families didn't claim them were used for anatomical studies.

These were involuntarily detained patients. Discharges were few, each one authorized only by a government psychiatrist. Although these were privately owned institutions, the psychiatrists who treated the inmates were provided by the Health Department.[63]

An APA task force sent to South Africa in 1979 found an "unduly high death rate" in the camps.

At the request of the United Nations, the World Health Organization investigated conditions at the hospitals and reported:

"The living conditions of the inmates are degrading, the staffing totally inadequate, and the standards of care extremely low, not only in comparison with the service available to the white population, but also in relation to elementary and essential human needs.

"The system of private institutions for mentally ill Africans [blacks] is used also as a tool for social repression, and some of the certified inmates may have been detained only because of trivial offenses against the pass laws."[64]

The report concluded: "Although psychiatry is expected to be a medical discipline which deals with the human being as a whole, in no other medical field in South Africa is the contempt of the person cultivated by racism, more precisely portrayed than in psychiatry."[65]

THE FUTURE OF HUMAN RIGHTS

As we turn the corner into the twenty-first century, modern thought is still unable to shake the doctrine of "otherness."

Instead of recognizing that humanity, by definition, is composed of individuals who are all uniquely themselves, psychiatric doctrine of today would have us believe it is all genetic and we are little more than a mix of who our ancestors used to be.

Individuals and entire races are denounced as inferior, ill, or as having a disorder, because they do not match up to manufactured psychiatric standards of how they are supposed to behave.

Failing to understand human behavior, thus hard pressed to improve it, yet insistent upon changing it, psychiatry has chosen to categorize it into classes of deviancy, relegating people, races, almost all of us, in fact, into some label of "otherness."

But the truth be told, "otherness" is a lie.

And it feeds on human rights.

If we were to set aside this false doctrine, we would find the strange foreigner or filthy Skid Row lunatic tries to communicate as we do. He has brothers, sisters, a mother. He has preferences in food, colors, people. Perhaps he plays a musical instrument. Perhaps he likes baseball. If we make any effort at all to understand him, we find he is no "other." He may think, believe, or behave differently. His mental abilities or his capacity to deal with life may not match our own.

But that doesn't make him "other."

It makes him human.

When his dignity becomes dispensable, it is only a matter of opinion—perhaps psychiatric opinion—as to whose is next.

CHAPTER XI

THE ECONOMICS OF DECEPTION:

PSYCHIATRIC FRAUD

MASSACHUSETTS PSYCHIATRIST RICHARD SKODNEK SAYS A VOICE made him do it.

He calls the voice, "The announcer."

"I still hear the announcer tell me," he wrote in 1995, "that the only way I can convince people I am troubled is to commit suicide in the courtroom."

Skodnek claimed he did his best to reason with the voice. "When I said they have metal detectors, he said to me, 'You can shove a pen deep into your brain through your ear.'"

Skodnek was in court because he was being prosecuted for Medicaid and Medicare fraud and for the intimidation of potential witnesses. He allegedly told the mother of one patient that he would be "forced" to release her daughter's psychiatric records if she cooperated with federal law enforcement agents.

Claiming his mental problems prevented him from seeing the wrongfulness of his deeds, the psychiatrist asserted his actions were motivated not by greed, but by a desire to "protect... his beloved patients."

Prosecutors were not sympathetic. They referred to Skodnek's emotional appeal as "self-serving hearsay."[1]

As this book went to press, Dr. Skodnek and the announcer were still bargaining for leniency.

It may come as no surprise to some that, although psychiatrists make up only 8 percent of physicians, they account for 18 percent of the doctors suspended from Medicare and Medicaid programs for acts of fraud and abuse—this according to a 15-year study sponsored by the Department of Justice.

It is the worst track record of all the medical disciplines studied.[2]

When the *Atlanta Journal-Constitution* investigated allegations of Medicaid overbilling by professionals in the mental health industry, it discovered that just 10 extremely well-paid psychiatrists and psychologists personally accounted for approximately 40 percent of the $31 million in children's mental health Medicaid billings paid by the entire state of Georgia for 1994.

The cost for the psychology program alone ballooned 11 times in four years.

One psychiatrist, James E. McClendon, billed the government $12 million for his services to youngsters over a two-year period. This one man accounted for 22 percent of the Georgia Medicaid funds paid out in mental health services for children that year.

When *Journal-Constitution* reporters tried to interview these top ten mental health billers, of the five they reached (not counting McClendon), it turned out *all* had invoiced under suspicious circumstances.[3]

Charges of fraud are not new to psychiatry. Most of us have heard the entire profession referred to as fraudulent or charlatan at one time or another. Unsubstantiated claims of special inner knowledge of the mind, of being able to cure the disturbed individual, of denial of the harm inherent in various treatments—such things lend themselves to accusations of quackery and hocus-pocus swindling.

But psychiatrists have managed to fend off such charges over the past two decades by claiming they are based merely on uneducated opinion.

Some acts of deception, however, are not so easily defended.

WHEN ENOUGH IS ENOUGH

April 28, 1992 was a dark day for the psychiatric profession.

It was the day U.S. Congresswoman Pat Schroeder leveled a stern finger of accusation into the face of the entire mental health industry and let forth with scathing rebuke.

"We are here this morning," she told the House Select Committee on Children, Youth and Families, "to shed light on, and we hope help put a stop to, one of the most disgraceful and scandalous episodes in the history of health care in America. I am referring to the unethical and disturbing practices in mental health care that are taking place from coast to coast."

Schroeder said her investigation had found: thousands of adolescents, children, and adults had been hospitalized for psychiatric treatment they didn't need; hospitals hired bounty hunters to kidnap patients with mental health insurance; patients were kept against their will until their insurance benefits ran out; psychiatrists were being pressured by hospitals to alter their diagnoses to increase profit; that hospitals "infiltrated" schools by paying kickbacks to school counselors who delivered students; bonuses were paid to hospital employees, including psychiatrists, for keeping the hospital's beds filled; and military dependents were being targeted for their generous mental health benefits.

"I could go on," she said, "but you get the picture. Clearly, this *BUSINESS* OF TREATING MINDS—particularly this *BIG BUSINESS* of treating *young minds* has not policed itself, and has no incentive to put a stop to the kinds of fraudulent and unethical practices that are going on."

According to a briefing she received from the Department of Justice, psychiatric hospitals and clinics were defrauding government programs and private insurers to the tune of hundreds of millions of dollars annually. Patients had been forcibly admitted into psychiatric treatment programs in situations where they posed no threat to the community or themselves. Often patients were subjected to batteries of unnecessary blood tests, X-rays, shock treatment, and other services. Mincing no words, she told the committee they were about to witness documents, affidavits, and testimony that would show a "systematic plan to bilk patients of their hard-earned dollars, strip them of their dignity, and leave them worse off than they were before they went for help."

Representative Schroeder set the stage for a cascade of evidence that would rock even the most hardened politicians on the committee.

One of the first matters addressed was a federal program called the Civilian Health and Medical Program of the Uniformed Services, otherwise known as CHAMPUS. The mental health insurance costs for CHAMPUS had soared between 1986 and 1989. She claimed this increase could be almost entirely attributed to the inpatient treatment of children and adolescents. Reviews by the GAO (General Accounting Office) of inpatient psychiatric claims had produced some rather alarming findings.

In a third of the patients studied, records indicated that the admission was medically unnecessary or failed to substantiate that the admission was medically necessary.

Two-thirds of the cases either did not meet critical quality-of-care criteria or lacked sufficient evidence to determine that they did meet the criteria.[4]

The GAO investigation also pointed out that nobody had been watching the store—the last audit of the program had been more than 13 years earlier, and it had warned of the lack of controls over psychiatric services.

Donald Mancuso, Assistant Inspector General for Investigations for the Department of Defense (DOD)—watchdogging for the CHAMPUS program—testified that psychiatric care was an area in which it is especially difficult to prove fraud. In many cases, individuals in need of help frequently fall prey to the greed of "unscrupulous health care practitioners."

Mancuso outlined the various "schemes" psychiatrists and mental health facilities use to line their pockets. "One scenario involves the 'emergency admission'" in which a doctor fraudulently claims the patient is being admitted as an emergency so his federal insurance will cover his hospitalization in a non-military hospital.

"Investigations have also disclosed a scheme known as 'contract max.' We have found the 'contract max' fraud in psychiatric care as it concerns hospital stays. Patients have actually been kept in the hospital for extended periods because the maximum stay allowed by their insurance had not been reached."

Another scheme involved "up coding" whereby providers would bill CHAMPUS for a higher level of service than actually provided. In one instance, it found that a doctor in the Midwest used personnel who lacked the proper medical credentials or qualifications to perform the services being billed. These services were then billed to CHAMPUS as if the doctor had personally performed them. Other investigations would show this to be a common practice used to defraud insurance companies.

Instances where treatment was billed but not provided were also found. One doctor, Michael J. Griffin, was indicted in Honolulu for billing marriage and family counseling sessions that never happened. The doctor was also alleged to have engaged in sexual relations with his patients, which he then billed to CHAMPUS as counseling sessions.

Mancuso cited the case of Dr. Pang S. Leu, a psychiatrist practicing in Petersburg, Virginia who was sentenced to 126 months incarceration, five years probation, fined $100,000, and ordered to pay $722,703 in restitution. Dr. Leu had submitted false claims for psychiatric services not rendered and had dispensed Halcion and Ritalin prescription drugs without a legitimate need or purpose. In this instance, not only CHAMPUS, but Medicare, the Virginia Department of Medical Assistance Services which operates Medicaid, and Blue Cross/Blue Shield of Virginia were defrauded.

Mancuso went on to tell how "some practitioners routinely waive the patient's portion of the payment, accepting the CHAMPUS payment as full payment. Although costing the patient less money, the effect is that the beneficiaries have less regard for the cost of their treatment and frequently fail to review or question their insurance billings, because they have no out-of-pocket expenses."

Testimony by Rear Admiral Edward D. Martin, U.S. Public Health Service, Deputy Assistant to the Secretary of Defense, revealed the massive costs being paid. From fiscal year 1986 to fiscal year 1989, CHAMPUS mental health costs almost doubled, reaching $613 million. This represented 25 percent of total CHAMPUS costs for that year. The overwhelming majority of this increase was accounted for by inpatient care costs for adolescents and children.[5]

Admissions reported for acute inpatient care increased 17 percent from 1990 to 1991. Inpatient substance abuse admissions went from 1,839 to 2,877, a jump of 56 percent.

CHAMPUS, it soon became obvious, was only the tip of the fraud iceberg.

Louis Parisi, Director of the Fraud Division of the Department of Insurance for the State of New Jersey, delivered a raw, unvarnished account of life in the trenches with widespread psychiatric fraud. "I am here today," he told the committee, "to describe our experiences with what I consider to be a glaring abuse of the public trust in some psychiatric hospitals."

He rolled off a catalog of abuses:

• Unnecessary tests followed by unnecessary treatments.

• Billing insurance companies higher charges than patients without insurance.

• Insurance companies being billed for services not provided.

• Diagnosis being determined based upon the coverage provided by the insured's policy.

• Services supposed to be provided by licensed physicians actually being provided by para-professionals or similar personnel with the licensed professionals signing claim forms indicating that these specialized services were performed by themselves.

• Confining patients in hospitals until their entire insurance benefits had been exhausted, thereby maximizing the financial reimbursement. The hospital would then discharge them immediately, claiming they were "cured."

• Ordering and performing exhaustive and extensive medical and psychological tests without sound medical reasons, simply to "run up the bill."

• Ordering medically unnecessary professional consultations, allegedly done to reward or gain the support of professional medical "friends."

• Placing the professional medical staff on a "commission" system whereby the doctors who had the most number of patients in the hospital for the longest period would be paid the highest salary or a "commission" on top of their base salaries.

"The condition of some private psychiatric hospitals," Parisi said, "and their substance abuse programs…is deplorable.

"A situation has developed in this country in the field of medical care where some hospitals and substance abuse centers can achieve a reputation for professionalism and a high level of patient care and that reputation is only a facade. The reputation for professional medical care has been replaced with a reputation for a sure-win moneymaker for the principals involved in the stock ownership and upper management levels of these billion dollar businesses."

Individuals and corporate employees often have group health insurance which, in New Jersey, he pointed out, will pay unlimited benefits for alcohol abuse, but not for other forms of substance abuse.

"All patients entering certain hospitals for drug treatment," Parisi claimed, "are asked by hospital staff if they are alcohol dependent and the type and amount of insurance they have. This is an apparent method of marking the patient as alcohol dependent to ensure health insurance payments, even if the patient answers the alcohol dependent question in the negative. Many questionnaires were checked positive by intake staffers contrary to the patient's true response."

The length of a hospital stay was often a function of the amount of insurance available. Patients were often released by hospitals on the very same day their benefits were terminated. "We even discovered situations where the local municipal police were called to a hospital to remove a patient from the facility," Parisi said. "The insurance benefits had terminated, but the patient had not been successfully treated and did not want to return to a life of substance abuse uncured."

Patients with adequate insurance who had been admitted to certain hospitals sometimes found that they no longer wanted to continue their stay. But the hospitals would often detain the patient to ensure continued insurance benefits.

Former hospital employees told investigators that monetary bonuses were paid to hospital staff doctors who could keep beds filled.

Parisi made no effort to hide his contempt. "If hospitals are expected by the governing bodies and the general public to treat and cure people of illness and maladies," he said, "how could such a corrupt policy ever achieve the desired result?"[6]

Texas State Senator Mike Moncrief presented the voluminous body of evidence he had amassed in September, 1991 as Chairman for the Texas Senate Interim Committee on Health and Human Services. "There is no question in my mind," he said at the outset, "that corporate profits have taken priority over patient care in many instances and that some health care providers have compromised their principles and their professional codes of ethics in pursuit of the almighty dollar."

He related how he had received a pamphlet in the mail from an anonymous source, promoting books and other materials published by a particular corporate chain of psychiatric hospitals. The pamphlet, called "Books as Hooks," said these items were inexpensive marketing tools that could increase a hospital's patient census. It contained the following quote from a substance abuse program director: "We've been using these books for three years...families love these books and they do help us fill the hospital."

In Texas, Moncrief had uncovered "some of the most elaborate, aggressive, creative, deceptive, immoral, and illegal schemes being used to fill empty hospital beds with insured and paying patients."

When Moncrief started holding public hearings on the issue, the Canadian government began cracking down on excessive charges it was being billed by private psychiatric hospitals in the United States. Many Canadian patients were being enticed by the prospect of complimentary airfares, limousine services, and luxury accommodations in treatment programs in sunny California, Florida, and Texas.

It was a gold mine while it lasted. The aggressive marketing resulted in claims from U.S. hospitals for Ontario patients alone increasing from $5.4 million in 1988 to $51.3 million just two years later. In 1990, approximately 2,500 Ontario residents were brought to the U.S. for treatment. One man was referred to as the "half a million dollar man." He reportedly received more than 20 months of treatment in five different Houston hospitals and returned to Canada a cocaine addict.

Moncrief said he was told that after the Canadian government put strict limits on reimbursement to U.S. hospitals, dozens of Canadian patients were dumped and stranded at the Houston airport with no return tickets.

"'Bounties' paid for Canadian patients also were extraordinary," he said, "ranging from $1,500 to $4,000 per patient. While these headhunting fees are a despicable practice and a probable violation of certain state and federal laws, the problem is even more insidious than it appears on the surface. We discovered instances where social workers, school counselors, probation officers, crisis hotline workers and even ministers were paid to refer paying patients to private psychiatric hospitals. These are the people in our communities we have all been taught to trust—not avoid."

He told of a 1-800 suicide hotline advertised in the San Antonio telephone book. Callers would be referred to a 1-900 number "where they make $2.00 a minute off of your call while you're deciding whether to take your life."

Repeatedly in his Texas hearings, throughout almost 80 hours of public testimony, witnesses gave accounts of how they were cured miraculously on the day their insurance benefits ran out—28 days seemed to be the magic number.

Others related experiences of having voluntarily sought treatment for such conditions as an eating disorder or chronic back pain and then finding themselves being held against their will. Still others told of having their diagnosis falsified by hospital personnel so it would match their insurance benefits.

Some of the former patients submitted itemized copies of their hospital bills to Moncrief's Committee. He presented samples which lent ample evidence of extreme fees, charges for services never rendered, over-medication, excessive therapy, duplicate billing, and other abuses.

"Once you have had the opportunity to review some of the bills more closely," he remarked, "I think your Committee also will be convinced that this is a major factor contributing to the out-of-control health care costs in this country."

He submitted evidence of one young woman being billed for eight, ten, and twelve hours of group therapy each day.

This same patient was billed on one day for 36 prescription drugs. Her itemized statement shows 8,400 milligrams of Lithobid (lithium—a drug given for "manic depression"). The *PDR* (*Physicians Desk Reference*—a doctor's guide to drugs) lists the maximum dose at 1,800 milligrams. This amount of lithium alone or in combination with the other drugs would have been lethal if it had actually been given to the patient.

A bill for another patient showed the same drugs being billed at different costs on different days. For example, the charges for a 10 milligram tablet of Mellaril ranged from $6.60 to $44.55.

One case involved a 16-year-old girl whose father reported that the private psychiatric hospital called his insurer almost daily to determine exactly when the insurance benefits would run out. His daughter was admitted for substance abuse treatment and was discharged after only 13 days, precisely on the day benefits were exhausted.

The girl's bill also reflected an excessive amount of therapy each day, sometimes as many as eight hours, even though school age patients were also supposed to be receiving academic instruction. On one particular day, she received $482 worth of "projective testing," $482 worth of psychological evaluation, and five additional hours of group therapy at a cost of $80/hour for a total of $1,364 worth of testing and therapy. Her $625/day semi-private room brought the grand total for that single twenty-four hours to just below $2,000.

The Senator commented, "This is not just unreasonable—it is outrageous. And it is fraudulent."

In closing, he told of a case reported to the Committee by the Chief of Police of Shenendoah, Texas, a small city outside of Houston with a large, 150-bed, private psychiatric hospital. The Chief said his department had responded to numerous complaints about this facility. One particularly memorable incident involved a four-year-old girl who was admitted to the hospital for evaluation after a physician concluded she may have been sexually molested by a family member. The child's mother was persuaded to check into the hospital with her young daughter for a few days to help the child get adjusted. Both were covered by CHAMPUS. Promptly after checking in, mother and daughter were separated and only allowed to see each other at meal times. When the mother demanded to be released, she said that several hospital employees overpowered her and gave her an injection. Mother and daughter were finally let go, but only after she contacted the Shenendoah Police Department.[7]

Perhaps the most condemnatory statement of all was that of a man who has a firm feel for what psychiatry is doing, Dr. Walter Afield, a 32-year veteran psychiatrist and CEO and Medical Director of The Mental Health Programs Corp., a company that reviews for insurance companies the practices of mental health facilities around the country. Dr. Afield graduated from Johns Hopkins University, did his residency at Harvard, taught at Harvard, and was the youngest person to be appointed a medical school chairman of a Department of Psychiatry in the U.S.

According to his assessment, corruption in the mental health industry is not only widespread—it is commonplace.

He delivered what he called "the Walter Afield thumbnail sketch of the history of psychiatry," pointing out that psychiatry originally started in the field of neurology. "Psychoanalysis was the rage in the early part of the century, and in some places, it is still a major influence. In the 1950s, tranquilizing drugs came into vogue and this was the next new wave of treatment. Psychotropic drugs were supposed to empty the state hospitals and cure mental illness. They didn't." In 1960, the new buzz word was community mental health. The latest fad, he said, "is now neurology and biology—back where we started. To say our profession is subject to fads is an understatement."

Afield reported that the late sixties brought the emergence of the private psychiatric chain hospital. Psychiatric Institutes of America (PIA) started in an office building in Washington and subsequently became a national company. Humana Hospital Corporation of America, Charter Hospitals and Community Psychiatric Centers also emerged. During the '80s, private psychiatric facilities flourished throughout the U.S.

As insurance controls were placed on general medical hospitals, many institutions, to bolster income, restructured delivery of services to include inpatient psychiatric and substance abuse beds. Psychiatric facilities and hospitals offering mental health services realized the income to be gained by providing services for these unmonitored benefits. It was a health benefit that paid big money for services rendered and no one ever questioned the expenditures.

Afield presented his views "regarding the elements of psychiatry in today's mental health delivery system and that impact as one of the major hoaxes on the American public."

In today's society, he said, mental health problems have become a commonly discussed topic. Most people know someone who has needed counseling or hospitalization for a mental health or substance abuse problem and has sought treatment. Health insurance has paid for this treatment, and in many cases, has been taken advantage of.

In Afield's words, "Mental illness is no longer taboo—it's big business."

He felt that 30, 45, or 60 days of unmonitored inpatient care was not the answer to the patient's needs—especially when the individual was not getting proper care for his primary problem. Oftentimes, facilities and attending physicians order expensive and, most of the time, unnecessary tests—just because the insurance benefit would pay for the service. Physicians hospitalized their patients for days before ever personally evaluating them. And he pointed out that housing patients in a motel was much cheaper and equally ineffective, but insurance doesn't pay for a motel room.

"Physicians affiliated with any of these inpatient programs 'dump' their troubled child or adolescent patient into a program to relieve the frustration of a stressed parent. These facilities and physicians are well aware that insurance will pay for the services rendered. Many parents see this type program as a way to get a rest from the ill-behaved child at someone else's expense."

331

According to Afield, most kids appear to be psychotic at various times in their lives. If they walk into a psychiatric hospital, they are going to be admitted and kept for a long period of time. This is a major disservice to the patient. Such hospitalization prevents them from getting state employment, federal employment, running for public office, eliminates their ability to get future medical insurance, and labels them with a diagnosis forever. Hospitalized patients involved in a treatment program receive unnecessary tests costing thousands of dollars for services that just aren't indicated. Such programs encourage brain mapping, nuclear magnetic resonance scanning, and a variety of things which nobody even understands in the mental health area. These tests become required services when a patient is locked into a specialized program because insurance pays for the service.

"My company," said Afield, "does mental health utilization review for payors all over the U.S. When a doctor or hospital calls to report an admission of a patient for depression, we ask certain questions regarding the case. In most cases, the doctor or facility will change their diagnosis to report a malady for a benefit which pays more money for services. The patient's diagnosis may change from substance abuse to depression within a matter of minutes. Depression pays the greater benefit.... Mental health care is determined by who is paying the bills, not by treatment needed for improvement. If you've got lots of good insurance, you're going to wind up in the hospital.

"I can give you multiple horror stories. I can talk about the problem. I can tell you very clearly that Florida is the most inept, Texas is the most corrupt. These are not the only states in the wrong—it's a national phenomenon. There are crooks and thieves out there taking advantage of the public."[8]

The picture being painted to Congress was undeniably clear.

The problem was large, pervasive, and for the most part unrestrained.

At this juncture, it was not a matter of if, but more a matter of how this rampant fraud would be brought down.

THE NME SCANDAL

The conditions reported to Congress were not new. Dishonest mental health operations have been with us for some time. But this aggressive approach of bounty hunters, 1-900 numbers, bonuses for filled beds—this was something relatively recent.

It was not news to the psychiatric profession, however. As far back as 1987, five years before the hearings, a *Psychiatric Times* article entitled, "Psychiatry's Time Bomb" had warned of it. The author, Adam Blatner, warned that the "proliferation of private psychiatric hospitals...poses a major threat to the psychiatric profession. It generates a significant pressure for admitting patients and keeping them in the hospital.... It is only a matter of time until the public, consumer groups, and [insurers] become aware of this situation."[9]

And, in a 1983 memo, a Los Angeles County mental health official warned about "teenaged mental patients" being placed in private hospitals, saying, "These facilities really are being used as detention centers and reform schools, not as hospitals." The official, Ralph Lopez, chief of the Health Facilities Division of the Los Angeles County Department of Health Services, cautioned county officials in charge of certifying hospitals that the private psychiatric facilities opening all over California at that time were "preying on parents' fears."

"These issues," he said, "need to be faced and resolved before the lid blows off somewhere."[10]

Indeed, the pressure was building. The problem Lopez alluded to, the recruitment of adolescent patients, became a stampede for income.

In Illinois the number of psychiatric beds for minors increased 66 percent between 1985 and 1988.[11]

Between 1980 and 1987, the number of Americans aged 10 to 19 who spent time in psychiatric hospitals rose by 43 percent.

Hospital Corporation of America, a chain of facilities, had a quarter of its beds designated for children or adolescents in 1983. In 1986 half the beds were so used.[12]

In addition to the heavy influx of juveniles, between 1983 and 1988 the number of all private psychiatric beds per 100,000 of population more than doubled. So did the rate of inpatient admissions.[13]

On August 26, 1993, the lid blew.

That was the day more than 600 FBI and other federal agents simultaneously raided the National Medical Enterprises (NME) offices in 14 different states and the District of Columbia.[14] NME owned one of the largest chains of psychiatric hospitals—more than 80—in the United States.[14]

An estimated 130 lawsuits had been filed against the company by patients. There were an additional 19 by insurers.

NME was under siege. But perhaps for good reason.

The storming of their offices was the culmination of two years of snowballing investigation into what was called "one of the most massive and pernicious health-care scandals of all time" in a complaint filed by two insurance companies.[15]

It all began on April 12, 1991, when a 14-year-old boy named Jeramy Harrell was apprehended at his grandparents' home in San Antonio by employees of a private security firm. The guards gave the impression of being official peace officers by flashing large police badges. It would turn out that the firm was being paid between $150 and $450 for each patient delivered to certain private psychiatric hospitals in the area.

Without even being examined by a physician, the young man was admitted to Colonial Hills, an NME-owned hospital, for a substance abuse problem. His records show he wasn't given a drug test until four days after admission, and the results were negative.[16]

Most important of all, however, was the fact that his own family could not get him out. His grandmother described the entire incident as reminiscent of her childhood in Nazi Germany.

After three days, Jeramy's 18-year-old brother got on the phone calling police, courts, even the Army, determined to get help. He finally hit paydirt when he reached the office of state senator Frank Tejeda.

Tejeda smelled civil liberties violations, serious ones.

Despite the senator's intervention, the hospital still would not comply. Finally, with a court order in hand, Tejeda personally went to Colonial Hills to take Jeramy out after six days of incarceration. Even then the hospital staff balked. "I'm leaving with that boy if I have to kick the damn door down!" Tejeda told them. Jeramy was released.

Then came the bill. Eleven thousand dollars for six days. The Harrells were stunned.

So was Tejeda. The event triggered discussions with his colleagues who had heard similar tales, horror stories of unauthorized detainments, people taken in on false charges, extravagant billing, bounties paid to counselors and community workers for bringing in patients.[17]

The stir caused new reports to come in. And it turned out, the situation was happening throughout Texas. As the investigation continued, the scandal mushroomed. And it was soon discovered that the same thing was happening in other states as well.

An October 20, 1991, article stated, "In the month since *The Dallas Morning News* first reported the allegations against [NME], the paper has received more than 250 calls regarding those allegations and raising other issues. Only three people defended the hospitals."[18]

The same newspaper reported, "The psychiatric community—some of whose members have lucrative ties to private hospitals—has been almost mute on the situation."

"This is a dreadful thing to be going on in our profession," conceded a prominent North Texas psychiatrist, who said that Dallas colleagues have been discussing the issue since the mid-1980s. She requested anonymity for fear of reprisals.

"Everybody would have a story to tell, and then we'd say, 'I don't see what we can do about it.' We just sort of shied away from it."[19]

Russell Durrett, one of the hospital's former financial controllers came forward with more bizarre tales. He explained how if a patient lost his job and thus his insurance, the medical facility would pay his premiums so he could maintain coverage and the hospital could then bill the insurer anywhere from $25,000 to $50,000.

"There was never anything identified to try to track what we did for our patients," he said. "We didn't really want to know. We really didn't care."

Durrett found routine falsification of records and inflated billings at the facility. Regional and corporate officials ordered financial officers there to create fake business expenses to hide monthly profits, he claimed. "We were making way too much profit, way too much money."[20]

Within six months of the Harrell incident, the investigation had reached four states.[21] And the stories kept coming.

In 1987, Florida resident Kelly Dewald voluntarily admitted herself to an NME facility in her state. She went in for anorexia but was put on antidepressants. Hallucinations and paranoia set in. After 34 days, when her insurance ran out, Kelly was summarily discharged and told her treatment was over.

"At this point I was left with nothing," Kelly said. "But one week after I stopped taking medication the violence, the fear and paranoia disappeared."

Her bill was $26,000.[22]

"For 11 months, I ate, slept, bathed, attended to personal hygiene …shackled to my bed. I was held in bondage for insurance money," John Deaton of Dallas told a congressional subcommittee on crime in 1994.

He had been strapped down after an altercation with a nurse.

His voice broke as he described his detainment at NME-owned Brookhaven Psychiatric Pavilion in 1988. "I honestly wanted help," he said. "I was 17, I was confused and I was well-insured." [23]

Eileen Vindsand, wife of a Florida fire fighter, said the stay of her 10-year-old son Jimmy at NME's Fair Oaks Hospital was a family nightmare. A school guidance counselor had recommended the facility in 1988 to evaluate the boy for hyperactivity and behavioral problems.

Once the hospital verified her insurance coverage, they promptly admitted Jimmy. When Mrs. Vindsand was later told she would not be allowed to see her son, she forced her way into his room and was shocked by what she discovered. "He was having what looked like grand mal seizures. He was terrified. He was flipping his head back and stuttering and his eyes were running back into his head."

When she demanded his release, the doctor in charge told her Jimmy had brain damage and that if she removed him the hospital could have her right of custody taken away.

"I believed it," the woman said. "They play off your emotions. They have M.D.s after their names. They are God."

Jimmy was released several days before his insurance ran out. His health returned after that and he outgrew his hyperactivity.[24]

In 1990, W.T. Gable took his 73-year-old Aunt Elsie to the psychiatric ward of the Regional Medical Center in Anniston, Alabama. Ms. Gable had been having trouble with recurring nightmares.

Gable said that after a week he wanted to take her out, but the doctor in charge refused to permit it, saying, "If you do, I'll fix it so that no doctor in town will touch her."

"Their intention," said Gable, "was to keep her there until the 6th, even before they knew what was wrong with her."

Ms. Gable was released on February 6, when her insurance coverage expired.[25]

In 1991, the state of Texas filed suit against NME to stop payment to it of $3.1 million from a crime victims' compensation fund, which paid for victims' psychiatric services.

That same year NME was forced to pay $400,000 in fines to the state of New Jersey, the largest such settlement in the state's history.

New Jersey psychiatrist Robert Stuckey, who had served as medical director of the alcoholic unit at Fair Oaks Hospital in that state from 1975-1985, admitted patients were taken in who did not need treatment and that their diagnoses were shaped to fit insurance coverage. "They were geniuses at assessing and diagnosing insurance," he said.[26]

One of the top executives in the chain of psychiatric hospitals, Peter Alexis, a former "administrator of the year," confessed to having paid up to $40 million in bribes to health care providers for referrals. He also admitted to monthly meetings in Washington in which other NME officials talked about soliciting and paying referral sources and disguising profits.[27]

Lawsuits and further investigation followed.

In 1992, a suit filed by a group of major U.S. insurance companies charged NME with trying to, among other things, "secure the hospitalization of thousands of patients who did not need hospitalization."[28]

By the day of the raid in 1993, agents of the FBI, Department of Health and Human Services, IRS, Defense Criminal Investigative Service, and the U.S. Postal Inspection Service were in on the sweep.[29]

At the five-story national headquarters in Santa Monica, California, federal authorities, armed with a search warrant, hauled out boxes and filing cabinets and loaded them into a large truck.[30]

According to a *Los Angeles Times* article the following day, "The National Medical case could prove to be the largest investigation ever of health fraud in the United States, a government source said, adding, 'I can't think of any case where this kind of effort has been expended.'"[31]

By April 1994, in a deal "that appears to dwarf previous corporate fraud settlements with the government," according to the *Daily News*, NME put out $375 million to settle fraud charges with the government.[32]

Within three years of the Jeramy Harrell incident, NME had divested itself of all its psychiatric hospitals, and the company's three founders had been forced out of their jobs.[33]

The house had come down and the mice had run away.

But they were not altogether gone.

Author Joe Sharkey remarked on the aftermath in his book *Bedlam*: "Yet, as anyone who watches television and reads the papers is aware, psychiatric hospitals, psychiatric wings of general hospitals, and addiction treatment centers are still eagerly trolling for customers who have insurance.

"And the profession of psychiatry, which was allowed through news media indifference to shrug off the hospital scandal and blame it almost exclusively on hospital operators, continues making bold strides into the general medical field, with its plans to become a standard component of much hospital treatment. Meanwhile the news media avidly continues to promote the claims by psychiatrists and psychologists that we are a nation suffering from an epidemic of mental illness that requires professional treatment."[34]

AND THE TREND CONTINUES

NME was not the only hospital chain to go down during this period, merely the largest.

Three similar hospital chains, Community Psychiatric Centers, Hospital Corporation of America, and Charter Medical Corporation, were required to make restitution to the state of Texas.[35] In 1991, Charter Medical settled, agreeing to pay over a half million dollars to the state crime victims' fund and to provide $1.6 million in charity psychiatric care.

Though the company admitted no wrongdoing in the settlement, when it was sued by a nursing supervisor who had charged she was fired for refusing to falsify patient records, a jury characterized the hospital's actions as beyond "all possible bounds of decency" and "intolerable in a civilized community."

Charter Medical filed for Chapter 11 bankruptcy later that year.

After such prominent beheadings in the public square, one might assume that psychiatric fraud would end abruptly. But, as Joe Sharkey pointed out in his book, it was not to be.

A 1995 article in the *John Cooke Fraud Report* by Jane Freeman of Managed Health Benefits, a Connecticut mental health cost containment company, tells us, "Fraud in psychiatry is alive and well and apparent in the delivery of every area of mental health and substance abuse treatment around the country."[36]

She cites the case of a 15-year-old boy sent to a psychiatric facility 1,500 miles away from home after stabbing his uncle. His medical records show minimal documentation of any treatment taking place. Entries did, however, contain reports of him using cocaine on hospital grounds, having sex with other patients, and not complying with treatment. Instead of ejecting him, the facility simply kept him until his benefits ran out.

She says it is still not uncommon to find in patients' bills several group therapy sessions held at the same time, all being charged to the patient as if he or she has attended all of them. In one case, a man was charged for 14 hours of group therapy a day.

Bills are also padded to cover air fares. Prospective patients are told not to worry about paying for airline tickets to distant facilities. The fare cost gets absorbed into the patient's bill—but is not specified as such because insurance companies would otherwise never pay for it.[37]

In 1993, while NME was shutting its psychiatric doors, bounty payments were alive and well across the country. A Florida woman, one of many operating a nationwide 1-800 number, was attracting customers via ads and telling them she could locate programs tailored just for them. What was actually occurring was that hospitals were paying big bonuses for every client pulled in. One reportedly paid $3,000 for any patient whose insurance covered at least 80 percent of costs.

When Cheryl Schillereff, an Arizona nurse and recovering addict who was seeking help for depression, called, she was referred to a hospital in Florida and told it was geared to medical professionals.

"It was just another run-of-the-mill treatment center," Schillereff said. "I could have gone five miles down the road for this kind of place."

When she tried to leave, she said counselors threatened to report her to the Arizona nursing board as unfit. She stayed. The hospital went out of business a few days later.[38]

In July 1995, in Texas again, after performing audits on 52 drug and alcohol treatment centers funded by the state, officials froze payments to 35 of them. Investigators expressed grave concerns about their financial management. The facilities were found to have significant record-keeping problems, and the state was seeking reimbursement for money improperly spent or unaccounted for.[39]

Also in 1995, Florida Medicare investigators discovered the astonishing fact that of all the billings for mental health outpatient services, 40 percent were bogus.[40]

In 1992, an entirely different broad-scale psychiatric fraud epidemic had started to come to light. At the forefront of this "scheme" was a referral apparatus that advertised nationally, advising the public to call 1-800 numbers in order to obtain assistance with personal problems such as being overweight or feeling in need of spiritual uplift.

Callers were handled by individuals who were trained to entice those with generous insurance benefits to one of the Southern California or other sunbelt hospitals.

Qualified callers were informed they would be transported, at no cost, by plane and limousine in most cases, to a desirable location, where their problem would be attended to in a relaxing environment over a period of several weeks, during which callers would enjoy guided tours, a warm climate, and a congenial atmosphere.

What callers were not told, however, was that they would, in fact, be placed in psychiatric institutions.

According to court documents, the hospitals "carefully concealed from insurers what really was happening in their facilities and instead wove an elaborate web of lies that included phony psychiatric diagnoses, fabricated medical histories, fake treatment records and bogus billings. Furthermore, illegal kickback arrangements [to recruiters] were used to sustain this wrongdoing."

In one single lawsuit brought by Aetna Life Insurance Company in 1994, approximately 25 "treatment centers" were named as defendants, notably many locations of Janet Greeson's A Place for Us, the Paracelsus Healthcare Corporation, and places with names such as the Christian Therapy Program, the New Life Treatment Centers, and the Humanistic Mental Health Foundation.[41]

A typical client was Donna Frisbie of Bryan, Ohio. She saw an ad on television for A Place for Us, claiming it could help people with weight problems. Donna called the number, explaining she also had a back problem that needed attention.

She was told it had the best doctors in the U.S. and could give her back surgery if needed. Donna was asked for her insurance particulars. "The next day," she says, "she called me back telling me that the insurance company ok'd everything. Little did I know what she meant by everything! Air fare, limos, trips to malls, trips to Venice Beach, etc. This she did not tell me."

Donna flew to Los Angeles and was taken by limo to the hospital. She knew something was wrong. When she said she didn't want to sign the admission papers, she was told her return ticket was for five weeks later; since she couldn't go home anyway, she may as well admit herself. Donna relented.

The next day she was taken to a psychiatrist who told her she was depressed but didn't know it. "I was put on antidepressants," she says, "which made me have a hard time functioning let alone even thinking."

"Meanwhile," she adds, "groups of us were taken out to meetings and some of the places were weird! One place was for sex addicted people. Our group just stood together acting afraid of the people."

Four weeks after her admission, Donna returned home with no weight lost and the same back problem. Her marriage had been "irreversibly damaged" and her hospital bill was a cool $65,000.[42]

Alexander English of Pennsylvania had a similar story. Looking for some help with his weight, he was told by a patient recruiter he could get help at "New Image" in Florida. When Alexander arrived he was taken not to New Image but to the United Behavior Center.

"As soon as I walked into the place the door locked behind me and I knew I was in the wrong place," he says.

After a long interview, he was taken to his room and informed he was in a mental institution. He was also informed he had been labeled suicidal.

He was put in with a group of 17 people, none of whom were there for the same reason as himself. "Most were recovering dope addicts, sex offenders, drug dealers, and people that were court committed.... I was to spend a great deal of time with these people."

On his third day, a psychiatrist prescribed him Prozac. Although Alexander only recalls seeing the doctor a few times, he was charged for 21 visits.

He was told he could leave anytime he wanted, but he would have to foot the bill himself—the insurance wouldn't cover anything unless he stayed the length of the program.

At one point he wrote a letter to his wife and when she received it, it had been tampered with.

"I felt like I had been kidnapped," he says, "and held under duress. There were always big, heavy-set guys around, football types, that were there for the sole purpose of pouncing people if anybody got out of hand. I was locked up with crazy people when my problem was that I was fat."

The stay did not help him with his weight.

The bill for 22 days: $24,590.[43]

As with NME, it was only a matter of time before some of the perpetrators among this new breed of psychiatric hoaxers were rounded up and brought to justice. But it always comes after much damage has been wrought and trusting people have paid dearly.

Keep in mind this crucial fact: While insurance companies are being cheated to the tune of tens of millions of dollars a year and all our premiums and medical costs are subsequently hiked up, there is also a very real human cost. Those individuals who are being subjected to psychiatric treatment, often unwillingly, are paying an incalculable cost in terms of their humanity. It is harm that cannot be counted in dollars.

Perhaps more sobering, it seems reasonable to assume that although the arms of justice have reached some, others will take the places of NME and similar institutions.

Indeed, the psychiatric field, with its vague diagnoses, its vague treatments, and such little expectancy of it actually helping, is and has always been a magnet of opportunity for those with a new potion to sell.

As Jane Freeman said in her fraud report, "As you read these final lines, new fraudulent schemes are being reimbursed and psychiatric patients, so often considered the most vulnerable of health care consumers, are being manipulated and deceived."

Or as Walter Afield said in 1994, "It's business as usual. Hasn't changed one bit."

FRAUD OF A DIFFERENT COLOR: FALSE MEMORY SYNDROME

One of the "new fraudulent schemes" perpetrated by some psychiatric practitioners is a different wrinkle on the oldest fraud in the profession: Creating new mental illnesses for which they can be reimbursed.

Holly Ramona of Napa Valley, California wanted some help for her compulsive appetite. Some advice perhaps, some useful guidance.[44]

Instead, the assistance she received would ultimately send her and her family down a corridor of nightmares into a world of manufactured madness.

It began when she went to see therapist Marche Isabella and psychiatrist Richard Rose.

Early in her treatment, Isabella told Holly that 70 to 80 percent of compulsive eaters have been sexually abused. The therapist also pointed out that Holly's fear of snakes could be attributed to sexual abuse. When Holly mentioned her long history of urinary infections, Isabella needed no explanations. It sounded like sexual abuse.

The therapist went one step further. When Holly said her father had once glanced at her in what might be construed as a suggestive way, Isabella labeled it as "emotional incest."

However, Holly's "memories" of sexual abuse did not come so readily as these psychiatric suggestions. After several months of treatment, she was still uncertain about the meaning of the "visions" she was having, and whether they were real or simply created. When placed under sodium amytal, she claimed to recall incidents of abuse, although she admitted the details were vague and she could not see her father's face clearly.

Apparently, however, Rose and Isabella did.

Isabella was on the phone to Holly's mother, telling her, "It's rape."

Holly's father Gary Ramona was in a state of shock.

His wife divorced him.

He was fired from his job as vice president for Robert Mondavi Winery, where he had supervised worldwide marketing and sales.

And he was crucified in the press, his reputation destroyed.

But Gary Ramona fought back. He hired a forensic expert who concluded Isabella's conclusion was "outrageous." And he took the matter to court. He showed home movies during the 1994 trial—scenes of family vacations, graduations and a cheerful, happy Holly Ramona.

He fought back. And he won.

But by then his life had been ruined.[45]

Ramona's case is not isolated.

Since the mid-1980s, hundreds of criminal and civil cases have been filed based on "recovered memories" of childhood sexual abuse. The numbers soared after publication of a book, *The Courage to Heal*, which became the bible of repressed memory advocates.

Authors Ellen Bass and Laura David wrote, "If you are unable to remember any specific instances, but still have a feeling that something abusive happened to you, it probably did." [46]

Meanwhile, psychiatrists themselves cannot even say what "repressed memory" is. "I have never been able to get two mental health professionals to agree on a definition of repressed memory," said Bill Craig, a Los Angeles attorney who defends clients facing accusations of abuse based on "recovered" memories.

No one is safe from accusation, even if they don't have children. This became painfully apparent to Cardinal Joseph Bernardin, one of the most respected members of the Roman Catholic hierarchy in the United States.

Bernardin had been a priest for more than 40 years, a bishop for nearly 30 and a cardinal for 10 when he suddenly found himself at the center of international press reports alleging he had sexually assaulted a 17-year-old aspirant to the priesthood.

His accuser, Steven J. Cook, claimed the incident had occurred 17 years previously and that details had only surfaced under hypnosis by a Philadelphia therapist named Michelle Moul. The lurid details of Cook's accusations became one of the key items aired repeatedly on a CNN special on priests and pedophilia.

As the case unfolded, however, and while the Cardinal was being por-trayed as a sexual predator in the press, Cook recanted his story. His attorneys concluded the memories had been fabricated and that the therapist was to blame. The suit was dropped.

But for the innocent cardinal the die had been cast. His name had been inextricably tied to a scandal that had no crime, no sin, and no victim. [47]

In December 1994, a Pennsylvania couple won a lawsuit against psy-chiatrist Judith Cohen who had "recovered" repressed memories of sexual abuse from their daughter.

When the 15-year-old, Nicole Althous, claimed to suddenly remember being sexually abused by her parents, Cohen informed the authorities—who promptly arrested the parents and put the child in foster care.

However, along with the girl's allegations were claims that her grand-mother flew around on a broomstick and that she herself had given birth to three children who had been murdered and tortured with a medieval thumbscrew device.

The parents' attorney remarked, "It didn't take a rocket scientist to realize that this kid was saying things that were impossible. She said she had a Caesarean birth, yet there was no scar. [The psychiatrist] was bombarded with information that was inconsistent with abuse, but she ignored it."

After a false arrest and extensive public humiliation, the charges against Nicole's parents were finally dropped.

"We were a family under siege," the mother said.

After a survey of more than 1,000 therapists, a San Diego psychologist concluded that psychologists and psychiatrists are "creating the very problem that they would then have to treat." The result, he warns, is that they are "propagating a cottage industry of discovering child abuse in their patients."[48]

Sometimes the psychiatrist does not even wait for the patient to be sure of what she has recalled. Dallas psychiatrist Wayne Jones calmly informed his patient Elaine's four daughters, aged 17 to 23, of their grandfather's alleged abuse of their mother.

Forty-eight-year-old Elaine, however, had very different memories of her childhood to those so confidently advanced for her by the psychiatrist. As she later stated, "I didn't have any recollection of my father abusing me until it was suggested that possibly he had. But once it had been suggested to me, my mind just took it from there. I was able to conjure up many things—very vivid images."

A jury found that Jones had slandered Elaine's parents and the psychiatrist was ordered to pay them $350,000.[49]

Harvard Law School Professor Alan Dershowitz wrote, "Because the 'theory' of repressed memory has never been scientifically validated...the law should never authorize a criminal prosecution solely on the basis of a 'recovered memory.'"

His comments followed an April, 1995 decision by U. S. District Court Judge D. Lowell Jensen in San Francisco to reverse the conviction of George Franklin, who had been jailed for the murder of an 8-year-old girl-friend of his daughter. The sole evidence convicting him of the 21-year-old unsolved murder were the recovered memories of his daughter, who had been "aided" by a therapist.[50]

When "Repressed Memory Syndrome" first appeared on the scene, it was hailed as a psychiatric breakthrough, a startling revelation of what lies at the root of some people's problems. However, like the beds at NME and the A Place for Us hotlines, psychiatrists and therapists seemed to waste little time in using this new twist to fill their couches with sexual abuse cases where none existed before. The rewards are more billable hours, expert witness fees in some cases, and media exposure promoting their services.

But in this instance, the price has not been paid by insurance companies. It has been paid with the happiness of families and the reputations of people who have done no wrong.

HOW MUCH MORE?

Fraud can only exist in the presence of tolerance.

Wherever psychiatric fraud is taking place, it is occurring under the knowing eyes of psychiatrists who are either participating or allowing it to happen.

That was visible in the words of the anonymous psychiatrist quoted in the *Dallas Morning News*, who said she and her fellows knew about the massive fraud in private psychiatric hospitals for at least five years (since the "mid-1980s"), yet did nothing about it.[51]

In reviewing the history of the profession, we see little hope of the doctors themselves reigning in the indecencies and excesses of the psychiatric community.

Fortunately, others outside the field have taken notice. The Texas legislature, for one, has learned to keep a watchful eye on this fruitful orchard of fraudulent activities.

Companies such as Walter Afield's and Jane Freeman's have found an immensely fertile field auditing psychiatric claims for signs of insurance abuse. As Freeman has said, it is visible in every area of mental health treatment across the nation.

Thus we are left to wonder about the future.

If, under the increasing scrutiny of an ever-more-dubious public, we keep peeling away, like an onion, the less-than-honest claims of the psychiatric profession, a question arises.... When we are finished, will anything be left?

Chapter XII

The Manufacture
of Madness

A well-known psychiatrist tells of visiting some friends, a couple with two children. In watching the young ones he could not help but notice how much they resembled their parents. The boy was mechanical like his father. The girl had the mother's inclination for art. Don't the genes breed true! he thought.

"I was about to say something of the sort," he writes, "when I remembered that these children were adopted and, beyond being human, had no genetic relationship to these parents."[1]

His experience points up the remarkable fact that much of what we see is actually an apparency. We only *think* we see it.

Trained in the psychiatric doctrine that mental traits are inherited, he saw an assumed reality that was different from the truth.

In a similar vein, a study reported in 1969 shows how what we are told can affect what we believe we see.

In this experiment, researchers wrote a script of an interview with a normal man. In it he spoke sensibly and clearly about his feelings and thoughts, remembered childhood events, was emotionally expressive but not excessively so, and showed no signs of major mental problems such as hallucinations, wild ideas, depression or disjointed thinking.

An actor was hired as the man being interviewed and he performed according to the script. The entire process was taped. The tape was then played to a group of students, practicing clinical psychologists, and practicing psychiatrists who were told the person on the tape "looked neurotic but actually was quite psychotic."

All were asked to indicate how the man being interviewed should be classified out of a list of various diagnoses, including *normal*. They were told, "Simply state what you actually heard—actually observed—this person say and do." When they were done, all were given a chance, if they wished, to change their diagnosis.

Significant numbers of the listeners found the man to be psychotic. One psychologist found four serious mental disorders. The majority found the actor to be neurotic. And only a small percentage—but no psychiatrists—thought he was normal or had "mild adjustment problems."[2]

The world's view of mental *illness* has been similarly colored over the past several centuries. We have been immersed in the incessant message from the psychiatric profession that people who are mentally troubled are, in fact, *sick*, and that this is generally caused by a physical failing in their brains.

This concept is so steeped in our thinking, we would be hard pressed to find someone who did not have at least some belief in this notion.

When seeing an individual with a psychiatric label, people often get images of chromosomes gone awry or misshapen brains.

But truthfully, as common an idea as this idea is, there is little evidence to back it up.

In 1960, Thomas Szasz jolted the international psychiatric community and free-thinking people around the globe with his now classic work *The Myth of Mental Illness*. Even today this book remains in print.

He stated: "We call problems in living 'mental illness'; individuals who consult psychiatrists or are compelled to submit to them by force or fraud are 'mental patients,' their complaints or the complaints of others about them are 'mental symptoms,' and the conditions imputed to them that allegedly 'cause' and 'explain' their conduct are 'mental disease'...we call psychiatric inquiries, whether invited by consenting clients or imposed on them against their will, 'diagnoses,' and psychiatric interventions, 'treatments'.... And since we even have a National Institute of Mental Health it is easy to see why the right-thinking person considers it unthinkable that there might be no such thing as mental health or mental illness. If that were so, we would be the victims of our own folly."[3]

Yet the "myth of mental illness" may well be just that.

As we have seen, when we treat the "mentally ill" as normal people—give them no psychiatric treatment at all—a great many improve. They snap out of their troubles.

Even the "incurable schizophrenic" gets better.

This is a simple way of measuring the truthfulness of any theory: *Does it work?*

When we examine the results of psychiatric doctrines, however, we find they have done little to reduce the numbers of the so-called mentally ill.

In fact, the opposite has occurred.

As psychiatry has grown, the tally of those with "mental disorders" has risen astronomically.

THE MOTHER LODE OF MENTAL ILLNESS

In the early 1800s the notion of the lunatic being *sick* was a foreign one. He was obviously strange in his behavior, perhaps destructive, but explanations as to *why* did not necessarily center on a physical malfunction.

This is because at that time the mind was viewed as a separate entity from the body. This had been the prevailing thought for centuries. In philosophy this is called dualism—two entities, mind and body.

In some cultures the madman was reviled, in others he was revered as divinely touched.

In the 1840s there was a single classification of mental problem in the U.S.—"idiocy/insanity."

By 1880, nearly four decades after the formation of the American Psychiatric Association, there were seven categories of mental disturbances: mania, melancholia, monomania (irrationality on one subject), pareses (syphilitic brain condition), dementia, dipsomania (alcoholism), and epilepsy.

The notion of mental *illness* began to set in during this time period. Up till then *sickness* meant an observable derangement of the body: infection, a cancerous organ, inflamed lungs.

But the budding profession of psychiatry initiated the practice of *declaring* illnesses they assumed were there instead of naming what they actually observed. They believed the "patient" must be sick because he behaved abnormally. By *declaring* his conduct as symptoms, they concluded they must be caused by an *illness*.

Not surprisingly, psychiatry has spent the past century unsuccesfully trying to prove this position.

No "brain lesions" have been found. No mutant nerve connections have been discovered. No substantiated genetic proof has come forth, even with modern technology.

After World War II came a considerable expansion of the number and types of mental illnesses. This was one of the results of the massive influx of psychiatrists into the military during the war.

The addition of new classes of illnesses may also explain why psychiatrists screened out and discharged record numbers of servicemen during this period.

In 1933, psychiatrists organized the first standard manual for the categorizing of "mental illnesses." It was called the *Standard Classified Nomenclature of Disease*. This went through two more revisions.

Then in 1952, the American Psychiatric Association published its own manual, the *Diagnostic and Statistical Manual for Mental Disorders* (*DSM*). This book defined 112 mental disorders. It included such things as:

1. Brain disorders (actual brain damage disorders)
2. Psychotic disorders (such as schizophrenia)
3. Neuroses of various sorts.
4. Personality disorders, i.e. a defect of personality, including alcoholism, drug addiction, and "learning disturbance."
5. Sexual deviation including homosexuality, transvestism, pedophilia, fetishism, sexual sadism, rape assault and mutilation.

There were no categories for infants or children, except for three "adjustment reactions" of infancy, childhood, and adolescence, respectively.

It is noteworthy that at the time, psychiatry was considerably confused. It was operating off of a mixture of two opposite beliefs: that the patient had a mental illness of physical origin and that his *illness* was a product of *dualism*, the concept that mind and body are separate.

As an example, schizophrenia—now considered a biological disease by modern psychiatry (though there is no evidence to support that theory)—was listed in 1952 under a category of "DISORDERS OF PSYCHO-

GENIC [mind-caused] ORIGIN OR WITHOUT CLEARLY DEFINED PHYSICAL CAUSE OR STRUCTURAL CHANGE IN THE BRAIN."

In 1968 the manual was revised and called *DSM-II*. By now, the number of disorders had jumped to 163. Included were:

1. 6 new schizophrenic disorders.
2. 13 new categories of alcoholic disorders.
3. 5 new neuroses.
4. 3 new personality disorders.
5. 6 new drug dependence disorders.
6. 8 new sexual deviance categories.
7. A whole new category of "Behavior Disorders of Childhood and Adolescence," listing 7 disorders.

This sudden outcropping of childhood disorders appeared only a few years after psychiatry had procured federal funding for treating "handicapped" children. (This funding is discussed in Chapter Eight.)

This is also the first time "hyperkinetic" appears as a diagnosis for youngsters—a concept that ultimately resulted in literally millions of children being placed on the addictive drug Ritalin and a financial bonanza for its maker.

Commentary in the *DSM-II* shows us these *disorders* are established by committee which votes on whether these disorders exist.

We are told, "In the case of diagnostic categories about which there is current controversy concerning the disorder's nature or cause, the Committee has attempted to select terms which it thought would least bind the judgment of the user. The Committee itself included representatives of many views. It did not try to reconcile these views but rather to find terms which could be used to label the disorders about which they wished to be able to debate."

In discussing schizophrenia, the manual says, "Even if it had tried, the Committee could not establish agreement about what this disorder is; it could only agree on what to call it."

In 1980, *DSM-III* was published. Sixty-one new mental disorders were added to bring the total to 224. Some interesting developments had occurred.

The category of Sexual Deviations was now changed to "Psychosexual

Disorders" with an addition of 14 new types. This followed on the heels of the APA's decision in 1974 to remove homosexuality from the manual as a form of deviancy.

This change was not the result of any scientific discovery or advance. It was precipitated by active lobbying from the homosexual community. To decide the issue, the APA took a vote from its membership. The result was 5,854 supporting and 3,810 opposed. On that basis, homosexuality went from a long-standing form of abnormal behavior to a scientifically-declared form of "sexual preference." [4]

Commenting on this, psychiatrist Walter Afield told us, "I was just talking last weekend to somebody who was on the commission to do the *DSM-IV* that was coming out, and I said, 'Well now, tell me, homosexuality used to be considered a disease and then it was not considered a disease. What's it going to be in *DSM-IV*?' And he said, 'Oh, we've totally cured it now. It doesn't exist.'" [5]

In the "Infancy, Childhood, and Adolescence," section, 32 new mental disorders were added, including:
- Attention Deficit Disorder
- Conduct Disorder
- Developmental Reading Disorder
- Developmental Arithmetic Disorder
- Developmental Language Disorder
- Developmental Articulation Disorder
- Separation Anxiety Disorder
- Overanxious Disorder

Illnesses stemming from the use of chemical substances went from 21 to 57. These included:
- Hallucinogen Organic Mental Disorders
- Cannabis [Marijuana] Organic Mental Disorders
- Tobacco Organic Mental Disorder (featuring tobacco withdrawal)
- Caffeine Organic Mental Disorder (covering caffeine intoxication)

The *DSM-III* Introduction tells us "there is no satisfactory definition that specifies precise boundaries for the concept 'mental disorder.'"

When a similar statement appeared in the follow-up volume, *DSM-III-R*, psychiatrist Matthew Dumont commented, "They say: '...while this manual provides a classification of mental disorder...no definition adequately specifies precise boundaries for the concept....' They then provide a 125-word definition of mental disorder which is supposed to resolve all the issues surrounding the sticky problem of where deviance ends and dysfunction begins. It doesn't.

"They go on to say: '...there is no assumption that each mental disorder is a discrete entity with sharp boundaries between it and other mental disorders or between it and no mental disorder.'

"This is a remarkable statement in a volume whose 500-odd pages are devoted to the criteria for distinguishing one condition of psychopathology from another with a degree of precision indicated by a hundredth of a decimal point [the *DSM* numerical code system]."[6]

The Introduction also tells us, "For most of the *DSM-III* disorders ...the etiology [cause] is unknown. A variety of theories have been advanced, buttressed by evidence—not always that convincing—to explain how these disorders come about."[7]

Additionally, they explain, "At the present time, however, there is no consensus in our field as to how to define 'neurosis.'"[8]

Seven years later, in 1987, the handbook was revised again to become the *DSM-III-R*.

The number of mental disorders increased from 224 to 253. The most dramatic increase occurred in the section, "Disorders Usually First Evident In Infancy, Childhood, or Adolescence," These included Pervasive Developmental Disorders, Developmental Expressive Writing Disorder, and Developmental Expressive Language Disorder.

There was an effort to include one hotly-debated "illness" called Paraphilic Rapism (later euphemistically changed to Paraphilic Coercive Disorder). It would have been assigned to any individual who had attempted rape or fantasized about it and experienced intense sexual arousal or desire associated with it for at least six months.

Public reaction was swift.

"Society as a whole is very upset with psychiatry explaining away criminal actions," claimed Roberta Roper in 1986. A Maryland activist for victims' rights, Roper became involved in her cause when her daughter was raped by two men who subsequently received light sentences. "Providing psychiatric—or pseudopsychiatric —explanations is not going to help the rape victim."

"I don't think the public has a whole lot of confidence in psychiatric evaluations," she added. "I don't see who benefits except the psychiatrists."[9]

Brooklyn district attorney Elizabeth Holtzman objected to "any attempt to define a disease by associating it with a crime."

"If psychiatrists say it exists, it exists," she said, "even though there's no scientific evidence." She commented, "I don't think psychiatrists can act as though they live in an ivory tower."

Assistant attorney general Lois Harrington claimed, "The only time we ever see psychiatrists in the courtroom is when they're telling us about a defendant's mitigating circumstances so sentences will be more lenient."

She noted, "This [rapism] is going to be absolutely devastating to victims."[10]

After considerable public furor, the APA voted to drop the alleged disorder.

However two other highly controversial diagnoses were added to *DSM-III-R*: Premenstrual Syndrome and Masochistic Personality Disorder.

Psychologist Paula Caplan served as a consultant to *DSM-III-R* committees in charge of approving these two disorders. In detailing this experience in her book *They Say You're Crazy*, Caplan tells of "the truly astonishing extent to which scientific methods and evidence are disregarded as the handbook is being developed and revised."[11]

When Masochistic Personality Disorder was proposed, there was an intense backlash among women's organizations as they feared it would be used primarily to label women as deliberate victims (as in abusive marriages).

Dr. Lenore Walker, the chair of the women's caucus of the Council of Representatives for the American Psychological Association, claimed that after women protested the suggested diagnosis, the APA tried to placate them by creating another diagnosis, *sadism*. Such an effort "shows the disrespect psychiatrists have for scientific research...." she said. "There was no talk of [a "sadism category"] before the flap over masochism."[12]

Another psychologist attending *DSM-III-R* hearings was quoted in *Time* magazine as saying, "The low level of intellectual effort was shocking. Diagnoses were developed by majority vote on the level we would use to choose a restaurant. You feel like Italian, I feel like Chinese, so let's go to a cafeteria. Then it's typed into the computer. It may reflect on our naivete, but it was our belief that there would be an attempt to look at things scientifically."[13]

Caplan quotes psychologist Lynne Rosewater's comments after attending hearings with Robert Spitzer, the psychiatrist overseeing the entire *DSM-III-R* project. "[T]hey were having a discussion for a criterion [about Masochistic Personality Disorder] and Bob Spitzer's wife [a social worker and the only woman on Spitzer's side at that meeting] says, 'I do that sometimes' and he says, 'Okay, take it out.' You watch this and you say, 'Wait a second, *we* don't have a right to criticize *them* because this is a "science"?'"[14]

After intense lobbying by women's groups and supporting factions such as the American Psychological Association and the American Orthopsychiatric Association, the APA voted first to change the name of Masochistic Personality Disorder to Self-Defeating Personality Disorder, then under further pressure, listed it under a new classification: disorders "needing further study."

In trying to explain why the APA didn't drop the diagnosis altogether, Caplan says, "The APA Board had had chances to defeat the proposals several times before but had nevertheless charged right ahead. As one senior APA official told me privately, Board members who leaned toward discarding all three categories [Rapism, Masochism, and PMS] were accused by their colleagues of 'giving in to the women.'"[15]

Premenstrual Syndrome was similarly bandied about and bartered. Women's groups and others expressed great concern over the potential for massive numbers of women being labeled as "mentally ill." Psychiatrists received support for PMS from drug companies—drugs was one of the few recommended treatments—and also claimed that by assigning the label to women it would allow them coverage for PMS (and psychiatrists payment for it) under some insurance policies.

In response to pressure, the APA changed the name of PMS to "Late Luteal Phase Dysphoric Disorder" and listed it as well as "needing further study" in the *DSM-III-R*.

Such an obfuscating move may be best explained by George Orwell's words: "The great enemy of clear language is insincerity. When there is a gap between one's real aims and one's declared aims, one turns...to long words...like a cuttlefish squirting out ink."[16]

DSM-IV was released in 1994.

Disorders increased from 253 to 374. The number of added categories created within the previous seven years exceeded the original 112 that were in the entire *DSM* of 1952.

The more biological slant of modern psychiatry is visible in the Introduction: "Although this volume is titled *Diagnostic and Statistical Manual of Mental Disorders*, the term *mental disorder* unfortunately implies a distinction between "mental" disorders and "physical" disorders that is a reductionistic anachronism of mind/body dualism."

Also: "The problem raised by the term 'mental' disorders has been much clearer than its solution, and unfortunately, the term persists in the title of *DSM-IV* because we have not found an appropriate substitute."

Once again we are told that although the manual provides a classification of mental disorders, it must be admitted that no definition adequately specifies precise boundaries for the concept of "mental disorder."

The term "Academic Disorders"—which covered the reading, arithmetic disorders in previous *DSMs*—has been changed to "Learning Disorders."

In describing the course of the Reading Disorder "illness," *DSM-IV* authors describe what sounds frighteningly similar to the routine result of poor teaching: "Although symptoms of reading difficulty (e.g., inability to distinguish among common letters or to associate common phonemes with letter symbols) may occur as early as kindergarten, Reading Disorder is seldom diagnosed before the end of kindergarten or the beginning of first grade because formal reading instruction usually does not begin until this point in most school settings. Particularly when Reading Disorder is associated with high IQ, the child may function at or near grade level in the early grades, and the Reading Disorder may not be fully apparent until the fourth grade or later. With early identification and intervention, the prognosis is good in a significant percentage of cases. Reading Disorder may persist into adult life."

Under "Learning Disorder Not Otherwise Specified," it says that a person might have such a disorder in reading, math, and/or written expression even though performance on tests measuring each individual skill is not substantially below what would be expected for that child.

Something else was notably absent in the *DSM-IV*. After continuous arm-twisting from interested groups, Self-Defeating Personality Disorder was removed.

Premenstrual syndrome, however, a highly profitable diagnosis, appeared, no longer under the banner of "needing further study," but as Premenstrual Dysphoric Disorder.

Psychiatrist Al Parides remarked that such diagnosis by consent or demand demonstrates that the *DSM* is not a scientific manual at all, but "a masterpiece of political maneuvering." He claims it turns the normal problems of life into psychiatric ones. "A child doesn't want to go to school and kicks the teacher when he goes to school. They work out the psychiatric diagnoses [as] a medical problem.... What they have done is medicalize many problems that don't have demonstrable, biological causes."

After her experience, Caplan concluded that the sheer mass of evidence was that the major players in the *DSM* continually ignore both scientific research and the harm suffered by patients due to the handbook's categories. She found this "incompatible with [the notion of] their being driven by only the most altruistic and balanced of motives."

Something is very wrong, she claims, when those at the top of the *DSM* hierarchy not only ignore scientific evidence and ignore proof of the harm they are doing but also admit that they don't want their patients to know what goes on in *DSM* meetings.[17]

The proliferation of mental illness created by this manual has not gone unnoticed by the general public. Indeed, its response has bordered on exasperation and incredulity.

Typical is a commentary on *DSM-IV* in the *Daily Messenger* by editor Mark Syverud. "Beware. A new book shows that an epidemic of mental illness is sweeping the nation," he writes.

He goes on to tell what this means for all of us.

"Does your 10-year-old dislike doing her math homework? Better get her to the nearest couch because she's got No. 315.4, *Developmental Arithmetic Disorder*.

"Maybe you're a teenager who argues with his parents. Uh-oh. Better get some medication pronto because you've got No. 313.8, *Oppositional Defiant Disorder*.

"And if your wife won't tell you that she snuck out to the outlet mall last Saturday, then she's definitely got 313.2, *Selective Mutism*.

"Omigosh! My family is full of psychos!

"Trust me, I am not making these things up. (That would be *Fictitious Disorder Syndrome*). The number of mental diseases identified in the manual has risen from 100 to 300 in the last 15 years. That translated to a virtual epidemic of madness sweeping the country. Only a decade ago, psychiatrists said one in 10 Americans had a mental illness. Now, according to the manual, half the population is mentally ill.

"How the other half stays sane remains a mystery.

"The manual will have to be updated annually because mental health professionals and defense lawyers keep discovering new illnesses. Just since the beginning of the year the experts have unearthed these new disorders:

"Lottery Stress Disorder (or LSD): A London psychiatrist discovered the outbreak among lottery losers who experienced "definition of mood and feelings of hopelessness" when their numbers didn't come in.

"Chronic Tax Anxiety Syndrome (CTAS): A Washington psychotherapist specializes in treating couples who suffer from excessive worry, sleeplessness and marital squabbling every April.

"Premenstrual Syndrome (PMS). It's not new, but now it has won recognition as a bona fide mental illness from the American Psychiatric Association.

"I know there are some cynics out there who will scoff at these new diagnoses. Maybe you think it's all psychobabble, just a gimmick to make money for the therapists. You wouldn't be caught dead on a psychiatrist's couch.

"You people are in serious denial. As a matter of fact, your unwillingness to seek professional help is itself a symptom of a serious mental problem. It's right here in the book: 15.81 *Noncompliance with Treatment Disorder.*"[18]

Doubtless, some psychiatrists may find Mr. Syverud's levity dangerous, a threat to the well-being of the millions of mentally ill who might not seek help after reading his views.

No doubt a few may even think something is seriously wrong with him—something new perhaps. Whatever it is, ultimately it will probably be found in the *DSM*.

THE FACTS VERSUS THE FICTION

Webster's defines *fiction* as "anything made up or imagined."[19]

It would seem that what we have seen in the *DSM* epitomizes this definition.

Quite literally it is the psychiatric process of creating or "making up" sickness.

Of course, they will protest that they do not make up the behavior they are talking about.

And this is true. The behavior exists.

But when psychiatrists group bundles of behaviors and emotions together and assign each bundle a name, *that* is a created entity.

It is also a *created* reality.

It did not exist before.

An example would be Attention Deficit Disorder.

For eons some children, like adults, have always been more active than others. Perhaps they play harder or wander mentally because of a short attention span.

Until the twentieth century parents simply dealt with this as a fact of life. They saw that individuals differ. They saw that some people, as children or adults, are difficult to tolerate. And the wise parents saw that children, like adults, learn to change their behavior for the better as time goes on.

However, psychiatry has deemed there is something wrong with these children. Some vague, unexplained defect in the brain. These doctors have identified certain conduct and claimed that any child who demonstrates this conduct has Attention Deficit Disorder.

Again, this is a created reality.

There is no evidence his brain is any different from anyone else's.

The child and parents thought he was normal when they walked into the psychiatrist's office. They think he is abnormal when they walk out.

Reality did not change. The child is still the same.

What changed was the reality of the family. They now "see" a disordered child, where before there was none.

As a normal child, he would have been tolerated, endured, disciplined, shipped off to relatives—whatever parents have done for thousands of years. And in all likelihood, he would have grown out of it with little significance made of the situation.

As an abnormal child, however, he would have been treated much differently by his parents, his teachers, and possibly his classmates. He would have been "special." Perhaps his behavior would have been "excusable." He would have been on years of medication. Instead of expecting the best of him, all (including the child) would treat him as limited by his "condition." He himself would, of course, think he had something inherently wrong with him that made him less than others. Most likely this sense of "abnormality" would be with him the rest of his life.

The only difference between these two scenarios is the *created reality*, Attention Deficit Disorder.

There is no physical evidence anywhere that such a "disease" actually exists.

There is an *actual* reality as to why this specific child behaves this way. He may have a lot of energy and no way to channel it. He may be eating improperly. He may have allergies. His parents and teachers may be intolerant of motion or children. His energy level and behavior may simply be normal for *him*.

The actual truth is bodies and individuals vary enormously in their idiosyncrasies, and they respond in very different ways to what happens in their environment.

To bundle a set of behavior and emotional characteristics and call them a "disease," implying they are caused by a single source—a biological malfunction—is *pure fiction*.

Even the psychiatrist's favorite "mental illness," *schizophrenia*, is concocted.

This is the classic insane person. Delusional, hallucinating, hearing voices, disassociated thought, talking to himself and nonexistent demons.

A century ago, psychiatrists observing this behavior simply assumed all people who do this are the same, that they have the same thing wrong.

Psychiatrists have believed it ever since.

There is no proof anywhere that this is true.

One man might be under phenomenal stress.

Another may be physically ill.

Another may be reacting to medication.

Yet the psychiatrist has invented the label *schizophrenia* which he then hangs on each of these individuals, implying they each have the same thing wrong with them—something incurable.

As a result all are given the same treatment, standardly a life sentence on powerful drugs.

Then there is *depression*, particularly as it involves the elderly. Writing in *The Atlantic Monthly's* April, 1995 issue, clinical psychologist Stanley Jacobson reports on a November, 1991 NIH Consensus Development Conference on the Diagnosis and Treatment of Depression in Late Life. The resulting report, a 22-page consensus statement announces that instead of all nine *DSM* symptoms for depression, a diagnosis can be made if any five are present. First and second on the *DSM* list are *depressed mood* and *loss of interest or pleasure.* The consensus downgraded these to positions five and six on the list.

"Now, the report would suggest," wrote Jacobson, "the major indicators of depression are the physiological symptoms: changes in appetite and weight, disturbed sleep, motor agitation or retardation, and fatigue and loss of energy."

It is hard not to imagine many elderly without some, if not all, of these symptoms as a natural consequence of old age.

Significantly, as Jacobson points out, now "Depression is thus all but divorced from the mind, converted to a discrete biological entity, a physical ailment as specific as high blood pressure or gallstones."

Jacobson says that the evidence for biological pre-eminence in depression is weak, and that the consensus statement could not recommend any specific diagnostic test for this "physical" illness. Nevertheless, the consensus statement concludes boldly that, "Depressed elderly people should be treated vigorously with sufficient doses of antidepressants and for a sufficient length of time to maximize the likelihood of recovery."

The obvious is completely missed by these "experts," according to Jacobson. He says, "Not once in its twenty-two pages does the consensus statement acknowledge that awareness of the proximity of death may be a contributing factor in late-life depression."

Perhaps, he suggests, "the experts need to be reminded that we are body *and* mind. Any and all threat of loss in late life may violate the balance of the system, shock the mind into awareness of the tenuousness of life, challenge the capacity to adapt to an essentially unwelcome reality, and lead to thoughts and feelings that appear, out of context, to be pathological, though they are as natural as being fearful of an approaching tornado."[29]

But, regardless of logic, the elderly are a hot market for mental health professionals. After all, everyone gets old, sooner or later. Which is why major hospitals send out mass mailings targeted to the elderly such as a

1995 brochure with headlines of symptoms: "Insomnia, Losses, Can't Drive, Limited Income, Illness, Loneliness, Death," and other of the normal problems faced by the elderly. The message concludes, "If you or a loved one are experiencing memory problems, puzzling moods and behaviors, or difficulties in managing activities of everyday life—call today for a free, confidential assessment."

Jacobson says tartly that "failure to credit the resilience and resourcefulness that successful aging requires (and that most people find within them) is a more significant public-health problem than late-life depression."[20]

Once again we have the manufacturing of madness.

That is the fiction of "mental illness."

There is, however, a true side to it.

There is such a thing as insanity.

What is true is that all people have a common urge to survive. They want survival for themselves, their families, their groups. This *is* the thrust that forwards an individual through life. He wants to survive and flourish.

We can define much of rational and irrational behavior by how well it aligns with survival.

At one time or another each of us does irrational things, behavior that is against survival. Too much alcohol, child beating, infidelity, destructive rages—we do things sometimes that are not logical and that hurt us and those we love.

Some people do this more than others. Some behave irrationally in one area and do well in another.

Some are so insane they cannot seem to survive on their own at all. And these people, it is true, need help.

For those who are not so disturbed, help can be fairly simple.

Down through the ages we have, as a race, managed to gather scraps of wisdom on how to deal with our human frailties.

Morals, as maligned as they are, have been a powerful tool in assisting us to rein in our weaknesses so that peace of mind and survival may prevail.

A remarkable amount of "mental illness" is, in actuality moral failure: intemperance, guilt, failure to self-discipline, sloth, lying, injustice, promiscuity—these things wreak havoc on the mind's well-being.

Virtually any and all "symptoms"—depression, feeling crazy, feeling persecuted, violent impulses, etc.—can and do develop when an individual betrays common-sense virtues.

As much as the psychiatrist likes to rail against morals as being too stressful and as much as he promotes the notion that "people can't help themselves," the truth is that all of us have managed to rise above our more base impulses when necessity has dictated.

It is not only possible, but, contrary to the psychiatrist's teachings, it is *necessary* to sanity.

Many an individual has undergone miraculous change of mental state by ending immoral behavior and deciding to live a "clean" life.

For some people, however, this may not be enough to resolve their troubles. They may need to talk their difficulties over with a friend, a family member, a religious counselor, or simply someone they trust.

Some may need to separate themselves from people or situations that make chronic trouble for them.

However, there are certain individuals who are simply so overwhelmed or disturbed that no amount of talk or moralizing will assist them.

They need help. And help is possible.

WHEN PHYSICAL ILLNESS OVERWHELMS THE MIND

In a 1967 article in the *American Journal of Psychiatry*, researchers Richard Hall and Michel Popkin wrote the following: "The most common medically induced psychiatric symptoms are apathy, anxiety, visual hallucinations, mood and personality changes, dementia, depression, delusional thinking, sleep disorders (frequent or early morning awakening), poor concentration, changed speech patterns, tachycardia [rapid heartbeat], nocturia [excessive urination at night], tremulousness, and confusion.

"In particular, the presence of visual hallucinations, illusions, or distortions indicated a medical etiology [cause] until proven otherwise. Our experience suggests this to be the most reliable discriminator [between medical and mental problems]. We were able to define a specific medical cause in 97 of 100 patients with pronounced visual hallucinations."[21]

This report is telling us that 97 percent of the cases of visual hallucinations they saw were *medical* in origin.

Visual hallucinations have always been a classic characteristic of the lunatic or *schizophrenic*. Given that millions of people have been lobotomized, shocked, extensively drugged, or relegated to the back wards of state hospitals for the rest of their lives because they were "seeing things," this 97 percent figure takes on a rather monolithic—and sobering—significance.

In and of itself this single psychiatric error may constitute the equivalent of a Medical Holocaust.

In this and other reports we are told studies have shown time and again that in a high number of patients, what appear to be "mental" problems are actually caused by physical ailments.

And these are generally ordinary medical problems that have nothing to do with psychiatry.

Hall and Popkin claim these mental symptoms are often the first or only signs of an underlying physical disorder.

This is not even new news.

In 1936, B.I. Comroe reported in the *Journal of Nervous Mental Disorders* that 24 out of 100 patients labeled *neurotic* developed organic disease within eight months of their initial diagnosis.[22]

A 1949 survey found that 44 percent of psychiatric patients were physically ill.[23]

A report published in 1965 cited a 42 percent incidence of "physical disease causative of initial psychiatric symptoms." The same researcher found 58 percent of the patients attending his psychiatric clinic suffered from some physical illness.[24]

A 1967 study in the *American Journal of Psychiatry* investigated 46 patients who had carcinoma (a type of cancer) of the pancreas, an illness which is very difficult to diagnose in its early stages. The result was that 76 percent had psychiatric symptoms which appeared to be closely related to the initial presence of the carcinoma growth. Symptoms of depression, anxiety, and premonition of serious illness were characteristic. The "psychiatric symptoms" appeared before any others in nearly half of the patients.[25]

Researcher Erwin Koranyi's 1972 study published in the *Canadian Psychiatric Association Journal* and presented to the Sixth World Congress of Psychiatry in 1977, showed that half of the people seeking psychiatric help in a clinic population had readily diagnosable physical problems which were often the sole cause for their mental symptoms.

In a 1977 study of the deaths of psychiatric patients, Koranyi found that 80 percent were physically ill at time of death. People had died from undiagnosed or misdiagnosed physical maladies such as cancer of the pancreas, water on the brain, bronchial cancer, syphilis, diabetes, and hardening of the arteries.

In 1979, Koranyi reported that out of 2,090 psychiatric patients referred to a Canadian outpatient clinic, 43 percent were suffering from one or more major, previously undetected physical illnesses, including hepatitis, syphilis, malaria, cancer, hypoglycemia, vitamin deficiencies, anemia, epilepsy, heart disease, asthma, and ulcers.

He stated: "Conditions believed to be primarily psychiatric or 'psycho-somatic' in nature, but in fact concealing a physical illness, may don the apparel of a depression, an anxiety state, apathy,...aggression, a variety of sexual problems, delusions, hallucinations, confusional states, or changes in the customary features of the personality. No single psychiatric symptom exists that cannot at times be caused or aggravated by various physical illnesses.[26]

A major report confirming these findings was presented at the 1980 convention of the American Psychiatric Association. It was found that out of 100 patients:

• 76 percent were found to be psychotic at the time of admission.

• 46 percent of the 100 patients were found to have a previously unrec-ognized or undiagnosed medical illness underlying or exacerbating their mental problems.

• 28 of these 46 patients (61 percent) showed a dramatic and rapid clearing of their mental problems following treatment for their medical condition.

• 18 more patients experienced a significant improvement of their mental condition following medical treatment.

• 80 percent of the patients studied were found to have a previously undetected physical disorder requiring treatment.

Illustrative of this phenomena is the case of Jeanette Wright of Bear Creek, Wisconsin. For thirty-five years she was labeled by psychiatrists as variously schizophrenic, manic depressive, and acutely psychotic. She was treated with large quantities of psychiatric drugs as well as electroshocks. After enduring this nightmare for most of her life, she was finally correctly diagnosed by a physician as having hypothyroidism.

She was cured in 11 days.

According to Dr. Douglas Hunt, author of a 1988 self-help book on anxiety disorders, "Many of the symptoms seen in patients with an over-active thyroid gland are also found in those with high levels of anxiety. Naturally, any highly anxious patients should be screened for thyroid disease to avoid misdiagnosis.[27]

Psychiatrists have access to this vast body of data; many know it. Why, then, do they not apply it?

In spite of the obvious role medical illness plays, Drs. E. Cheraskin and W. M. Ringsdorf, Jr. of the University of Alabama, wrote in 1974, "In an informal survey of psychiatrists in the Washington, D.C., area a highly placed American Psychiatric Association official found that not one had ever requested medical information of any sort when accepting a new patient for treatment. Only rarely did they ask a patient if he was taking any drugs before prescribing their own favorite medication, despite the possibility that their prescription could be fatally incompatible with something already in the patient's medicine chest."[28]

Nutrition also plays a factor.

In 1975, Carlton Fredericks, a world-renowned nutritionist, detailed cases of patients who responded immediately to vitamin and mineral therapy after having shown no improvement through conventional psychiatry.

Dr. H. L. Newbold taught traditional psychiatry at Northwestern University Medical School until he found the connection between nutritional disorder and mental unrest. In his 1975 *Mega-Nutrients for Your Nerves*, Newbold describes hundreds of case histories, including his own, where mild anxiety and depression were eliminated by implementing the latest scientific knowledge about nutrition.[29]

George Watson, former professor of philosophy of science at the University of Southern California, became aware that many mental and emotional disorders stem from the physical malfunction of the body's metabolism. In his 1972 book *Nutrition and Your Mind: The Psychochemical Response*, he describes research in which more than 300 subjects yielded significant improvement rates:

"The rate of improvement we have found among those suffering from virtually every kind of mental illness is very high—about 80 percent—and we have seen dramatic case histories of complete clinical remissions in what heretofore have been considered almost intractable illness."[30]

Eric Braverman, director of research at the Atkins Center in New York City and Carl Pfeiffer, director of the Brain Bio Center in Rocky Hill, New Jersey, documented the therapeutic effect of amino acids (the constituents of protein) on mental and physical health. In their 1987 *The Healing Nutrients Within: Facts, Findings, and New Research on Amino Acids*, these doctors presented hundreds of clinical studies on the medical application of these nutritional substances. Amino acids, they asserted, can be used to treat depression and are an alternative to psychiatric drugs. [31]

Anorexia nervosa, a condition marked by loss of appetite and self-starvation to the point of death, has also been shown to diminish with doses of zinc or amino acids. [32]

Former psychiatrist William H. Philpott, now a specialist in nutritional brain allergies, reports, "Mental illness and an assortment of physical diseases can result from a low concentration in the brain of any one of the following vitamins:

"Thiamine (B-1), niacin (B-3), pyridoxine (B-6), hydroxocobalamin (B-12), pantothenic acid (B-5), folic acid and ascorbic acid (C).

"Volunteers fed a diet which was low in pantothenic acid very quickly became emotionally upset, irritable, quarrelsome, sullen, depressed, and dizzy.

Symptoms resulting from B-12 deficiencies range from poor concentration to stuporous depression, severe agitation and hallucinations.

Evidence showed that certain nutrients could stop neurotic and psychotic reactions and that the results could be immediate." [33]

Academic or behavioral problems, often called Attention Deficit Disorder by the psychiatric world, can also respond to nutritional measures. A study published in 1986 correlates a modification of diet in 803 New York City public schools with significantly improved test scores. For four years, amounts of sugar and food additives were lowered in the children's diets, after which these children's academic performance improved 16 percent against the national average. [34]

There may also be a direct correlation between diet and some criminal behavior. Studies at juvenile facilities in Virginia, Alabama, and California reveal that restricting foods with high allergy potentials dramatically reduced antisocial behavior. [35]

Nonpsychiatric methods have also been shown to cure phobias. In 1986,

Dr. Harold Levinson, associate professor of psychiatry at New York University Medical Center, proposed that most "phobias" are due to an easily diagnosable inner-ear dysfunction and not to emotional illness. In his book *Phobia Free* Levinson points out that 90 percent of all phobias are due to a hidden physical problem and respond to motion sickness medications and rest.[36]

Dr. Douglas Hunt, one of America's foremost experts on phobias, cured his own with a nutritional program of vitamins, minerals, and amino acids. In *No More Fears* Hunt writes that anxieties can originate from nutritional deficiencies and explains how such deficiencies come about and how nutritional supplementation can bring about positive results.[37]

Dr. Alan Goldstein, professor of psychiatry at Temple University in Philadelphia, agrees that vitamin deficiencies can worsen phobias. In his 1987 book, *Overcoming Agoraphobia: Conquering Fear of the Outside World*, he outlines his highly effective, drug-free program that has helped hundreds of people conquer their fears. Goldstein discovered that even the most severe phobias can be overcome by breathing from the diaphragm, putting one's attention on the present, and looking at things around one's immediate environment. He points out that tranquilizers are addictive and create psychological dependency, destroying the patient's ability to regain control over his own responses to his problems. "I have never seen anyone who was able to change his or her self-perception of 'sick' to 'well' while on drugs," Goldstein says.[38]

According to 1989 findings by the Board on Environmental Studies and Toxicology of the National Academy of Sciences, one in seven Americans is sensitive to household chemicals.[39] This sensitivity can bring about manifestations of mental problems. The same is true of high levels of heavy metals, like lead or cadmium, in the body.

Pediatrician Doris Rapp explains in *The Impossible Child* how children's allergies to common household items can cause trouble for youngsters, yet can be detected and effectively treated.[40]

Dr. John Nash Ott (originator of time-lapse photography) discovered that long periods under fluorescent lights cause some people to become tense and irritable. He found that emotional behavior improves dramatically when full-spectrum lights, designed to approximate natural daylight, are used instead.[41]

Even periods of withdrawal from being bombarded by sensory stimulation produces radical improvements in a variety of mental disorders.

In his 1990 book *Rickie*, psychiatrist Frederic Flach tells the harrowing story of what happened to his own daughter when he turned her over to the mental health system. After an emotional outburst at the age of thirteen, Rickie was institutionalized and diagnosed as schizophrenic. For ten years she suffered the ordeal of private and state mental hospitalizations, including restraints, drugs, and electric shocks.

When a prominent psychiatrist recommended lobotomizing Rickie, Flach finally rebelled against the practices of his profession and sought alternatives. Dr. Melvin Kaplan discovered Rickie had a visual perception problem; Dr. Carl Pfeiffer of the Brain Bio Center found Rickie also had a metabolic imbalance. Extensive vitamin treatment and special glasses containing prisms freed Rickie from her former "psychiatric" symptoms and restored her to a productive life.

All of the "respected" psychiatrists Flach consulted during the ten years of Rickie's ordeal had shunned such alternative treatment. Flach related that, because of his own psychiatric training, the idea that diet could overcome mental problems "struck me as preposterous." Yet Dr. Pfeiffer confided to Flach that other physicians had also turned to the nutritional program at the Bio Center, when it was their child or loved one who needed help.

In the 1974 book, *Psychodietetics*, authors Cheraskin, Ringsdorf, and Brecher remark, "All our research, everything in our clinical experience over the past twenty-five years, has convinced us that you can improve your emotional state by improving your nutrition: by making sure that every body cell receives optimal amounts of every essential nutrient."

In short, there is a great deal of nonpsychiatric help available to those who seek it.

These are *not* created realities.

These are actual physical solutions to real medical problems.

They are the real answers to what is actually wrong with the mentally troubled—a far cry from the pat, unsolvable response, "mental illness."

TRULY HELPING THE MENTALLY DISTURBED

The first action one can take to help those in mental distress is to *not* tell them they are mentally ill. Do not tell them they have a psychiatric disorder.

369

They are having enough trouble as it is. They do not need a barrage of advice on how mentally sick they are or how wrong they are.

More than anything they need rest and security.

Secondly, do not put them in a mental institution with conditions the way they are today in these facilities; this only adds to the environmental disturbance they must deal with and overloads an already overwhelmed mind.

In rare instances, a judicious use of drugs may initially be necessary to deal with violence or extreme situations such as life-threatening sleeplessness, starvation, etc.

As soon as possible, the person should receive a full, searching examination by a medical doctor.

This should be done to *find* what is wrong, not to see if anything is there. Nutritional deficiencies should be investigated as well.

A great many things could be the cause.

Hall and Popkin list:
• 21 medical conditions that can cause anxiety
• 12 conditions that can cause depression
• 56 conditions that can cause mental disturbance in general
• 40 types of drugs that can create "psychiatric symptoms"

The 1986 book, *Ill Not Insane,* lists over 140 medical problems which can cause mental troubles.[41]

Treat what is found in the medical exam. Get further tests if nothing is showing.

The insane individual is commonly in pain and may not even know it. His "switchboard" may be so overloaded by such stimuli that he can no longer function and behaves strangely.

In addition to any medical treatment required, *let the individual rest in a safe environment with no harassment and with ample food.*

He may have to rest a short time or long, depending on his condition and on him. Tolerance and patience are the jewel virtues in helping such an individual.

Note: people with extensive histories of past psychiatric treatment may have a hard time. Drugs and electroshock take their toll on the mind and nervous system and the natural healing mechanisms can be altered or, in extreme circumstances, destroyed in such people. Whatever the circumstances, any effort is well worth trying.

When treated as above he has a chance to come out of it.

Unlike those treated with shock and drugs, he will truly understand what occurred and will not spend the rest of his life wondering what is "wrong" with him.

And he will probably not relapse as the medical condition has been found.

However, if the psychosis recurs, do the program again. The medical condition could have returned or he may have something new or something that was missed the first time.

A LOOK TOWARD TOMORROW

Standard medical (nonpsychiatric) treatments can cure many—perhaps most—cases of "mental illness."

Rest and food in an unharassed environment can help a great many more.

And these are nonviolent means. No intrusive drugs, cutting, or shock.

It gives the mentally disturbed a truly humane chance to live again.

In 1978, psychiatrist E. Fuller Torrey, then director of St. Elizabeth's Hospital, a mental institution in Washington, D.C., predicted that psychiatrists will have no more patients when physical illnesses are referred to appropriate and more competent specialists, and when people with simple "problems of living" are referred to nonpsychiatric professionals who use educational approaches.

"With nobody left to call a patient," he wrote, "psychiatry will wither and die."[42]

Chapter XIII

...The Single Most Destructive Force...

It has been said that evidence speaks for itself.

Of course, for this to be true, evidence must be heard and understood. And it must be viewed with an intent toward knowing the truth.

In Chapter I we posed the question: Is psychiatry, as Thomas Szasz has claimed, "the single most destructive force that has affected the American society within the last fifty years"?

This is a staggering accusation. In fact, it slanders an entire occupation that purports internationally to do nothing but help others.

Yet nothing—certainly no good—would be served by a critical inquiry into a profession that had done no wrong.

Still as we noted when the question was posed, there was a ring of truth in Szasz's contention.

And, in fact, by reviewing the mountain of documentation of what psychiatry has *really* done, what other conclusion can we come to?

An honest inquiry into the driving force behind our soaring crime, drug abuse, immorality, and illiteracy finds *psychiatry* at the helm at every turn.

This pernicious influence has been so pervasive, so cancerous, it has become hard to grasp, hard to see, and almost impossible to believe.

It is true, the evidence speaks for itself.

A simple look at the statistics speaks volumes.

Soaring crime, illiteracy, and social decay have paralleled the increase in psychiatric funding and the rise in numbers of psychiatrists.

And the patterns psychiatry follows again and again are exceedingly clear.

1. *Psychiatry falsely claims to be a science.*

Continuously we hear these doctors refer to the "scientific" basis of their profession. When *Time* referred to Robert Spitzer's *DSM* hearings as "a bit of old-fashioned horse trading," Spitzer fired a letter off to the magazine, asserting, "We are scientists and not horse traders."[1]

The truth is their findings, pronouncements and treatments have no scientific basis. Witness the fact that their members are massively splintered into all manner of theories.

Their ideas of "mental illness" are a product of faith, not scientific proof. They have believed in schizophrenia for a century, yet have no evidence it exists.

When we try to fit psychiatry into the narrow definition of a true science, it fails the test miserably.

But, as we have seen, by promoting itself as a *science*, psychiatry has placed itself before the public, the government, and the courts as a medical discipline based on proven laws. Through this, it has claimed authority. Yet its members have shown themselves to be incapable of resolving the problems of the human condition. They are ridiculed as frauds in our judicial system. Nonpsychiatric physicians scoff at them.

The emperor has no clothes.

While their non-scientific basis may make for laughable theories and claims, their presence in our society as *scientists* has done grave damage.

It is no joke.

Wearing the mantle of science, they have slipped into our education system, our court rooms, our homes, our offices, our legislatures, our government, and our minds. As we have abundantly shown, their entry into each realm, like an ape at the helm, has brought a sudden crash onto the rocks. And these are usually rocks that society, using common sense, avoided for centuries until psychiatrists came along.

This assertion that psychiatry is a science has brought untold ruin to those who have innocently opened their doors to psychiatric help.

2. *Despite its declared altruistic motives, psychiatry is a business with the*

primary motive of making money for its practitioners.

If we look at the actions we have recounted in previous chapters with the realization that psychiatry is a business, their actions become much clearer.

It explains why the APA would push for the government funding of psychiatric training. It explains why there was such a drive to open community mental health centers around the country to create a near-infinite demand for psychiatry. It offers a reason why psychiatric services and illness seem to follow where the money is.

When government funds were made available for "handicapped children," mental disorders for youngsters suddenly appeared in the *DSM* a few years later. Yet, when government funding of community mental health centers was cut and the insane were left out on the street, no concerted psychiatric action was taken to help these people as there was no financial gain in it.

Though psychiatrists knew of psychiatric fraud long before the NME debacle, they kept quiet so as not to let the actions of their colleagues impair their reputation, or their income. Fraud continues to be widespread in psychiatry because the prime directive is to make money.

While they ostensibly worked their way into the armed services to reduce the number of mentally ill in the military, they used their position to create the government-funded NIMH and to broadcast to the country that an epidemic of mental illness was sweeping the nation.

By treating patients with pills and electroshock, they can see far more clients per day than by doing it the old-fashioned way of listening to the person's problems. By claiming the mainly natural difficulties of the elderly are "depression" or some other "disorder," Medicare and Medicaid can be tapped.

The APA's annual campaigning of "Mental Illness Awareness Week"— this is an activity of commerce intended to drive in business.

While all the "disorders" found in the *DSM* may be touted as scientific, they are simply voted by consensus. And only the most naive consumer doesn't see the fact that it is just a method to create more customers. Additionally, all these "diseases" allow psychiatrists to collect insurance money for "treating" everyday problems. Insurance companies normally will not pay for mental health services without proof there is an actual mental ailment. The *DSM* is so broad and vague psychiatrists can use it to find such an illness for any client who walks in the door.

Even ECT and psychosurgery are promoted in spite of the harm they do because they are highly profitable.

If we try to understand the actions of psychiatry from a humanitarian standpoint, all is not logical. If we look at them from a business standpoint —and from the standpoint of a quest for power—their actions may be unconscionable, but at least they are explainable.

3. *When psychiatry enters an area, the amount of "mental illness" increases.*

As we saw in Chapter IV, this became exceedingly visible when psychiatrists entered the military hierarchy in World War II. Suddenly we saw a mushrooming of rejection rates. Huge numbers of recruits became unfit for duty. Psychiatric discharges from the armed services rose astronomically.

While promising to save the American taxpayers money by reducing the amount of war veteran "mental illness" they would have to pay for, the *actual* result of psychiatric presence in the military was a continuous doubling of the numbers and cost of psychiatric discharges.

We saw the same phenomena in ensuing years. The number of psychiatrists in the U.S. increased tenfold since the war, and the number of "mental illnesses" reported in the *DSM* tripled.

In the mid-1800s "mental illness" was judged to strike one in a thousand, according to census takers. After World War II the figure being promoted was one in ten. Then we heard it was a third of the population. Now it is a half.

Psychiatrist Ron Leifer laughed at his profession's incessant "discovery" of "mental illness." "Everyone is neurotic," he said. "I have no trouble giving out diagnoses. In my office, I only see abnormal people. Out of my office, I only see normal people. It's up to me. It's just a joke. This is what I mean by this fraud, this arrogant fraud.... To make some kind of pretension that this is a scientific statement is...damaging to the culture.... The more popular psychiatry becomes, the more mentally ill people there are. This is good business."

Our courts have been no less spared. Psychiatrists have found greater and greater numbers of "syndromes" and "disorders" to explain away the most heinous and trivial of crimes. Only public outrage prevented them from declaring rapists not responsible for their behavior.

No one doubts they will "discover" more.

In our educational system, we find that the more funds made available to this profession, the more learning disabled and ADD children found.

When they try to judge dangerousness in the courtroom, study after study shows they always err. Their expertise is nil.

In short they see "illness" where it is not.

This is good for business. It is good for the psychiatrist's "self-esteem" as it makes him feel useful. It is good for the psychiatric community as a whole.

But it is *devastating* to our society. Perfectly healthy people, who may be troubled for the moment, are told they are "sick." Our children are told they are "disabled" or "special." Vast numbers of money and man-hours are lost through the psychiatric treatment of people who have simple problems in living.

The excuse of "mental disorder" is used to make acceptable every form of irresponsibility; wrecking marriages, student's hopes, careers, and standards of conduct people expect of themselves in everyday life.

This is no small thing.

Instead of a culture premised on high personal accountability, achievement, and demand for self-improvement, psychiatry has dealt us a society of victims, "sick" people who avoid stress, and have a pat excuse for every failure in living.

This is the legacy of their "discoveries."

4. *When psychiatry enters an area, conditions worsen, and it brings out the worst in people.*

Again, the evidence is overwhelming.

When they worked their doctrines and methods into our educational system, we saw literacy, competence, and test performance plunge.

The more they pervaded our children's schools with their emphasis on self-esteem, the child's feelings, and avoidance of stress, the more we saw teen pregnancies and abortions shoot out the roof. Where once stood kids whose worst crimes were throwing paper wads and lying, we now find weapon-brandishing youngsters who would put a bullet in your head as soon as look at you.

Educators, parents, law enforcement officials have asked: what kind of influence could possible turn children into such monsters? When we look at the massive influx of psychiatrists and their treatments into our children's lives, along with their Ritalin, their assault on morals and literacy, their call to do what feels good—when we see how this intrusion has coincided with the degradation of our children, what else can we conclude?

We cannot ignore the fact that psychiatric doctrines have not only damned these kids to lives of mediocrity, but to moral vacuums as well. Crime has soared, particularly youth crime. And in place of rambunctious, hard-to-control children, we have over a million youngsters downing powerful addictive drugs daily as they walk a bewildered path toward an already tarnished future.

How many parents of the 1950s would have believed the escalating drug culture among our youth since the 1960s? Such depravity would have been unfathomable. Yet within a generation, psychiatrists took the discovery of mind-altering chemicals and made "getting high" a household phrase. Instead of warning against the perils of drugs, these doctors intoxicated themselves with them, promoted them, spread them throughout our culture, and continue to hawk their "value" to this very day.

In the meantime, the abuse of these chemicals eats at the foundations of schools, families, marriage, law and order, and social well-being like a hoard of rats. Sexual mores and personal responsibility have plummeted into an abyss from which they have yet to see daylight again.

In our courts, the concept of personal accountability has become a joke. Psychiatrists have gradually reduced the insanity defense until any of us can claim the right to a pardon.

In keeping with this, psychiatrists have paraded through the media and talk shows to promote the latest illness that is striking the nation, explaining how we are all excusable because we are victims of sexual abuse, mental abuse, social abuse, or any other blameworthy source.

The result of all this is that we now live in a society where illiteracy is rampant, the family unit is an endangered species, marriage is ridiculed, decency and morality are archaic notions, and television screens across the land encourage these destructions with all the concern of a yawning hangman.

This same deterioration happened when psychiatry entered the military. Instead of delivering desperately-needed able-bodied men, psychiatrists screened out and discharged servicemen in droves, as though the armed services and the nation had an endless supply. Psychiatrists, in fact, promoted *malingering*—a practice any traditional general would have recognized as fatal to a well-disciplined military. These doctors encouraged the serviceman to look at his weakness and fears instead of his duty and capabilities. As a result, far more ended up on psychiatric disability than did in World War I.

After psychiatrists carried out their plan to empty the state hospitals by using community mental health centers, we find after billions spent, the insane have, in reality, been ignored and left to wander and sleep in our streets.

When they were allowed to formulate policy for the screening of the so-called undesirable in Hitler's Germany, they answered the call by slaughtering hundreds of thousands of innocent people and laying the foundation for the Holocaust.

In caring for our elderly, we find these doctors treat our old ones with drugs and more drugs, turning productive final years into a surreal tailspin toward death.

When psychiatry enters an area, things not only worsen, they often degenerate into conditions so sordid and decayed, they shock and demoralize. They seem unbelievable.

Who would have thought in 1960 that we would see the savage crime that stalks our streets today? Children killing children. Mothers killing babies. Kids sucking cocaine into their young bodies. Gangs running the streets of cities and towns.

What teacher at the turn of the century would have believed that our children would be allowed to leave school illiterate? That almost half the teachers would fail to pass a 6th grade math test? That universities would lower their passing requirements to appeal to the student's "self-esteem?"

We repeat the chilling 1945 words of G. Brock Chisholm, president of the World Federation for Mental Health: "The pretense is made…that to do away with right and wrong would produce uncivilized people, immorality, lawlessness and social chaos."

5. *Psychiatric treatments do more harm than good.*

Psychologist Paula Caplan wrote, "Masses of research have been done by and about mental health professionals and the work we do, but very little has been well done, and even less has produced conclusive or even very reliable information."[2]

Since they are based on unproven theories, most of the treatments of psychiatry are little more than expediencies.

Psychosurgery makes people less troublesome and more cooperative. So do ECT and drugs. These things also derange an individual's thinking and emotional responses so he cannot resolve the problems that beset him. They prey on physical health and mental well-being. Psychiatric treatments not only prevent the person from learning to deal with life, they encourage him to avoid his difficulties by diving into a world of chemical tranquility or the fog of brain damage.

As we have seen, even "talk therapy" performs no better than none at all.

The ultimate lesson of such treatments is that the incompetent individual "needs" such help to face life.

Yet the real evidence clearly shows that most people do fine without such help. And if they recover on their own, they are not left with the debilitating effects of drug and shock. Nor are they stuck with the stigma of a *DSM* label and a record of psychiatric hospitalization.

The psychiatrist's idea of "improved" is a dramatically far cry from the common man's. These doctors see dulled emotions and numbed sensibilities, and say they have done something for the person. The few success stories that psychiatry seems to muster of patients improved by their treatments are moot points. Since people recover on their own anyway, and in as good or greater numbers than those getting treatment, it is only common sense that some will recover in spite of psychiatric care.

The damaging effect of psychiatric therapies becomes very visible in the treatment of the insane. After years of treating *schizophrenia*, these doctors conclude it is virtually incurable, something the individual lives with the rest of his life. Obviously, they get this impression from the results they have had in "treating" these people.

Yet as we saw in the Vermont study and with the French patients in World War II, a large number of these patients recover with no psychiatric help at all.

If *with* treatment *none* recover, what else can we conclude but that treatment itself is harmful?

There is, of course, little doubt that the effects of ECT—brain damage, memory loss, mental confusion—are far too debilitating to offset any momentary relief this treatment could possibly give.

Drugs, with their often powerful side effects, can leave the person addicted, weak, "someone else," not there, contorting with tardive dyskinesia, or any of a thousand other bizarre reactions.

For some, psychiatrists will prescribe drug treatment for the rest of their lives, believing this is necessary to deal with their incurable biological "mental illness." Any hope of recovery or *belief* that one *has* recovered is dashed as the psychiatrist "knows" the person can't be allowed off the medication.

When people recover just as well or better without treatment, how could harmful drugs and shock be construed as anything but a detriment?

6. *The psychiatric profession is incapable of policing itself.*

When Walter Freeman roamed the country lobotomizing patients for years, there was no outcry from the profession to stop him.

Psychiatrists across the country are perfectly aware of the destructive effects of ECT, yet instead of coming forward to a government body, they remain silent and try not to offend their fellows for using a different "methodology." (10 or 20 honest organized psychiatrists protesting publicly could most likely outlaw the treatment.)

Instead of turning their colleagues in for psychiatric rape, 92 percent choose to stay silent. When the APA issued a statement opposing psychiatric sexual assault, the number of complaints against psychiatrists did not go down. It went up.

When the NME scandal hit, exposing runaway psychiatric fraud, we saw psychiatrists were well aware of it for years beforehand and did *nothing* to turn the matter around. It took a 14-year-old boy and a state senator to bring down an outrage that an entire nation of psychiatrists let slide. Even after NME, we saw that fraud roars on in psychiatry. Hundreds, thousands of doctors blithely watch it eat insurance and taxpayer money and ruin the lives of trusting patients.

While blacks rotted in concentration camp conditions in South Africa, no concerned group of psychiatrists raised a collective hand to bring it to the world's attention. It took a church digging for access that psychiatrists had at their fingertips to unearth these wretched human rights violations and bring change through their exposure.

As German psychiatrists carried out their "destruction of life devoid of value," it would be folly to think that psychiatrists in other countries—

even the U.S.—were unaware of these activities. One cannot dispose of several hundred thousand mental patients without notice.

Yet there are no banner headlines in the newspapers of World War II declaring these atrocities. No psychiatrist raised his voice in rage at this butchery.

But since these doctors, as a group, are acknowledged to be among the most immoral, what else should we expect?

With a group that has the highest rate of drug abuse, the highest rate of Medicare fraud, the highest rate of alcoholism, the highest rate of trouble from infidelity—and one that teaches young and old alike that morality is a joke—does anyone honestly expect psychiatrists to rise above their misdeeds and reform their profession?

It isn't going to happen.

How can it?

Their entire philosophy is premised on the notion that personal responsibility is not possible.

7. Psychiatrists are generally incapable of seeing themselves as the cause of the problem.

While it is abundantly clear that with the increase in numbers of psychiatrists, there has been an increase in "mental illness," a great many psychiatrists see this and other psychiatrically-caused problems backwards.

They present it as: due to the rise in mental illness, more psychiatrists are needed.

The same goes for the soaring crime and decline in education. They do not see themselves as even vaguely related to the cause. They see some mysterious influence creating these conditions and claim greater numbers of psychiatrists are needed to remedy the situation.

In looking at the fact that the more government money psychiatrists have been given, the worse the country has become, these doctors claim it happened because they weren't given *enough* money to stem the decay in time.

When looking at a patient degenerating from drugs, shock, or confinement, such psychiatrists claim the problem is that the patient wasn't brought to them soon enough.

When patients manifest psychotic behavior as a result of withdrawing from toxic psychotropic drugs, the psychiatrist usually blames it on the patient's "mental illness." He is oblivious that the drugs have done any harm at all.

In witnessing the moral decay wracking our schools, they blame it—as did Chisholm—on the stressful moral upbringing children are under and advocate even more "liberal" teachings.

Such reasoning is weaved throughout their texts and journals. Since their avowed intention is to help, they cannot grasp that they are doing harm. Or even if their actions are destructive, since it is all in the name of science and they are the authorities doing their best, it seems unreasonable to them that anyone should complain.

Psychiatrists do not believe they should be held liable for the damage done to their patients or to society. This, of course, is the ultimate irresponsibility.

THE ROUTE OUT OF THE MADNESS

As bad as it may seem as we watch the insanity in our streets, homes, schools, and society, there is a road out.

It is essentially the reverse of the path that brought us into this madness.

If we care anything at all about the quality of life for ourselves, our children, and the future, we *must* consider this. This is not a nightmare we will wake from until change takes place.

Like the delinquent youth who has abandoned his upbringing and taken up with bad company, we must ask ourselves whether we want to keep hanging with a crowd that has no future—indeed, associates who will likely destroy us.

Or have we had enough.

1. *Stop government funding of psychiatry.*

Let's be honest.

Psychiatry is no branch of medicine. As such it is a hoax.

It is at best a spurious philosophy.

It should be treated and named as one.

Thus its atheistic philosophy will not be cloaked in the trappings of "scientific fact," and run into our schools, our children's minds, and our culture without being recognized for what it is.

Any legitimacy given to it as a "science" should be removed because that is patently and demonstrably untrue.

The government should not be funding NIMH to study psychiatry's philosophical tenets. That is a violation of separation of Church and State.

After forty years and billions of dollars spent at NIMH, we have only bloated numbers of "mentally ill" and no useful form of help. In the meantime, we keep hearing about some coming breakthrough.

How foolish are we supposed to be?

Obviously these people are guessing in the dark, and wasting our money on their very expensive hobby. In two centuries they have made *negative* progress.

The government should not be putting its money into theoretical programs with a history of failure. The taxpayer does not want his money wasted paying "experts" on living who, in fact, live more incompetent lives than the man in the street.

That's foolhardy.

If psychiatry believes it is such a successful mental science, let it earn its daily bread on its own merits like the rest of the business world has to.

Stop government funding of psychiatric *training*, psychiatric *research*, and psychiatric *treatment*.

Since medical doctors can treat the insane for physical ailments—and can do it better—there is no practical reason why psychiatry, its practitioners, or its institutions should receive government money.

2. Ban shock treatment and psychosurgery.

How is it possible that in an age such as ours, with technological developments snowballing us into a space-age future, that we are still permitting people—in fact, many of our elderly—to have electricity raked through their brains in the guise of treatment?

Does anyone really believe this can be good for people?

This is little more than a modern form of medieval barbarism.

Shock treatment damages brains, memories, and personalities.

It is not even safe to make it available to people "if they choose," because psychiatrists consistently mislead the public by claiming it is "safe and effective,"—a statement even a five-year-old would immediately disagree with.

This "treatment" doesn't even help. It only "works" by trauma to the head.

No civilized society would approve of a baseball bat to the skull as treatment. The same standard should be applied to shock treatment.

As to psychosurgery, we amply covered this human experimentation in Chapter VI. Even veteran M.D.s vomited after watching Freeman rip through healthy brain tissue.

Psychosurgery's very existence is a mournful chapter in human history.

Electroshock and psychosurgery should be banned.

3. *All vestiges of psychology and psychiatry should be removed from our schools.*

Schools are for learning.

They are not for psychiatric experiments on young minds.

We once had successful methods of education in our schools. They should be used so that children of today and tomorrow can read and write with confidence and have a future to look forward to.

Any changes introduced into standard successful teaching methods should be gauged by how well they improve student performance.

Students should be challenged to be competent, not to "feel good." If they are encouraged toward true achievement, they won't need "self-esteem" classes. They'll feel *great* because they genuinely are capable in their own eyes.

All death education, extraneous sex education, group therapy, feel-good sessions, values-neutral studies—*all* teachings of this incestuous family of subjects should be stopped.

Schools are for learning.

No child should ever be adjudicated by school counselors or teachers as "hyperactive," "learning disabled," "dyslexic," or having ADD or any other such manufactured ailment.

He is a child.

He is a human being.

He is not a mental disorder.

If he is a disciplinary problem he should be treated as one, assuming he has teachers who have made a genuine effort to tolerate the youngster.

Instead of referring his parents to a psychiatrist, have them consult a nutritionist or a medical doctor or perhaps look into a different school or more workable setting. If the child is having trouble learning, find out what he missed earlier in his studies and help him understand that. Also ensure the school is using standard successful teaching methods.

Never consign a child to an oblivion of believing he is stupid by calling him "learning disabled."

Any teaching that morals or virtue or values are "opinion" and that there is no good or bad should be purged from texts and curricula. These are ruinous falsehoods.

Any psychology- or psychiatrically-based courses in teachers' colleges should be removed. They have absolutely no place in a teacher's training. Teachers are not here to fiddle with kid's minds. They are here to teach.

School programs and methods should be combed carefully for all remnants of psychiatric and psychological thought and these should be ejected.

This is the *only* way we can assure our schools are turning out competent, literate, and well-educated students who understand the world around them and have the basic tools for survival and achievement in the adult world.

4. *Remove psychiatry from our entire judicial system.*

Psychiatrists are the butt of jokes in our courts.

To let this go on as if we don't know why is foolish.

They are made fun of because they are not scientists, yet they are pretending to be.

Justice in one of Man's noblest pursuits.

Our court rooms have been established for meting out equitable treatment based on a search for the truth.

To have psychiatrists denigrate our halls of justice with pretentious theorizing, while they sell their opinions to the highest bidder is blasphemous to all that is decent in us.

Our courts are for justice.

They are about truth.

Psychiatrists have nothing but opinion—and even that provokes whispers and titters from the gallery.

They are not experts.

They should not be adjudicating whether someone is "fit to stand trial," because they don't know any better than the average man.

They have no place in a court of law.

Their presence should be banned. Their theories should be banned since they have no basis in fact.

The insanity defense should be removed from our laws. Several states have already done this and justice has not suffered.

Judges and juries have always had the option of showing leniency and mercy toward a hopeless lunatic where it is morally right to do so. That has not changed.

Abolishing the insanity defense and all of its inbred offspring—"diminished capacity," "irresistible impulse," "temporary insanity"—is imperative if we are to restore faith in our judicial system. Psychiatrists, psychologists, and all such pretended "experts" have no place in our courts.

Neither should they be in our prisons.

Our penal system is degraded enough without adding the insanity of psychiatric drugs and counseling to the mix.

Prisoners shouldn't be on drugs.

It is simply one more barrier between them and personal responsibility.

Since psychiatric counseling in prisons has been *proven* by their own studies to be useless, why confuse inmates' minds with more of it? What good can come of a philosophy that teaches him he is not responsible for his condition?

Better rehabilitation measures are available outside of psychiatry. They should be sought, piloted, and used.

5. *Outlaw involuntary commitment.*

The practice of psychiatrists holding the power of incarceration in their hands should end.

No one should be imprisoned in a hospital against his will.

The only reason alternatives have not been created in lieu of involuntary commitment is because no one has had to.

The majority of such commitments are for the benefit of family and police and have nothing to do with humane treatment of the mentally disturbed. If someone is violent or breaking the law, he should be dealt with, as are all people who do such things. We don't need psychiatrists for that.

We *do* need other sources of refuge.

Particularly we need places of asylum where the mentally disturbed can get medical help, rest, safety, and food, without degradation and terror.

As Dr. Thomas Szasz recommends in his book, *Psychiatric Slavery*, "old age homes, workshops, temporary homes for indigent persons whose family ties have been disintegrated, progressive prison communities—these and many other facilities will be needed to assume the tasks now entrusted to mental hospitals."

A great many would *want* to go to such a place, because they know at heart that is what they need.

Who wants to be put in a mental hospital?

Sane or not, human beings have certain inalienable rights.

One of them is *liberty*.

No psychiatrist or court should be allowed to take that away unless the individual has been arrested and charged with a crime.

All coercive practices used to force people into mental hospitals should be made illegal.

Any psychiatrist found to be using threats or malicious measures to get people to "accept" psychiatric treatment or who hospitalizes a patient against his will should be charged with assault and false imprisonment.

6. *Declare psychiatric rape illegal.*

There is no excuse for a therapist who takes sexual liberties with his patients.

Whether "consent" is obtained or not is irrelevant.

For a trusted counselor to prey upon the weak or misuse his position for sexual gratification is a violation of the deepest confidence.

The fact that psychiatrists and psychologists don't censure their colleagues swiftly and severely for it speaks against these professions.

This practice is wrong and it is damaging.

Psychiatric rape is already a crime in many states.

There is no reason it should not be universally illegal .

7. *Take treatment of the insane out of the hands of psychiatrists.*

Trusted with the care for our mentally disturbed, psychiatry had failed utterly to provide any humane solutions to their plight.

Poor souls have been electrically tortured, chemically imprisoned, mutilated, dumped into the streets, and forgotten in the back wards of snake pits called mental hospitals.

Today millions contort, grimace and tremble—and will to their graves—because of nerve-damaging drugs that they trustingly swallowed in the belief that it was for their own good.

Instead of receiving solace from their demons, they have been treated like experimental animals subjected to tests of yet newer theories, labeled with degraded names, and locked away—usually against their will—in houses of madness surrounded by howling wretches worse off than themselves. As a final pitch into a deeper hell, they are told by their caring doctor they will always be this way.

This is insanity in itself.

These people need rest.

They need medical care.

They need food and security.

Psychiatrists are not needed for any of this.

The insane need help.

They don't need more torture.

They should be treated with the dignity all of us deserve and would wish for ourselves if we were in their position.

The Future Beckons

Some people scoff at the idea of creating a better world where insanity, crime, and even war are distant memories.

They scoff because they think it is impossible.

It may be.

But only the most cynical of us would not want to try.

Man is capable of great evil, it is true. But there is still a native decency in us all that makes us want happiness for ourselves, those we hold dear, and even those we hardly know.

Even young Anne Frank saw this light of hope through the blackness of Nazi persecution as she and her family huddled for months in fear of jackbooted soldiers capturing them.

"In spite of everything," she wrote, "I still believe that people are really good at heart."[3]

The good is there to be cultivated.

It cannot be nurtured in a world where psychiatric doctrine and thought permeate our culture with the philosophy that we are mere animals who have no hope of finding happiness outside of a medicine cabinet.

But if we work diligently to weed out these falsehoods and provide real education, justice, asylum, and rehabilitation, there is abundant hope.

And where hope lives, dreams—even dreams of a better world—can come true.

The Citizens Commission on Human Rights

The Citizens Commission on Human Rights (CCHR) was established in 1969 by the Church of Scientology to investigate and expose psychiatry's violations of human rights and to eliminate harmful practices in the field of mental health.

CCHR was formed at a time when the victims of psychiatry were a forgotten minority group, warehoused under dreadful—often terrifying—conditions in institutions around the world. "Treatment" was both brutal and barbaric; those under psychiatric care were mercilessly experimented upon with therapeutically unproven mind-altering drugs, electric shock and psychosurgery. In short, they were being assaulted, sexually abused, irreversibly damaged or killed—all under the guise of "mental healing."

CCHR members include doctors, lawyers, civil and human rights representatives and other professionals who saw, and continue to see it as their duty "to expose and help abolish any and all physically damaging practices in the field of mental health." Co-founder of CCHR is internationally acclaimed author and Professor of Psychiatry Emeritus, Dr. Thomas Szasz. Today, there are more than 120 CCHR chapters in 27 countries around the world.

CCHR has achieved legislative reforms worldwide including: banning the use of ECT and psychosurgery for children under the age of 16; banning other harmful psychiatric treatments; legal representation and legal rights for mental patients; legislation protecting against insurance fraud and "bounty hunting"; and the creation of patient rights' codes.

CCHR works with law enforcement and health insurance fraud agencies and district attorney's offices and carries out legislative reform work with congressmen and senators and other concerned individuals and groups.

While CCHR offers assistance to persons whose rights have been violated by psychiatrists, this does not include medical or legal advice.

CCHR recommends that persons who feel they suffer adverse reactions from psychiatric treatments, seek competent medical examination by non-psychiatric, caring medical specialists.

CCHR documents cases involving many different kinds of psychiatric abuses such as, but not limited to, involuntary commitment (false imprisonment), forced treatment (drugs, electric shock and psychosurgery), sexual abuse or rape by psychiatrists and psychologists, child abuse (drugging, sexual assault), criminal assault or other physical abuse, fraud (especially health insurance fraud), and experimentation.

It assists victims of such psychiatric abuse and their families and friends to take the appropriate action necessary to bring the perpetrator(s) of the abuse to justice. Often the person wants to use his or her case to help CCHR expose the need for legislative reforms to prevent such abuse from happening again. In this way, CCHR's actions include assisting the individual in filing criminal, disciplinary or other complaints, arranging for the individual to participate in radio, TV or other media interviews, and meeting with legislators, educators and other authorities.

The international headquarters of CCHR is located at:

Citizens Commission on Human Rights

6362 Hollywood Boulevard

Los Angeles, California 90028

213-467-4242

800-869-2247

REFERENCE NOTES

CHAPTER I
WHAT IS HAPPENING TO US?

1. William J. Bennett, "Quantifying America's Decline," *Wall Street Journal*, March 15, 1993.

2. "Where Are Morals Heading?," *Awake!* (Watchtower Bible and Tract Society of New York), August 8, 1993, p. 4.

3. *Europe 2000-Human Resources*, "Crime: UK tops EC crime rate," April 1992, Vol. 4, Section 3.

4. Thomas Szasz, *The Myth of Mental Illness*, Revised edition, (New York: Harper and Row, 1974), back cover.

5. Interview, Thomas Szasz, September 17, 1993.

6. Robin McKown, *Pioneers in Mental Health*, (New York: Dodd, Mead and Co., 1961), p. 192.

7. As quoted in Emil Kraepelin, *One Hundred Years of Psychiatry*, (New York: Philosophical Library, Inc., 1961), p. 11. Translated from the German essay written in 1917.

8. J.R. Kantor, *The Scientific Evolution of Psychology*, (Chicago: The Principia Press, 1969), p. 186.

9. Harvey Mindess, *Makers of Psychology: The Personal Factor*, (New York: Insight Books, 1988), p. 32.

10. Quoted in Paolo Lionni and Lance Klass, *The Leipzig Connection* (Portland, Ore.: Heron Books, 1980), p. 8.

11. Clarence J. Karier, *Scientists of the Mind*, (Chicago: University of Illinois Press, 1986), p. 28.

12. E.M. Thornton, *The Freudian Fallacy*, (New York: The Dial Press, 1984), pp. 144-45.

13. Quoted in Peter Gay, *A Godless Jew*, (New Haven, Connecticut: Yale University Press, 1987), p. 6.

14. Sigmund Freud, *The Future of an Illusion*, SE XXI, p. 38.

15. Interview with Dr. Al Parides, December 17, 1993.

16. Kraepelin, *op. cit.*, p. 9.

17. David B. Larson, et al., "Systematic Analysis of Research on Religious Variables in Four Major Psychiatric Journals," *The American Journal of Psychiatry*. Vol. 143, No. 3 (March, 1986), pp. 329-334.

18. "Report of the Task Force on Religion and Psychiatry: Phase III," *American Journal of Psychiatry*, 135:6, June 1978, p. 776. The report lists 25 percent as atheist and 33 percent as agnostic.

19. Parides, *op. cit.*

20. *Webster's New World Dictionary*, (New York: The World Publishing Company, 1988), p. 86.

21. *Statistical Abstracts of the United States*, 1994, p. 69. This is based on a continental population of approximately 375,000,000.

22. Henry Chu and John Dart, "Christ on Campus," *Los Angeles Times*, April 3, 1994, p. B6.

23. George Washington as quoted in Our Ageless Constitution, (Ashboro, North Carolina: W. David Stedman Associates, 1987), p. 132.

24. Benjamin Franklin, "The Autobiography of Benjamin Franklin," in Charles W. Eliot (ed.), *The Harvard Classics*, (New York: P.F. Collier and Son, 1937), Vol. 1, pp. 79-80.

25. G. Brock Chisholm, "The Reestablishment of Peacetime Society—The William Alanson White Memorial Lectures, Second Series," *Psychiatry: Journal of the Biology and the Pathology of Interpersonal Relations*, February 1946, p. 9.

26. *Ibid.*, pp. 7,9.

27. *Ibid.*, p. 9.

28. John Steinbecker, *The Child Seducers*, (Fullerton, CA: Educator Publications, 1970).

29. William Menninger, "Presidential Address," *New Directions in American Psychiatry 1944-1968*, (Washington, D.C.: American Psychiatric Assn., 1969), p. 79.

30. Amy Wallace and Bob Pool, "Jurors' Rift Emerged Early and Ran Deep," *Los Angeles Times*, January 29, 1994, p. A28.

31. *Ibid.*

32. *Ibid.*, p. A1.

33. *Ibid.*, p. A28.

34. John Taylor, "Irresistable Impulses, Unbelievable Verdicts," *Esquire*, April 1994, pp. 96-97.

35. Howard P. Rome, "Presidential Address," *New Directions in American Psychiatry 1944-1968*, *op. cit.*, p. 319.

36. "No Sexual Harrassment Allowed," a brochure written by the California Chamber of Commerce, 1993, Sacramento, Calif.

37. *Wall Street Journal*, Pop Culture and Drugs, February 26, 1995.

38. *TV Times*, April 3-9, 1994, p. 44, found in *Los Angeles Times*, April 3, 1994.

39. Barnaby Conrad, *The Complete Guide to Writing Fiction*, (Cincinnati, Ohio: Writer's Digest Books, 1990), pp. 172-3.

40. D. Ewen Cameron, "Presidential Address," *New Directions in American Psychiatry 1944-1968*, *op. cit.*, p. 119.

41. Chisholm, *op. cit.*, p.8.

42. Thornton, *op. cit.*, p. 144.

43. Interview, Dr. William Glazer, December 14, 1993.

44. Quoted in Brian Doyle, "The Impaired Psychiatrist," *Psychiatric Annals*, Vol. 17, No. 11, November 1987, p. 760

45. H.J. Eysenck, "What's the Truth About Psychoanalysis?," *Reader's Digest*, January 1960, p. 41.

46. In the 1920s the psychiatric Mental Hygiene movement published tracts, giving advice on marriage, child rearing, and such. The "Spock" referred to is Dr. Benjamin Spock, an advisor on the raising of children in the 1960s.

47. Inez Robb, "How to Stay Married," *Reader's Digest*, June 1960, p. 169.

CHAPTER II
A LOOK BEHIND
THE WIZARD'S SMOKE:
DOES PSYCHIATRY
ACTUALLY WORK?

1. Emil Kraepelin, *One Hundred Years of Psychiatry*, (New York: Philosophical Library, Inc., 1961), p. 26. Translated from the German essay written in 1917.

2. Karl Bowman, "Presidential Address," *New Directions in American Psychiatry 1944-1968*, (Washington, D.C.: American Psychiatric Assn., 1969), p. 15.

3. William Menninger, "Presidential Address," *New Directions in American Psychiatry*, p. 71.

4. "Mental Illness," *World Book Encyclopedia*, 1984, p. 331.

5. American Psychiatric Assn. Campaign Kit 1989, opening letter by Harvey Ruben, M.D.

6. *Ibid.*, Section on "About this year's campaign," p. 1.

7. *Ibid.*, Section on "About legislators," p. 2.

8. *Ibid.*, opening letter.

9. *Ibid.*, Section on "About the public," p. 11.

10. *Ibid.*, Section on "About the public," p. 2.

11. *Ibid.*, "Let's Talk About Mental Illness," column #1.

12. Interview, Walter Afield, January 11, 1994.

13. APA Campaign Kit 1989, Section on "About the Media," p. 3.

14. Senate Joint Resolution 55, February 7,

1989.

15. "Giving Mental Illness Its Research Due," *Science*, May 30, 1986, p. 1085.

16. Joan McCord, "A Thirty-Year Follow-Up of Treatment Effects," *American Psychologist*, March 1978.

17. "Thirty-year follow up: Counseling fails," *Science News*, November 28, 1977.

18. C.B. Truax and K.M. Mitchell, "Research on Certain Therapist Interpersonal Skills in Relation to Process and Outcome," in A.E. Bergen and S.L. Garfield (eds.) *Handbook of Psychotherapy and Behavior Change*, (New York: John Wiley and Sons, 1971), p. 340.

19. N.A. Cummings, "Turning Bread into Stones," *American Psychologist*, 1979, *34*, pp.1119-20.

20. E. Fuller Torrey, *Nowhere To Go*, (New York: Harper & Row, 1988), p. 18.

21. Phil Brown, *The Transfer of Care*, (London: Routledge and Kegan Paul, 1985), p. 134.

22. James V. McConnell, *Understanding Human Behavior: An Introduction to Psychology*, (New York: Holt, Rinehart and Winston), p. 587.

23. *Ibid.*

24. Thomas Kiernan, *Shrinks, Etc.*, (New York: Dial Press, 1974), p. 55.

25. *Ibid.*, p. xii.

26. *Ibid.*, p. 56.

27. Bernie Zilbergeld, *The Shrinking of America*, (Boston, Mass.: Little, Brown and Co., 1983), p. 26.

28. Karl Menninger, "The Course of Illness," *Menninger Clinic Bulletin*, Vol. 25, No. 5 (September 1961).

29. P.M. Boffey, "Schizophrenia: Insights Fail to Halt Rising Toll," *New York Times*, March 16, 1986, pp. 1, 32.

30. Stanley Peele, *Diseasing of America*, (Lexington, Mass.: Lexington Books, 1989), p. 16.

31. "Schizophrenia," *Diagnostic and Statistical Manual of Mental Disorders*

(Third Edition—Revised), (Washington, D.C.: American Psychiatric Assn., 1987), p. 191.

32. "Schizophrenia," *Diagnostic and Statistical Manual of Mental Disorders*, Third Edition, (Washington, D.C.: American Psychiatric Assn., 1980), p. 185.

33. S.B. Gaze and E. Robins, "Suicide and Primary Affective Disorder," *British Journal of Psychiatry*, No. 117, 1970, pp. 437-8.

34. Reading File, "Suicide," *Children Today*, November-December 1984, p. 5.

35. Robert C. Haynes and Janice K. Marques, "Patterns of Suicide Among Hospitalized Mentally Disordered Offenders," *Suicide and Life-Threatening Behavior*, Vol. 14 (2), Summer 1984 (Human Sciences Press).

36. D.P. Kraft and H.M. Babigian, "Suicide by Persons With and Without Psychiatric Contacts," *Archives of General Psychiatry*, Vol. 33, February 1976.

37. B. Barraclough, et al., "A Hundred Cases of Suicide: Clinical Aspects," *British Journal of Psychiatry* (1974), 125, pp. 367-8.

38. Marjorie Wallace, "Coroners criticized over mental patients," *London Times*, January 21, 1986, p. 3.

39. Interview with Thomas Szasz, September 17, 1993.

40. Zilbergeld, *op. cit.*, p. 169.

41. Kiernan, *op. cit.*, p. 81.

42. J. Hillman and M. Ventura, *We've Had 100 Years of Psychotherapy and the World's Getting Worse*, (San Francisco, Calif.: Harper, 1993).

43. Walter Fisher, Joseph Mehr, Philip Truckenbrod, *Power, Greed, and Stupidity in the Mental Health Racket*, (Philadelphia: Westminster Press, 1973).

44. H. H. Strupp and S. W. Hadley, "Specific vs. Nonspecific Factors in

Psychotherapy," *Archives of General Psychiatry*, 1979, 36, p. 1134.

45. J.A. Durlak, "Comparative Effectiveness of Paraprofessional and Professional Helpers," *Psychological Bulletin*, 1979, *86*, pp. 88-89.

46. *Psychiatry's Multibillion-Dollar Fraud*, CCHR, 1993.

47. Fisher et. al., *op. cit.*, p. 117.

48. Zilbergeld, *op. cit.*, p. 148.

49. Jeffrey Mervis, "NIMH Data Points Way to Effective Treatment," *American Psychological Assn. Monitor*, July 1986, 1, p. 13.

50. Stanley Peele, *Diseasing of America*, (Lexington, Mass.: Lexington Books, 1989), pp. 14, 15.

51. Interview with Leonard Frank, January 4, 1994.

52. Interview with Lucille Barry, January 7, 1994.

53. Jonas Robitscher, quoted in Zilbergeld, *op. cit.*, p. 11.

54. Nathan Hale, Jr., *Freud and the Americans*, (New York: Oxford University Press), p. 235.

55. Paul Appelbaum quoted from interview in Rael Jean Isaac and Virginia Armat, *Madness in the Streets*, (New York: The Free Press, 1990), p. 345.

56. Tipper Gore claimed 28 percent—in an editorial reply.

57. Ronald D. Laing, *Wisdom, Madness, and Folly* (New York: McGraw-Hill, 1985), p. 126.

58. Council on Scientific Affairs, American Medical Assn., "Results and Implications of the AMA-APA Physician Mortality Project," *Journal of the American Medical Association*, Vol. 257, No. 21, June 5, 1987, p. 2950. The suicide rate in the general population is given as 12.3 per 100,000 vs. 61 per 100,000 for psychiatrists. Also see below.

59. Harvey D. Campbell, "The Prevalence and Ramifications of Psychopathology in Psychiatric Residents: An

Overview," *American Journal of Psychiatry*, 139:11, November 1982, p. 1406. The rate for residents is 106 per 100,000.

60. C.L. Rich, F.N. Pitts, Jr. "Suicide by Psychiatrists: A Study of Medical Specialists Among 18,730 Consecutive Physician Deaths During a Five-Year Period, 1967-72," *The Journal of Clinical Psychiatry, 41*, August 8, 1980, p. 261.

61. W. Freeman, "Psychiatrists Who Kill Themselves: A Study in Suicide," *American Journal of Psychiatry*, Vol. 124, No. 6, December 1967, p. 847.

62. *Journal of the American Medical Association*, *op. cit.*, pp. 2949-53.

63. David W. Previn, "Physician Suicide: The Psychiatrist's Role," in Stephen C. Scheiber and Brian B. Doyle (eds.), *The Impaired Physician*, (New York: Plenum Publishing Corp., 1983), p. 44.

64. Thomas Maeder, "Wounded Healers," *Atlantic Monthly*, January 1989, p. 38.

65. *Ibid.*

66. *Ibid.*

67. LeClair Bissell and Jane K. Skorina, "One Hundred Alcoholic Women in Medicine," *Journal of the American Medical Association*, June 5, 1987, p. 2940.

68. William McAuliffe, et al., "Psychoactive Drug Use Among Practicing Physicians and Medical Students," *New England Journal of Medicine*, September 25, 1986, p. 808.

69. Merian Kirchner, "What Makes Other Marriages Lousy," *Medical Economics*, October 1, 1979, pp. 42-3.

70. Stephen B. Seager, *Psych Ward*, (New York: G.P. Putnam's Sons, 1991), pp. 17-18.

71. *Ibid.*, p. 211.

72. Maeder, *op. cit.*

73. A. Bergin quoted by Zilbergeld, *op. cit.* p. 23.

74. Thomas Szasz, *Insanity: The Idea and*

its Consequences, (New York: John Wiley and Sons, 1987), p. 245.

75. J. Leven, *Satan, His Psychotherapy and Cure by the Unfortunate Doctor Kassler,* (New York: Knopf, 1982), p. 466.

76. N. Gartrell, et al., "Psychiatrist-Patient Sexual Contact: Results of a National Survey, I: Prevalence," *American Journal of Psychiatry,* Vol. 143, No. 9, September 1986, p. 1126.

77. *The Daily Report,* August 2, 1988, p. A8.

78. Sheldon H. Kardener, et al., "A Survey of Physicians' Attitudes and Practices Regarding Erotic and Nonerotic Contact with Patients," *American Journal of Psychiatry,* October 1973, p. 1080.

79. Gartrell, *op. cit.,* p. 1126.

80. "Sex and Psychotherapy," *Newsweek,* April 13, 1992, p. 53.

81. Erica E. Goode, "The Ultimate Betrayal," *U.S. News & World Report,* March 12, 1990.

82. Kardner, *op. cit.,* pp. 1077-81.

83. J. Foreman, "Counselors Profile Therapist-Offender," *Boston Globe,* August 31, 1986, p. 8.

84. J.C. Holroyd and A.M. Brodsky, "Psychologists Attitudes and Practices Regarding Erotic and Nonerotic Physical Contact With Patients," *American Psychologist,* 32:843-49, 1977.

85. Kenneth S. Pope, et al., "Sexual Intimacy in Psychological Training," *American Psychologist,* Vol. 32, No. 10, August 1979, p. 682.

86. Clifford L. Linedecker, *Children in Chains,* (New York: Everest House, 1981), p. 108.

87. Letterhead, Rene Guyon Society, 256 So. Robertson Bl., Beverly Hills, CA 90211.

88. Linedecker, *op. cit.,* p. 108.

89. *Ibid.,* p. 109.

90. *Ibid.,* p. 108.

91. Bowman, *op. cit.,* p. 25.

92. Winfred Overholser, "Presidential Address," *New Directions in American Psychiatry,* pp. 55, 61.

93. Harvey J. Tompkins, "The Presidential Address: The Physician in Contemporary Society," *American Journal of Psychiatry,* 124:1, July 1967, p. 40.

94. John P. Spiegel, "Presidential Address: Psychiatry—A High-Risk Profession," *American Journal of Psychiatry,* 132:7, July 1975, p. 693.

95. Joseph T. English, "Presidential Address: Patient Care for the Twenty-First Century: Asserting Professional Values Within Economic Restraints," *American Journal of Psychiatry,* 150:9, September 1993, p. 1293.

96. Carl Binger, *Revolutionary Doctor: Benjamin Rush, 1746-1813,* (New York: W.W. Norton and Co., 1966), pp. 246-47.

97. Bowman, *op. cit.,* p. 15.

98. Kiernan, *op. cit.,* p. xi.

99. Thomas Szasz, *The Myth of Mental Illness,* Revised ed., (New York: Harper and Row, 1974), p. 94.

100. *Ibid.*

101. Fisher, et al., *op. cit.,* pp. 117-18.

102. Carl Rogers, quoted by Zilbergeld, *op. cit.,* p. 114.

103. Chu and Trotter, *op. cit.,* p. xix.

104. Doyle, *op. cit.,* p. 760.

105. Jean Starobinski, *A History of Medicine,* (New York: Hawthorne Books, 1964), pp. 31-33.

CHAPTER III
FROM LUNATIC ASYLUMS
TO LIVING ROOMS

1. American Psychiatric Assn., *One Hundred Years of American Psychiatry,* (New York: Columbia University Press, 1944), p. 16.

2. Quoted in F. Alexander and S. Selesnick, *The History of Psychiatry,* (New York: Harper and Row, 1966), p. 122—Quoting B. Rush *Medical Inquiries and Observations upon the*

Diseases of the Mind, 5th ed., pp. 106-7, Gregg and Elliott, 1835.

3. Thomas Szasz, *The Manufacture of Madness*, (New York: Harper and Row, 1970), pp. 146-47.

4. Quoted in Walter Bromberg, *From Shaman to Psychotherapist*, (Chicago: Henry Regnery Co.), p. 107.

5. *Ibid.*

6. *Ibid.*

7. Szasz, *op. cit.*, p. 45—Referencing B. Rush, *Medical Inquiries, etc.*, p.110.

8. *Ibid.*, p. 157. Quoting B. Rush from William Stanton's *The Leopard's Spots*, p. 13.

9. Quoted in Martin Gross, *The Psychological Society*, (New York: Simon and Schuster), 1978, p. 16.

10. As quoted in "Bosnia: The Minds Behind Purification," published by CCHR, January 1994, pp. 11-12.

11. As quoted in "Bosnia: Ending the Religious Genocide," *The Crusader*, August 1993, pp. 1, 6.

12. David Hothersall, *History of Psychology*, (Philadelphia: Temple University Press, 1984), p. 268.

13. Charles Darwin, quoted in Bernhard Schreiber, (San Francisco: Section 5 Books, 1983), pp. 11-12.

14. Schreiber, *op. cit.*, p. 11.

15. Quoted in Lenny Lapon, *Mass Murderers in White Coats*, (Springfield, Mass., Psychiatric Genocide Research Institute, 1986), p. 75.

16. *Ibid.*, pp. 75-76.

17. Lapon, *op. cit.*, p. 76.

18. Quoting Katzen-Ellenbogen's trial testimony in Lapon, *op. cit.*, p. 88.

19. Hans Georg Guse and N. Schmacke, "Psychiatry and the Origins of Nazism," *International Journal of Health Services*, Vol. 10, No. 2, 1980.

20. Quoted in Robert Castel, Francoise Castel, and Anne Lovell, *The Psychiatric Society*, (translated by Arthur Goldhammer), (New York: Columbia University Press, 1982), pp.

46-47. He gives source as Carlos F. MacDonald, "Presidential Address," *American Journal of Insanity*, July 1914, 71:9.

21. Quoted in Lapon, *op. cit.*, p. 78.

22. *Ibid.*

23. Adolf Hitler, *Mein Kampf*, translated by Ralph Manheim, (Boston: Houghton Mifflin Co., 1971), p. 255. (Quoted in L. Lapon, *op. cit.*, p. 80.)

24. Lapon, *op. cit.*, p. 83.

25. Quoted in Schreiber, *op. cit.*, p. 18.

26. Schreiber, *op. cit.*, p. 28.

27. *Ibid.*, p. 79.

28. *Ibid.*, p. 41.

29. Joseph Harsch, *Pattern for Conquest*, as quoted in B. Schreiber, *op. cit.*, p. 45.

30. Michael Burleigh, *Selling Murder*, directed by Joanna Mack, Domino Film Production, 1991.

31. *Ibid.*

32. "Medical killings led Nazis to mass murder," *L.A. Daily News*, (Los Angeles), September 28, 1986.

33. Frederic Wertham, *A Sign For Cain*, (London: Robert Hale Ltd., 1966), p. 180.

34. As quoted by Lapon, *op. cit.*, p. 21—taken from Mitscherlich and F. Mielke, *The Death Doctors*, (London: Elek Books, 1962), p. 248.

35. Wertham, *op. cit.*, pp. 164-65.

36. *Ibid.*, p. 181-82.

37. G. Brock Chisholm, "The Reestablishment of Peacetime Society," *Psychiatry: Journal of the Biology and the Pathology of Interpersonal Relations*, Vol. 9, No. 1, p. 3.

38. *Ibid.*, p. 9.

39. *Ibid.*, p. 1.

40. Charles S. Ascher, quoted in J. B. Matthews, "The World Health Organization," *American Opinion*, May 1958, p. 11.

41. *Ibid.*, p. 12.

42. *The New York Times*, Biographical Edition 11, (New York: The New

York Times Company, February 5, 1971), p. 315.

43. C. P. Blacker, quoted in Schreiber, *op. cit.*, p. 71.

44. Wertham, *op. cit.*, p. 190.

45. Lapon, *op. cit.*, p. 119.

46. Robert Lee Hotz, "Genetics, Not Parenting, Key to Temperament, Studies Say," *Los Angeles Times*, February 20, 1994, pp. A1, A38.

47. Robin McKown, *Pioneers in Mental Health*, (New York: Dodd, Mead and Co., 1961), p. 185.

48. *Ibid.*, p. 208.

49. Quoted in Schreiber, *op. cit.*, p. 20.

50. McKown, *op. cit.*, pp. 185-86

51. Clarence J. Karier, *Scientists of the Mind*, (Chicago: University of Illinois Press, 1986), p. 28.

52. Robert Castel, et al., *The Psychiatric Society*, translated by Arthur Goldhammer, (New York: Columbia University Press, 1982), pp. 34-35.

53. E. Fuller Torrey, *Nowhere to Go*, (New York: Harper and Row, 1988).

54. Castel, et al., *op. cit.*, p. 36.

55. C.L. Dana, "The Future of Neurology," *Journal of Nervous and Mental Disease*, 40, 1913: pp. 753-57.

56. Castel, et al., *op. cit.*, pp. 41-44.

57. Schreiber, *op. cit.*, pp. 17-18.

58. Bromberg, *op. cit.*, pp. 219-20.

59. Castel, et al., *op. cit.*, p. 38.

60. Torrey, *op. cit.*, p. 50.

61. F. Williams, "Is There a Mental Hygiene?" *Psychoanalytic Quarterly, 1* (1932), 113-20.

62. Quoted in *Ibid.*, p. 37.

63. Wertham, *op. cit.*, p. 163.

64. Torrey, *op. cit.*, p. 51.

65. "Mental Health and World Citizenship," a statement prepared for the International Congress on Mental Health, London, 1948. Published by the World Federation for Mental Health.

66. John R. Rees, "Strategic Planning for Mental Health," *Mental Health*, Vol.

1, No. 4, pp. 103-06.

67. Chisholm, *op. cit.*, p. 9.

68. Quoted in Bromberg, *op. cit.*, p. 222.

69. Bromberg, *op. cit.*, p. 223.

70. *Ibid.*, p. 226.

71. Torrey, *op. cit.*, p. 214.

CHAPTER IV
THE TENDRILS OF INFLUENCE

1. E. Fuller Torrey, *Nowhere to Go*, (New York: Harper and Row, 1988), p. 164.

2. The beginning NIMH budget was $7.5 million. It is now in the hundreds of millions.

3. Albert Deutsch, "Military Psychiatry," *One Hundred Years of American Psychiatry*, published for American Psychiatric Association, (New York: Columbia University Press, 1944), p. 420-21.

4. *Ibid.*, p. 425.

5. *Ibid.*, p. 424.

6. *Ibid.*, p. 429.

7. William Menninger, "Psychiatric Experience in the War, 1941-46," in Bernard Hall (ed.), *A Psychiatrist for a Troubled World*, (New York: Viking Press), p. 528.

8. William Menninger, *Psychiatry in a Troubled World*, (New York: The Macmillan Company, 1948), p. 12.

9. Deutsch, *op. cit.*, p. 423.

10. A. H. Chapman, *Harry Stack Sullivan, The Man and His Work*, (New York: G.P. Putnam's Sons, 1976), p. 12.

11. *Ibid.*, pp. 50-51.

12. Deutsch, *op. cit.*, p. 430.

13. Menninger, *A Psychiatrist for a Troubled World*, p. v.

14. *Ibid.*, p. xvi.

15. Lawrence J. Friedman, *Menninger, The Family and the Clinic*, (New York: Alfred A. Knopf, 1990), p. 83.

16. *Ibid.*, p. 84.

17. *Ibid.*, p. 90.

18. *Ibid.*, p. 311.

19. *Ibid.*, p. 82.

20. *Ibid.*, p. 81.

21. Menninger, *op. cit.*, p. 675.
22. *Ibid.*, p. 452.
23. *Ibid.*, p. 453.
24. *Ibid.*
25. *Ibid.*, p. 454.
26. *Ibid.*
27. U.S. Labor Party publication, "The Tavistock Mother."
28. Deutsch, *op. cit.*, p. 439.
29. Robert Felix, *Mental Illness, Progress and Prospects*, (New York: Columbia University Press, 1967), p. 28-29.
30. Menninger, *op. cit.*, *A Psychiatrist for a Troubled World*, pp. 341, 347
31. Felix, *op. cit.*, p. 29.
32. Deutsch, *op. cit.*, p. 424.
33. Menninger, *op. cit.*, p. 530.
34. *Ibid.*, p. 268.
35. *Ibid.*, p. 535.
36. *Ibid.*, p. 269.
37. *Ibid.*, p. 531.
38. *Ibid.*
39. Edward Strecker, "Military Psychiatry: World War I," *One Hundred Years of American Psychiatry*, (New York: Columbia University Press, 1944), p. 391.
40. *Ibid.*, p. 396.
41. Karl Bowman, 1946 Presidential Address to the American Psychiatric Association, *New Directions in American Psychiatry 1944-1968*, (Washington, D.C.: American Psychiatric Association, 1969), p. 15.
42. Felix, *op. cit.*, p. 29.
43. *Ibid.*
44. *Ibid.*, p. 30.
45. Robert L. Robinson, "Robinson Remembers Thirty Years of APA," *Psychiatric News*, November 16, 1979, p. 1.
46. Elizabeth Brenner Drew, "The Health Syndicate," *The Atlantic Monthly*, December 1967, p. 76.
47. *Ibid.*
48. Steven Foley and Henry Sharfstein, *Madness and Government*, (Washington, D.C.: American Psychiatric Association Press, 1983), p. 12.
49. Francis Braceland, "Robert Hanna Felix, Eighty-Ninth President, 1960-61, A Biographical Sketch," *New Directions in American Psychiatry, 1944-1968*, *op. cit.* p. 235.
50. Foley and Sharfstein, *op. cit.*, p. 20.
51. *Ibid.*, p. 19.
52. Torrey, *op. cit.*, p. 62.
53. Foley and Sharfstein, *op. cit.*, p. 29.
54. Torrey, *op. cit.*, p. 163.
55. Torrey, *op. cit.*, p. 164.
56. Foley and Sharfstein, *op. cit.*, p. 25.
57. Drew, *op. cit.*, p. 76.
58. *Ibid.*, p. 78.
59. Robinson, *op. cit.*, p. 21.
60. Drew, *op. cit.*, p. 79.
61. *Ibid.*
62. *Ibid.*, p. 76.
63. Foley and Sharfstein, *op. cit.*, p. 23.
64. Torrey, *op. cit.*, p. 65-66.
65. Albert Deutsch, *The Story of GAP*, (New York: Group for the Advancement of Psychiatry, 1959), p. 8.
66. Robinson, *op. cit.*, p. 1.
67. William Menninger, "Presidential Address," *New Directions in American Psychiatry, 1944-1968*, *op. cit.*, p. 70.
68. Minutes from the October 21, 1947 meeting of Psychological Strategy Board. Obtained from National Archives.
69. W.A. Higginbottom, *Ibid.*, p. 1.
70. Martin A. Lee and Bruce Shlain, *Acid Dreams, The CIA, LSD and the Sixties Rebellion*, (New York: Grove Press, 1985), p. 20.
71. Quoted in John Marks, *The Search for the Manchurian Candidate*, (New York: Times Books, 1979), p. 63.
72. *Ibid.*, p. 135.
73. L. Macdonald, "Breakthrough," in B. Burstow and D. Weitz (eds.), *Shrink resistant: The struggle against psychiatry in Canada*, (Vancouver: New Star Books, 1988), pp. 206-10.

74. Quoted in Marks, *op. cit.*, pp. 135-36.

75. *Ibid.*, p. 138.

76. Quoted in Marks, *op. cit.*, p. 137.

77. Leonard Rubenstein, "The CIA and the Evil Doctor," *The New York Times*, November 7, 1988.

78. Torrey, *op. cit.*, p. 213.

79. Mike Gorman, *Community Mental Health Journal*, *12* (1976) pp. 119-27.

80. Foley and Sharfstein, *op. cit.*, p. 35.

81. *Ibid.*, p. 42.

82. J.R. Ewalt, Foreword in Grunebaum, (ed.) *The Practice of Community Mental Health*, (Boston: Little, Brown and Co., 1970).

83. 1945 National Neuropsychiatric Institute bill, House Hearings, p. 30.

84. William C. Menninger, "Presidential Address," *New Directions in American Psychiatry 1944-1968*, *op. cit.*, p. 73.

85. Robert Felix, *Mental Health and Social Welfare*, (New York: Columbia University Press, 1961), p. 21.

86. Torrey, *op. cit.*, p. 65.

87. Quoted in Foley and Sharfstein, *op. cit.*, p. 44. Original source: Plank adopted at quadrennial convention, Los Angeles, July 1960, and quoted by Senate President John E. Powers, Massachusetts, at Governor's Conference on Mental Health, Chicago, Illinois, 10 November 1961.

88. *Ibid.*, pp. 45-48.

89. *Ibid.*, p. 49.

90. Leo H. Bartemeier, M.D. "Memorial for William C. Menninger," Clarke & Way, Inc., 1967.

91. Message from the President of the United States, February 5, 1963. Found in *Ibid.*, p. 166.

92. P. Collier and D. Horowitz, *The Kennedys: An American Drama*, (New York: Warner Books, 1984)

93. Foley and Sharfstein, *op. cit.*, p. 63.

94. Torrey, *op. cit.*, p. 118.

95. Isaac and Armat, *op. cit.*, p. 97.

96. Quoted in Franklin Chu and Sharland Trotter, *The Madness Establishment*, (New York: Grossman Publishers, 1974), p. 57.

97. *Ibid.*, pp. xi, xiii.

98. *Ibid.*, p. 203-04.

99. Torrey, *op. cit.*, p. 25.

100. Isaac and Armat, *op. cit.*, p. 92.

101. A.F. Panzetta, "Whatever Happened to Community Mental Health: Portents for Corporate Medicine," *Hospital and Community Psychiatry*, *36* (1985): pp. 1174-79.

102. Foley and Sharfstein, *op. cit.*, p. 100.

103. Isaac and Armat, *op. cit.*, p. 84. From an interview done by the authors.

104. John A. Talbott, "Presidential Address: Our Patients' Future in a Changing World: The Imperative for Psychiatric Involvement in Public Policy," *The American Journal of Psychiatry*, p. 1003.

105. Message from the President of the United States, May 15, 1979. Found in Foley and Sharfstein, *op. cit.*, p. 182.

CHAPTER V
VOLTAGE THROUGH THE BRAIN

1. As quoted in Emil Kraepelin, *One Hundred Years of Psychiatry*, (New York: Philosophical Library, Inc., 1961), pp. 92-94. Translated from the German essay written in 1917.

2. Erwin H. Ackerknecht, *A Short History of Psychiatry*, (New York: Hafner Publishing Co., 1959), pp. 33-34.

3. Walter Freeman and James Watts, "Physiological psychology," *Annual Review of Physiology*, 6:535, 1944.

4. Lee Coleman, "Introduction," in *The Case Against ECT*, (Los Angeles: Citizens Commission on Human Rights), p. i.

5. Max Fink, "Impact of the Antipsychiatry Movement on the Revival of Electroconvulsive Therapy in the United States," *The Psychiatric Clinics of North America*, Vol. 14, No. 4, December 1991, p. 793.

6. Ugo Cerletti, "Electroshock Therapy," in Arthur M. Sackler *et al.* (eds.), *The Great Physiodynamic Therapies in Psychiatry: An Historical Reappraisal*, (New York: Hoeber-Harper, 1956), pp. 92-94.

7. 1941 Discussion of Roy R. Grinker, Norman A. Levy, and H.M. Serota, "Disturbances in brain function following convulsive shock therapy," *Archives of Neurology and Psychiatry*, 47:1028-29, June 1942.

8. William Menninger, *Psychiatry in a Troubled World*, (New York: The Macmillan Co., 1948), p. 294.

9. Lawrence Kolb and Victor H. Vogel, "The use of shock therapy in 305 mental hospitals," *American Journal of Psychiatry*, 99:90-93, July 1942.

10. Report No. 1, Group for the Advancement of Psychiatry, September 15, 1947.

11. Abraham Myerson, in discussion of Franklin G. Ebaugh, et al., "Fatalities following electric convulsive therapy: a report of 2 cases with autopsy findings," *Trans. Amer. Neurol. Assoc.*, 68:39, June 1942.

12. Ugo Cerletti, "Old and new information about electroshock," *American Journal of Psychiatry*, 107:93-94, August 1950.

13. Theodore L. Dehne, commenting in Philadelphia Psychiatric Society, "Symposium: complications of and contraindications to electric shock therapy," *Archives of Neurology and Psychiatry*, 49:786-791, May 1943.

14. W.H. Kay, *We Can't All Be Sane!*, (Los Angeles: Collectors Publications, 1965), pp. 117-19.

15. Cyril J.C. Kennedy and David Anchel, "Regressive electric-shock in schizophrenics refractory to other shock therapies," *Psychiatric Quarterly*, 22(2):317-320, 1948.

16. David Rothschild, et al., "Regressive shock therapy in schizophrenia,"

Diseases of the Nervous System, 11:148, May 1951.

17. Reported in Louis Lowinger and James Huddleson, "Complications in electric shock therapy," *American Journal of Psychiatry*, 102:495-497, March 1946.

18. Report of the Task Force on Electroconvulsive Therapy of the American Psychiatric Association, (Washington, D.C.: American Psychiatric Association, 1978), p. 6.

19. H. Richard Beresford, "Legal issues relating to electroconvulsive therapy," *Archives of General Psychiatry*, 25:100-101, August 1971.

20. John Maurice Grimes, *When Minds Go Wrong*, (New York: Devin-Adair, 1954), p. 130.

21. Robert Morgan, "The isolation, description, and treatment of the pathological behavior of ECT-damaged patients," unpublished research proposal, February 1966, pp. 5-6.

22. "From lobotomy to physics to Freud...an interview with Karl Pribram, APA *Monitor*, American Psychological Association, Sept.-Oct., 1974, p. 9.

23. James W. Thompson and Jack D. Blaine, "Use of ECT in the United States in 1975 and 1980," *American Journal of Psychiatry*, May 1987, p. 557.

24. Gary Aden, "The International Psychiatric Association for the Advancement of Electrotherapy: A Brief History," *American Journal of Social Psychiatry*, 4, No. 4 (1984): 9-10.

25. Report of the Task Force on Electroconvulsive Therapy of the American Psychiatric Association, *op. cit.*, pp. 3, 5.

26. Angelo Figueroa, "S.F. supervisors vote against shock therapy," *San Francisco Examiner*, February 12, 1991.

27. Resolution 129-91, San Francisco Board of Supervisors, January 29, 1991, p. 2.

28. Quoted by Leonard Frank, *op. cit.*, pp. 170-171.
29. Interview with Michael Chavin, August 15, 1994.
30. Lee Goodman, "A Current Affair," *The Key West Citizen*, June 30, 1994.
31. Richard Abrams, "Interview with Lothar Kalinowsky," *Convulsive Therapy*, 4, pp. 25-39.
32. Cerletti, *op. cit.*, pp.92-94.
33. Abrams, *op. cit.*, p. 30.
34. Cerletti, *op. cit.*
35. David J. Impastato, "The story of the first electroshock treatment," *American Journal of Psychiatry*, 116:1113-1114, June 1960.
36. Cited in F.J. Ayd, Jr., "Guest editorial: Ugo Cerletti, M.D. 1877-1963," *Psychosomatics*, 4, A6-A7.
37. Cerletti, *op. cit.*, p. 106
38. R.M. Mowbray, *Scotland Medical Journal*, 4:375, July-August, 1959.
39. Evelyn Crumpton, et al., "The role of fear in electroconvulsive treatment," *Journal of Nervous and Mental Diseases*, 136: 29-33, January 1963.
40. Sylvia Plath, *The Bell Jar*, (New York: Harper and Row, 1971), pp. 117-18.
41. 1978 Report of the Task Force on Electroconvulsive Therapy of the American Psychiatric Association, p. xi.
42. *Ibid.*, p. 4.
43. Fink, *op. cit.*, p. 793.
44. C.P.L. Freeman and R.E. Kendell, "ECT: I. Patients' Experiences and Attitudes," *British Journal of Psychiatry*, 137, 1980, p. 15.
45. November 27, 1990 San Francisco Board of Supervisor hearings on Electroshock, p. 83.
46. Lee Coleman, "Introduction," in Leonard Frank (ed.), *The History of Shock Treatment*, (San Francisco, Calif., 1978), p. xiii.
47. Quoted in Lawrence Kolb and Victor Vogel, "The use of shock therapy in 305 mental hospitals," *American Journal of Psychiatry*, 99:90-93, July 1942.
48. Leonard Frank, "Electroshock: Death, Brain Damage, Memory Loss, and Brainwashing," *The Journal of Mind and Behavior*, Vol. 11, Nos. 3 and 4, Summer and Autumn 1990, p. 500[254].
49. C. Edward Coffey, et al., "Brain Anatomic Effects of Electroconvulsive Therapy," *Archives of General Psychiatry*, 48:1013-1021, November 1991.
50. Fink, *op. cit.*, p. 793.
51. J. Easton Jones, "Non-ECT," *World Medicine*, 1974, p. 24.
52. Statistical Abstracts of the United States, U.S. Department of Commerce, 1987, p. 79. In 1975, 27,063 suicides were recorded. In 1980, there were 26,869.
53. *Ibid.*
54. Alec Roy, "Risk Factors for Suicide in Psychiatric Patients," *Archives of General Psychiatry*, Vol. 39, September 1982, p. 1093.
55. A.E. Hotchner, *Papa Hemingway*, (New York: Random House, 1966), p. 308-44.
56. Freeman and Kendell, *op. cit.*, p. 13.
57. Letter from A.E. Bennett, "Electroconvulsive Therapy," *Correspondence*, Vol. 14, No.2.
58. David Sharp, "A Bolt for the Blues," Special Report, November 1991-January 1992.
59. Bruce Finley, "Electroshock: quick fix or cure?" *Denver Post*, October 21, 1990.
60. November 27, 1990 San Francisco Board of Supervisor hearings on Electroshock, p. 23.
61. Fred Frankel, *Massachusetts Journal of Mental Health*, 3:3-29, (Winter), 1973.
62. Interview with Thomas Szasz, September 17, 1993.
63. Chavin, *op. cit.*

64. Frank, "Electroshock," *op. cit.*, p. 494 [248].

65. Chavin, *op. cit.*

66. Eric Pace, "Lothar Kalinowsky, A Psychiatrist, 92; Used Electroshocks," *The New York Times*, June 30, 1992, p. D23.

67. Lothar Kalinowsky, "Additional remarks on the danger of premedication in electric convulsive therapy (Letter to editor), *American Journal of Psychiatry*, 113:79-80, July 1956.

68. Lothar Kalinowsky and P. Hoch, *Shock Treatments, Psychosurgery, and Other Somatic Treatments in Psychiatry*, (New York: Grune and Stratton, 1952), p. 139.

69. Freeman and Kendell, *op. cit.*, p. 14.

70. Marilyn Rice, "The Rice papers," *Madness Network News*, April 1975, pp. 4-8.

71. Lothar Kalinowsky, Deposition in Marilyn Rice v. John E. Nardini and Psychiatric Institute of Washington, (Superior Court, D.C., Civil Action No. 703-74), March 12, 1976.

72. Peter Breggin, *Toxic Psychiatry*, (New York: St. Martin's Press, 1991), p. 192.

73. Aden, *op. cit.*

74. "Doctors of Desire," *San Francisco Examiner*, August 4, 1991, p. A-18.

75. Rex Dalton, "Epidemic of psychotherapist-patient sex worsens," *San Diego Union*, January 1, 1989.

76. *San Diego Union*, September 27, 1989.

77. Dalton, *op. cit.*

78. A. Podnov, *Psychiatry*, 1969, pp. 138-41.

79. Edward Babayan, *The Structure of Psychiatry in the Soviet Union*, (New York: International Universities Press, 1985), pp. 36-37.

80. *Ibid.*, p. 294.

81. Bernard J. Alpers, "The Brain Changes Associated with Electrical Shock Treatment: A Critical Review," *The Journal-Lancet*, November 1946.

82. Walter Freeman and James Watts, "Physiological psychology," *Annual Review of Physiology*, 6:535, 1944.

83. Bernard J. Alpers and Joseph Hughes, "The brain changes in electrically induced convulsions in the human," *Journal of Neuropathology and Experimental Neurology*, 1:172-177, April 1942.

84. Paul H. Hoch, Discussion and concluding remarks (Round Table on ECT), *Journal of Personality*, 17:48, 1948.

85. I.M. Allen, "Cerebral Lesions from Electric Shock Treatment," *New Zealand Medical Journal*, Vol. 58, 1959, p. 375.

86. Donald I. Templer, et al., "Cognitive Functioning and Degree of Psychosis in Schizophrenics given many Electroconvulsive Treatments," *American Journal of Psychiatry*, pp. 123, 443.

87. R.J. Grimm, "Convulsions as therapy: The outer shadows," *Psychiatric Opinion*, *15*, 30-31; 45-47.

88. Raymond Levy and Robin Jacoby, "Correspondence," *British Journal of Psychiatry*, 1982.

89. 1978 Report of the Task Force on Electroconvulsive Therapy of the American Psychiatric Association, *op. cit.*, p. 4.

90. *Ibid.*, p. 77.

91. American Psychiatric Association, *The Practice of Electroconvulsive Therapy: Recommendations for Treatment, Training, and Privileging*, (Washington, D.C.: American Psychiatric Association, 1990), p. 68.

92. Charles H. Kellner, in Charles H. Kellner (ed.), "Electroconvulsive Therapy," *The Psychiatric Clinics of North America*, Vol. 14, No. 4, December 1991, p. xiii.

93. "Proposed Rules," *Federal Register*, Vol. 55, No. 172, September 5, 1990, p. 36586.

94. Leon A. Weisberg, et al., "Intracerebral

hemorrhage following electroconvulsive therapy," *Neurology*, November 1991, p. 1849.

95. Donald Templer and David Beleber, "Can ECT Permanently Harm the Brain?" *Clinical Neuropsychology*, Vol. IV, No. 2, pp. 64-65.

96. Richard Weiner, "Does electroconvulsive therapy cause brain damage," *The Behavioral and Brain Sciences*, Vol. 7 (1984), p. 21.

97. Lee Coleman quoted in Adrian Tame, "Shock Treatment," *Penthouse*, (1987).

98. Interview with Linda Andre, August 29, 1994.

99. Freeman and Kendell, *op. cit.*, pp. 14-15.

100. Angela Alioto, 1990 San Francisco Hearings, *op. cit.*

101. *Ibid.*, p. 10.

102. Irving Janis, "Psychologic effects of electric convulsive treatments," *Journal of Nervous and Mental Diseases*, 111:369-70, 1950.

103. Freeman and Kendell, *op. cit.*, p. 13.

104. L.R. Squire, "Memory and electroconvulsive therapy," [Letter], *American Journal of Psychiatry*, 139, p. 1221.

105. Pope Paul XII, quoted in P. Winner, "The Pope on psychoanalysis," *New Republic*, October 20, 1952, p. 8. According to Winner, the pope was referring to "lobotomy, other forms of surgical intervention and, by implication, shock treatment."

106. David Richman, "Brain Burns," in *Frank's History*, *op. cit.*, p. 136.

107. Andre, *op. cit.*

108. Rael Jean Isaac and Virginia C. Armat, *Madness in the Streets*, (New York: Free Press, 1990), p. 199.

109. *Ibid.*, p. 199.

110. John Friedberg, "Shock Treatment, Brain Damage, and Memory Loss: A Neurological Perspective," *American Journal of Psychiatry*, 134:9, p. 1012.

111. The Report of the Royal Commission into Deep Sleep Therapy, Vol. 1, p. 48.

112. *Ibid.*, Vol. 4, p. 43.

113. *Ibid.*, Vol. 6, p. 96.

114. *Ibid.*, Vol. 2, p. 1.

115. *Ibid.*, Vol. 2, p. 14.

116. *Ibid.*, Vol. 2, p. 1.

117. *Ibid.*, Vol. 2, p. 2.

118. *Ibid.*, Vol. 2, p. 15.

119. *Ibid.*, Vol. 2, p. 18.

120. *Ibid.*, Vol. 2, p. 98.

121. *Ibid.*, Vol. 2, p. 37.

122. Frank, "Electroshock," *op. cit.*, p. 498[252].

123. Cases "A" through "J," CCHR files, Citizens Commission on Human Rights, 6362 Hollywood Bl., Suite B, Los Angeles, California 90028.

124. Fink, *op. cit.*, pp. 794-99.

CHAPTER VI
DESTROYING THE BRAIN
TO SAVE THE MIND

1. Joann Ellison Rodgers, *Psychosurgery*, (New York: HarperCollins, 1992), p. xvi.

2. *Ibid.*, xvii.

3. *Ibid.*, xv.

4. *Ibid.*, p. 1.

5. Quoted in Alan W. Scheflin and Edward Opton, *The Mind Manipulators*, (New York: Paddington Press, 1978), p. 245.

6. *Ibid.*

7. L. G. Kiloh et al., *Physical Treatments in Psychiatry*, (London: Blackwell Scientific Publications, 1988), p. 277.

8. Rodgers, *op. cit.*, p. 8.

9. *Ibid.*, p. 37.

10. Rael Jean Isaac and Virginia C. Armat, *Madness in the Streets*, (New York: The Free Press, 1990), p. 178.

11. Scheflin and Opton, *op. cit.*, p. 282.

12. Isaac and Armat, *op. cit.*

13. "The psychosurgical question," *Frontiers of Psychiatry*, p. 1.

14. Rodgers, *op. cit.*, p. 12.

15. *Ibid.*, p. 11.

16. Lenny Lapon, *Mass Murderers in White*

Coats, (Springfield, Mass.: Psychiatric Genocide Research Institute, 1986), p. 84.

17. Glenn Frankel, "Psychosurgery's Effects Still Linger," *The Washington Post*, April 6, 1980, p. A1.

18. H. T. Ballantine, Jr., "Historical Overview of Psychosurgery and Its Problematic," *Acta Neurochirurgica*, Suppl. 44, p. 126, 1988.

19. Glenn Frankel, "D.C. Neurosurgeon Pioneered 'Operation Icepick' Technique," *The Washington Post*, April 7 1980, p. A1.

20. *Ibid.*

21. Walter Freeman, "Psychosurgery," in Silvano Arieti (ed.), *American Handbook of Psychiatry*, Vol. Two, (New York: Basic Books, Inc., 1959), p. 1521.

22. *Ibid.*, p. 1522.

23. Walter Freeman and James Watts, *Psychosurgery*, (Springfield, Ill.: Charles C. Thomas, 1942), pp. 96-97.

24. Quoted in Scheflin and Opton, *op. cit.*, p. 258.

25. Quoted in *Ibid.*, p. 259.

26. Martin Porter, "Night of the Human Tomatoes," *High Times*, March 1979, p. 64.

27. E. Fuller Torrey, *Nowhere to Go*, (New York: Harper and Row, 1988), p. 106.

28. Quoted in Porter, *op. cit.*

29. Isaac and Armat, *op. cit.*, p. 380.

30. Quoted in Rodgers, *op. cit.*, p. 44.

31. Frankel, *op. cit.*

32. Quoted in *Ibid.*

33. Quoted in *Ibid.*

34. Quoted in *Ibid.*

35. *Ibid.*, p. 179.

36. Rodgers, *op. cit.*, p. 38.

37. Quoted in *Ibid.*

38. Quoted in *Ibid.*, p. 5.

39. *Ibid.*, p. 38.

40. Quoted in Frankel, *op. cit.*

41. Isaac and Armat, *op. cit.*, p. 179.

42. Frankel, *op. cit.*

43. Freeman, *op. cit.*, p. 1522.

44. Frankel, *op. cit.*

45. *Ibid.*

46. Rodgers, *op. cit.*, p. 21.

47. Jamie Talan, "Patients living legacy to age of lobotomies," *Denver Post*, December 23, 1990.

48. "Modified Prefrontal Leucotomy," *British Medical Journal*, September 11, 1971, Vol. 3, p. 595-96.

49. Freeman, *op. cit.*, p. 1523.

50. *Ibid.*

51. *Ibid.*

52. Quoted in Scheflin and Opton, p. 256.

53. Frankel, *op. cit.*

54. *Ibid.*

55. Frankel, "Psychosurgeries Effects," *op. cit.*

56. Porter, *op. cit.*

57. *Ibid.*

58. William Arnold, *Shadowland*, (New York: McGraw-Hill Book Co., 1978), as quoted in *Psychosurgery* by Joann Rodgers, p. 39.

59. Review of *Great and Desperate Cures* by Elliot Valenstein, *Los Angeles Times*.

60. Isaac and Armat, *op. cit.*, p. 179.

61. Rodgers, *op. cit.*, p. 3.

62. "Psychosurgery called resurging menace of brain mutilation," *Frontiers of Psychiatry*, p. 1.

63. Scheflin and Opton, *op. cit.*, p. 321.

64. *Frontiers of Psychiatry*, *op. cit.*

65. Rodgers, *op. cit.*, p. 42.

66. "Report on psychiatry and human rights," Council of Europe, March 15, 1994, Document 7040, p. 14.

67. Quoted in Isaac and Armat, *op. cit.*, p. 193.

68. Interview with Robert Shaw, November 5, 1994.

69. Quoted in Rodgers, *op. cit.*, p. 218.

70. Quoted in *Ibid.*, pp. 65-66.

71. Frankel, "D.C. Neurosurgeon," *op. cit.*

72. Frankel, "Psychosurgery's Effects," *op. cit.*

73. Edward Babayan, *The Structure of Psychiatry in the Soviet Union*, (New York: International Universities Press,

1985), p. 36.

74. *Ibid.*, pp. 293-94.

75. Scheflin and Opton, *op. cit.*, pp. 282-83.

76. Glenn Frankel, "Today's Psychosurgeons Defend Techniques," *The Washington Post*, p. A1, April 8, 1980.

77. *Frontiers of Psychiatry, op. cit.*, p. 5.

78. John O'Neill and Robert Haupt, "How they put metal plates in Bruce's brain," *Sydney Morning Herald*, August 4, 1988.

79. Report of the Royal Commission into Deep Sleep Therapy, Vol. 2, p. 38.

80. *Ibid.*, p. 11.

81. *Ibid.*, p. 7.

82. *Ibid.*, p. 38.

83. *Ibid.*, p. 13.

84. O'Neill and Haupt, *op. cit.*

85. *Ibid.*, p. 11.

86. Kiloh et al., *op. cit.*, pp. 277-333.

87. *Psychosurgery*, Appendix, The National Commission for the Protection of Human Subjects of Biomedical and Behavioral Research, U.S. Dept. of Health, Education, and Welfare, Publication No. (OS)77-0002, p. I-32.

88. Robert Haupt and John O'Neill, "Podio Case the Ultimate Tragedy," *The Sydney Morning Herald*, August 4, 1988.

89. Report of the Royal Commission into Deep Sleep Therapy, *op. cit.*, Vol. 2, p. 44.

90. *Ibid.*, pp. 40-41.

91. *Ibid.*, pp. 39-40.

92. *Ibid.*, p. 38.

93. *Ibid.*, p. 45.

94. *Ibid.*, pp. 47-48.

95. Everett R. Holles, *The New York Times*, p. 18, column 1.

96. Report of the Royal Commission into Deep Sleep Therapy, Vol. 2, pp. 45-46.

97. Quoted in Rodgers, *op. cit.*, p. 134.

98. Quoted in Scheflin and Opton, *op. cit.*, p. 310.

99. Report of the Royal Commission into Deep Sleep Therapy, Vol. 2, pp. 47-48.

100. K. Sano and Y. Mayanagi, "Posteromedial Hypothalamotomy in the Treatment of Violent, Aggressive Behavior," *Acta Neurochirurgica*, Suppl. 44, p. 145.

101. L.V. Laitinen, "Psychosurgery Today," *Acta Neurochirurgica*, Suppl. 44, 158-162, 1988.

102. P. Cosyns, "Psychosurgery and Personality Disorders," *Acta Neurochirurgica*, Suppl 44, p. 124, 1988.

103. Quoted in Rodgers, *op. cit.*, p. 181.

104. Quoted in *Ibid.*, p. 204.

105. Quoted in *Ibid.*, p. 70.

106. Quoted in Scheflin and Opton, *op. cit.*, p. 272.

107. H. Thomas Ballantine, "Historical Overview of Psychosurgery and its Problematic," *Acta Neurochirurgica*, Suppl. 44, p. 127, 1988.

108. Rodgers, *op. cit.*, p. 180.

109. Interview with Robert Shaw, November 5, 1994.

110. Rodgers, *op. cit.*, pp. 177-78.

111. Mark A.J. O'Callaghan and Douglas Carroll, *Psychosurgery: A Scientific Analysis*, (Lancaster, England: MTP Press, Ltd., 1982), p. 115.

112. Quoted in *Ibid.*, p. 44.

113. *Ibid.*, pp. 39, 43.

114. Scheflin and Opton, *op. cit.*, p. 324.

115. Quoted in Rodgers, *op. cit.*, p. 52.

116. *Ibid.*, p. 83.

117. *Ibid.*, p. 83.

118. K. Sano and Y. Mayanagi, "Posteromedial Hypothalamotomy in the Treatment of Violent, Aggressive Behavior," *Acta Neurochirurgica*, Suppl. 44, 1988, pp. 148, 150.

119. Ballantine, *op. cit.*, p. 127.

120. Scheflin and Opton, *op. cit.*, pp. 274-75.

121. *Ibid.*, p. 273.

122. Frankel, *op. cit.*

123. Rodgers, *op. cit.*, pp. 128-32.

124. Scheflin and Opton, *op. cit.*, p. 319.
125. Individual Rights and the Federal Role in Behavior Modification, A Study Prepared by the Staff of the Subcommittee on Constitutional Rights of the Committee on the Judiciary, U.S. Senate, November 1974, pp. 326, 328.
126. Quoted in Rodgers, *op. cit.*, p. 46.
127. Individual Rights, *op. cit.*, p. 349.
128. Rodgers, *op. cit.*, pp. 79-80.
129. Scheflin and Opton, *op. cit.*, p. 274.
130. Rodgers, *op. cit.*, p. 76.
131. O'Callaghan and Carroll, *op. cit.*, p. 95.
132. Michael Miller, "Brain Surgery Is Back In a Limited Way To Treat Mental Ills," *The Wall Street Journal*, December 1, 1994.
133. Isaac and Armat, *op. cit.*, pp. 189-91.
134. Interview with John Barrella, December 21, 1994.
135. Rodgers, *op. cit.*, p. 210.
136. Miller, *op. cit.*
137. Quoted in Rodgers, *op. cit.*, pp. 204-05.
138. *Ibid.*, p. 50.
139. Quoted in Isaac and Armaat, *op. cit.*, p. 192.

CHAPTER VII
THE ALMIGHTY PANACEA–DRUGS

1. Ronald K. Siegel, Ph.D., *Intoxication*, (New York: Pocket Books, 1989), p. x
2. *Ibid.*, p. viii
3. "France must control 'artificial paradise' of tranquilizers," *The Financial Times Limited*, March 22, 1994.
4. "Fate and Distribution of Cocaine, Diazepam, Phencyclidine [PCP] and THC [marijuana]: A Technical Review," Foundation for Advancement in Science and Education, research bulletin, August 1985.
5. "Office Visits to Psychiatrists—United States 1985," Data from the National Health Survey, Vital & Health Statistics, Series 13, No. 94, p. 2.
6. "Drugs-Facts," from *Executive News Service*, 1989.
7. William E. McAuliffe, Ph.D., et al., "Psychoactive Drug Use Among Practicing Physicians and Medical Students," *New England Journal of Medicine*, Vol. 315, No. 13, September 25, 1986, pp. 805, 808.
8. David Solomon (ed.), *LSD—The Consciousness-Expanding Drug*, (New York: G.P. Putnam's Sons, 1964), pp. 24-25.
9. Seymour Rosenblatt, M.D. and Reynolds Dodson, G.P., *Beyond Valium—The Brave New World of Psychochemistry*, (New York: Putnam's Sons, 1981), pp. 18-19.
10. Peter D. Kramer, M.D., *Listening to Prozac*, (New York: Viking [The Penguin Group], 1993), p. 248.
11. Lester Grinspoon, M.D. and James B. Bakalar, J.D., "The Amphetamines: Medical Uses and Health Hazards," *Psychiatric Annals* 7:8/August 1977, p. 9.
12. *Ibid.*, p. 13.
13. Judith P. Swazey, *Chlorpromazine in Psychiatry—A Study of Therapeutic Innovation*, 1974, p. 34.
14. "Thorazine Therapy," *Dendron Monthly News*, August 1988, issue #7.
15. *Ibid.*
16. Judith P. Swazey, *Chlorpromazine in Psychiatry*, Massachusetts Institute of Technology, 1974, p. 160.
17. Heinz E. Lehmann, "Therapeutic Results with Chlorpromazine," *Canadian Medical Association Journal*, Vol. 72: 1955, pp. 91-99, cited in David Richman, Dr. Caligari's Psychiatric Drugs, (Berkeley, Calif.: Network Against Psychiatric Assault, 1984), 20.
18. "Dr. Caligari's Psychiatric Drugs," (Berkeley, Calif.: Network Against Psychiatric Assault, 1987), p. 20.
19. *Ibid.*, p. 23.
20. *Ibid.*
21. Louis Engel, "What you need to know

about psychiatric drugs," *The Millenium Whole Earth Catalog*, p. 176.

22. Rosenblatt, *op. cit.*, p. 45.

23. *Ibid.*

24. Arnold Bernstein and Henry L. Lennard, "The American Way of Drugging," Society, May/June 1973, Vol. 10, No. 4, p. 14.

25. *Ibid.*, pp. 21-22.

26. Milt Freudenheim, "The Drug Makers Are Listening to Prozac," *The New York Times*, January 9, 1994.

27. Rosenblatt, *op. cit.*, p. 46.

28. *Dorland's Pocket Medical Dictionary*, 23rd edition, (Philadelphia: W.B. Saunders Company, 1982).

29. Dr. William Glazer interview, December 14, 1993.

30. Rosenblatt, *op. cit.*, pp. 164-65.

31. *Listening to Prozac, op. cit.*, p. 57.

32. Ron Leifer Interview, January, 1994.

33. Lorne J. Brandes et al., "Stimulation of Malignant Growth in Rodents by Antidepressant Drugs at Clinically Relevant Doses," *Cancer Research*, Vol. 52, July 1, 1992, p. 3796

34. "Fate and Distribution of Cocaine, Diazepam, Phencyclidine [PCP] and THC [marijuana]: A Technical Review," *op. cit.*

35. Interview with Dr. Al Parides, December 17, 1993.

36. "The American Way of Drugging," *op. cit.*, p. 22.

37. P.M. Boffey, "Schizophrenia: Insights Fail to Halt Rising Toll," *The New York Times*, March 16, 1986, pp. 1, 32.

38. Sidney M. Wolfe, M.D. et al.,"Worst Pills Best Pills," p. 157.

39. Walter Afield interview, January 11, 1994.

40. Joe Graedon, "Side effects depress patient," *The Columbus Dispatch*, October 21, 1986, p. 3C

41. *Dr. Caligari's, op. cit.*, p. 30.

42. *Ibid.*, p. 61.

43. "The PDR Family Guide to Prescription Drugs," (Montvale, New Jersey: Medical Economics Data, 1993), pp. 523-24.

44. Mike Masterson and Chuck Cook, "Mentally sound given psychoactive drugs," *The Arizona Republic*, June 26, 1988.

45. *Ibid.*

46. *Ibid.*

47. From documented cases on file at the Citizens Commission on Human Rights.

48. Dr. Caligari's, *op. cit.*

49. *Ibid.*, p. 47.

50. From documented case on file at the Citizens Commission on Human Rights.

51. Toxicology Sheet of Joseph Wesbecker, prepared by Dr. Richard Greathouse, coroner of Jefferson County, Kentucky; interview with Richard Greathouse, WKLY-TV, Louisville, October 19, 1989, 11 p.m.

52. Richard F. Gatehouse, Jefferson County, Kentucky Coroners Inquisition on Joseph Wesbecker, November 22, 1989.

53. LaTonya Turner, News, WFMV TV, Nashville, August 6, 1990, 6 p.m.

54. Richard I. Shader, M.D., Alberto DeMascio Ph.D., et al., *Psychotropic Drug Side Effects: Clinical and Theoretical Perspectives*, (Baltimore, Md.: The Williams & Wilkins Company, 1970), p. 134.

55. "Listening to Prozac," *op. cit.*, p. 102.

56. *Ibid.*, p. 226.

57. *Ibid.*, p. 291.

58. D.G. Workman, M.D., and D.G. Cunningham, "Effect of Psychotropic Drugs on Aggression In A Prison Setting," *Canadian Family Physician*, November 1975, pp. 63-66.

59. Jerrold F. Rosenbaum, M.D., et al., "Emergence of Hostility During Alprazolam Treatment," *American Journal of Psychiatry*, June 1984, Vol. 141, No. 6, pp. 792-93.

60. David L. Gardner, M.D. and Rex W. Cowdry, M.D., "Alprazolam-Induced Dyscontrol in Borderline Personality Disorder," *American Journal of Psychiatry*, January 1985, Vol. 142, No. 1, pp. 98-100.

61. Paul H. Soloff, M.D., et al., "Paradoxical Effects of Amitriptyline on Borderline Patients," *American Journal of Psychiatry*, December 1986, Vol. 143, No. 12, p. 1603.

62. Louis A. Gottschalk, et al., "Effects of Imiprimine on Anxiety and Hostility Levels," *Psychopharmacologia*, Vol. 7, pp. 303-10.

63. T.J. Feuerstein and R. Jackisch, "Why do some antidepressants promote suicide?", *Psychopharmacology*, Vol. 90, 1986, p. 422.

64. Javad H. Kashani, M.D., et al., "Hypomanic reaction to amitriptyline in a depressed child," *Psychosomatics*, Vol. 21, No. 10, October 1980, pp. 867, 872.

65. John N. Herrera, Ph.D., et al., "High Potency Neuroleptics and Violence in Schizophrenics," *The Journal of Nervous and Mental Disease*, Vol. 176, No. 9, September 1988, pp. 558-61.

66. Jerome L. Schulte, M.D., "Homicide and Suicide Associated with Akathisia and Haloperidol," *American Journal of Forensic Psychiatry*, Vol. 6, No. 2, 1985.

67. "Prescription for Murder—Psychiatric Drugs Create Killer," *Freedom*, November/ December 1988, pp. 16-17.

68. Michael Bunch, "2 now dead in domestic tragedy; daughter, a witness, traumatized," *The San Diego Union*, April 18, 1991.

69. Richard Hooks, "Therapist Forced to Choose: Protect Patient or Society?" *The San Bernardino Sun*, October 5, 1986.

70. Herbert D. Kleber, M.D., "Detoxification From Narcotics," *Substance Abuse: Clinical Problems and Perspectives*, edited by Joyce H. Lowinson, M.D. and Pedro Ruiz, M.D., (Baltimore and London: Williams & Wilkins, 1981), p. 318.

71. *Ibid.*

72. "The Nightmare of Methadone," *Freedom* Magazine, Vol. 21, October 1988, pp. 20-23.

73. *Ibid.*

74. Ray Belew, "Methadone 'victory' rate: 1 percent" *The Columbus Dispatch*, July 2, 1987, p. 1A.

75. "The Nightmare of Methadone," *op. cit.*

76. Marsha Rosenbaum, et al., "Money for Methadone: Preliminary Findings from a Study of Alameda County's New Maintenance Policy," *Journal of Psychoactive Drugs*, Vol. 19, January-March, 1987, p. 40.

77. "Methadone: N.Y. hooked on a cure, War on addiction and chaos," *The Denver Post*, August 20, 1989.

78. *Ibid.*

79. Spencer Rumsey, "Part II; Addiction and Obsession," *Newsday*, November 19, 1992, p. 68.

80. "Human Testing of Hallucinogen Backed," *The Washington Post*, August 27, 1993, p. A11.

81. Martin A. Lee and Bruce Shlain, *Acid Dreams*, (New York: Grove Press, Inc., 1985), p. xiv.

82. *Ibid.*, p. 13.

83. *Ibid.*, p. xiv.

84. *Ibid.*, p. 12.

85. *Ibid.*, p. 24.

86. *Ibid.*, p. 48.

87. *Ibid.*, p. 22.

88. *Ibid.*, pp. 22, 189.

89. *Ibid.*, pp. 20, 69.

90. "LSD—The Consciousness-Expanding Drug," *op. cit.*, pp. 232-33.

91. "Listening to Prozac," *op. cit.*, p. 247.

92. Walter Afield interview, January 11, 1994.

CHAPTER VIII
PSYCHIATRY, JUSTICE AND CRIME

1. Barbara Kantrowitz, "Wild in the streets," *Newsweek*, August 2, 1993, p. 43.

2. Adam Walinksy, "The Crisis of Public Order," *The Atlantic Monthly*, Vol. 276, No. 1, July 1995, p. 47.

3. "Sourcebook of Criminal Justice Statistics—1993," Bureau of Justice Statistics, U.S. Dept. of Justice, p. 352.

4. "The Crisis of Public Order," *op. cit.*, p. 44.

5. Michael Newton, "Mass Murder, An Annotated Bibliography," (New York: Garland, 1985)

6. "The Crisis of Public Order," *op. cit.*, p. 47.

7. *Harper's Index*, *Harper's Magazine*, May 1995, p. 11.

8. John Taylor, "Irresistible Impulses," *Esquire*, April 1994, p. 97.

9. Todd R. Eastham, "Backlash Developing Against Power of Psychiatrists," *Los Angeles Times*, January 11, 1981.

10. *Ibid.*

11. Linda A. Teplin, "Mental Health and Criminal Justice," (Beverly Hills, Calif., Sage Publications, Inc., 1984), p. 30.

12. "Backlash Developing Against Power of Psychiatrists," *op. cit.*

13. *Webster's New World Dictionary of the American Language*, Prentice Hall Press, Second College Edition, 1986, p. 50.

14. Thomas Szasz, M.D., "Insanity—The Idea and its Consequences," (New York: John Wiley & Sons, 1987), p. 229.

15. "Mental Health and Criminal Justice," *op. cit.*, pp. 28-29.

16. Benjamin Rush, M.D., "Medical Inquiries and Observations Upon the Diseases of the Mind," 1812.

17. Thomas Szasz, M.D., "The Therapeutic State—Psychiatry in the Mirror of Current Events" (New York: Prometheus Books, 1984), p. 124.

18. Thomas Szasz, "Insanity—The Idea and its Consequences," *op. cit.*, p. 237.

19. Karl Menninger, M.D., "The Crime of Punishment," (New York: The Viking Press, 1968), p. 115.

20. Aron C. Mason, "The Psychiatric Subversion of Justice—The Public Menace Destroying the Court System," *Freedom* Magazine, Vol. 21, Iss. 6.

21. "The Crime of Punishment," *op. cit.*, p. v, 120.

22. *Ibid.*, p. 120.

23. *Ibid.*, p. 121.

24. *Ibid.*, p. 121.

25. *Ibid.*, p. 122.

26. "The Psychiatric Subversion of Justice…," *Freedom* Magazine, *op. cit.*

27. J.R. Rees, M.D., "Strategic Planning for Mental Health," *Mental Health*, Vol. 1, No. 4, October 1940, p. 104.

28. "Mental Health and Criminal Justice," *op. cit.*, pp. 30-31.

29. Lee Coleman, M.D., "The Reign of Error—Psychiatry, Authority, and Law," (Boston: Beacon Press, 1984), p. 49, 254 quoting from *Durham v. United States* 214 F.2d 862 (D.C. Cir. 1954).

30. Julius Schreiber, M.D., "The Durham Decision—A Beacon in the Dark," *Mental Hygiene*, Volume XL, 1956, The National Association for Mental Health, Inc., p. 300.

31. Thomas S. Szasz, M.D., "The Manufacture of Madness," (New York: Harper & Row, 1970), p. 317.

32. "Robinson Remembers 30 Years of APA," *Psychiatric News*, November 16, 1979.

33. Ralph Adam Fine, Escape of the Guilty, (New York: 1986), pp. 224-26 and introduction from the Williamson Alanson White Memorial Lectures, Second Series, Major General G.B. Chilsholm, Vol. 9, February 1946.

34. Albert Deutsch, "The Durham

Decision—A Beacon in the Dark," *op. cit.*, pp. 297-8; "The Story of GAP," (New York: Group for the Advancement of Psychiatry, 1959), p. 18

35. Coleman, *op. cit.* p. 82-83.

36. Bernard L. Diamond and David W. Luisell, "The Psychiatrist as an Expert Witness: Some Ruminations and Speculations," *Michigan Law Review*, Vol. 63, No. 8, June 1965, p. 1342.

37. Alfred K. Baur, M.D., "Legal Responsibility and Mental Illness," *Northwestern University Law Review*, Vol. 57, No. 1, March-April 1962, p. 15.

38. Seymour L. Halleck, "A Critique of Current Psychiatric Roles in The Legal Process," *Wisconsin Law Review*, Vol. 1966, No. 2, Spring, p. 389.

39. *Ibid.*, p. 390.

40. "Mental Health and Criminal Justice," *op. cit.*, p. 262.

41. "Psychiatry in the Sentencing Process,"—*A Report of the Task Force on The Role of Psychiatry in the Sentencing Process*, American Psychiatric Association, Washington, D.C., July 1984, pp. 6-7.

42. "No Blame, No Shame," *Freedom Magazine*, Vol. XXVII, Iss. 1, September 1994, p. 9.

43. "Experts or Hired Guns," *Freedom Magazine*, Vol. 27, Iss. 6, p. 14.

44. *Ibid.*

45. Bruce J. Ennis, "Prisoners of Psychiatry—Mental Patients, Psychiatrists and the Law", (New York: Harcourt Brace Jovanovich, Inc., 1972), p. 227.

46. Joseph J. Cocozza & Henry J. Steadman, "The Failure of Psychiatric Predictions of Dangerousness: Clear and Convincing Evidence," *Rutgers Law Review*, Vol. 29, No. 5, Late Summer 1976, pp. 1098-99, 1101.

47. Brief Amicus Curiae for the American Psychiatric Association to the Supreme Court of the United States in *Estelle v. Smith*, case No. 79-1127, October term, 1979, p. 8.

48. Melitta Schmideberg, M.D., "The Promise of Psychiatry: Hopes and Disillusionment," *Northwestern University Law Review*, Vol. 57, No. 1, March-April 1962, p. 26.

49. Thomas Szasz, "Insanity—The Idea and its Consequences," *op. cit.*, p. 5.

50. Steve Marshall, "Number of serious crimes committed by juveniles soars," *USA Today*, July 25, 1994.

51. "Kids and crime," (graphics), *USA Today*, June 2, 1994.

52. Marshall, *op. cit.*

53. "The Crisis of Public Order," *op. cit.*, p. 49.

54. Interview with Danny Black, August 1, 1995.

55. Michael S. Brunner, "Retarding America—The Imprisonment of Potential," (Portland, Oregon: Halcyon House, 1993), pp. 55, 56, 59.

56. Colin Wilson and Donald Seaman, "The Encyclopedia of Modern Murder," (New York: Arlington House, 1983), pp. ix-x.

57. Michael Newton, *Mass Murder, An Annotated Bibliography*, (New York: Garland, 1985)

58. "The Crisis of Public Order," *op. cit.*, p. 46.

59. Isabel Wilkerson, "2 Boys, a Debt, a Gun, a Victim: The Face of Violence," *The New York Times*, May 16, 1994.

60. D.G. Workman, M.D., and D.G. Cunningham, "Effect of Psychotropic Drugs on Aggression in a Prison Setting," *Canadian Family Physician*, November 1975, pp. 63-66.

61. "Mental Health and Criminal Justice," *op. cit.*, p. 68.

62. "Drugs—Facts," *Executive News Service*, 1989.

63. Richard Lacayo, "When Kids Go Bad," *Time*, September 19, 1994, p. 61.

64. "Sourcebook of Criminal Justice Statistics—1993," Bureau of Justice Statistics, U.S. Dept. of Justice, p. 327.

65. Harold I. Kaplan, Alfred M. Freedman, Benjamin J. Sadock, 3rd edition, (Baltimore: Williams and Wilkins, 1980).

66. Sam Vincent Meddis, "Population of prisoners tops 1 million," *USA Today*, October 28, 1994.

67. Crime and Punishment (Graphics and data), *Time*, February 7, 1994, p. 58.

68. *Ibid.*, p. 68.

69. "The Promise of Psychiatry: Hopes and Disillusionment," *op. cit.*, p. 20.

70. Douglas Lipton, *The Effectiveness of Correctional Treatment—A Survey of Treatment Evaluation Studies*, (New York: Praeger Publishers, 1975), p. 209.

71. *Ibid.*, p. 211.

72. *Ibid.*, p. 227.

73. *Ibid.*, p. 307.

74. *Ibid.*, p. 213.

75. *Ibid.*, p. 315.

76. Gene Kassebaum, et al., *Prison Treatment and Parole Survival: An Empirical Assessment*, (New York: John Wiley & Sons, Inc., 1971), pp. 285-87.

77. Carl R. Rogers, Ph.D., *On Becoming A Person*, (Boston: Houghton Mifflin Company, 1961), p. 276.

78. Samuel Chavkin, *The Mind Stealers—Psychosurgery and Mind Control*, (Boston: Houghton Mifflin Company, 1978), p. 80.

79. *Ibid.*, p. 67.

80. *Ibid.*, p. 68.

81. *Ibid.*, p. 74.

82. *Ibid.*, p. 74.

83. *Ibid.*, p. 75.

84. *Ibid.*, p. 91.

85. *Ibid.*, p. 108.

86. *Ibid.*, p. 52.

87. Alan W. Scheflin and Edward M. Opton Jr., *The Mind Manipulators*, (New York: Paddington Press Ltd.,

1978), pp. 298-300.

88. *Ibid.*, p. 104.

89. *Ibid.*, pp. 104-05.

90. "The Effectiveness of Correctional Treatment…," *op. cit.*, pp. 330-31.

91. *Ibid.*, p. 553.

92. Henry J. Steadman, et al., "Developing Jail Mental Health Services: Practice and Principles," National Institute of Mental Health, Alcohol, Drug Abuse, and Mental Health Administration, Public Health Service, U.S. Dept. of Health and Human Services, 1986, pp. 39, 41.

93. *Ibid.*, p. 42.

94. *Ibid.*, p. 35.

95. "Mental Health and Criminal Justice," *op. cit.*, p. 75.

CHAPTER IX

THE BREAKDOWN OF EDUCATION

1. "SAT National Mean Scores From 1951-1992" & "SAT Summary Data for COLLEGE BOUND SENIORS 1971-72 through 1993-94," tables from the Educational Testing Service; "On Further Examination—Report of the Advisory Panel on the Scholastic Aptitude Test Score Decline," College Entrance Examination Board, New York, 1977, p. 6; "The Teacher's Almanac 1987-88," Facts On File Publications, New York, 1987, p. 131.

2. James A. Weed, Ph.D., "Suicide in the United States: 1958-82," from "Mental Health, United States 1985," Alcohol, Drug Abuse, and Mental Health Administration, Public Health Service, U.S. Department of Health and Human Services, pp. 135-36, 150-54; "Statistical Abstract of the United States," Bureau of the Census, U.S. Dept. of Commerce, 1988, p. 82, 1990, p. 86, 1993, p. 99.

3. "Statistical Abstract of the United States," 1940 through 1985 (various years), 1988, 1990, 1994, 1995.

4. Samuel L. Blumenfeld, "The New Illiterates: And How to Keep Your

Child From Becoming One," (Boise: The Paradigm Company, 1988), p. 23.

5. The National Commission on Excellence in Education, "A Nation At Risk," Washington, D.C.: U.S. Govt. Printing Office, 1983, pp. 5-6.

6. Graph: "Total Expenditure Per Pupil in Average Daily Attendance in Public Elementary and Secondary Schools in Constant Dollars," U.S. Department of Education, National Center for Education Statistics, "Statistics of State School Systems," various years; "Revenues and Expenditures for Public Elementary and Secondary Education," Common Core of Data survey, various years; and unpublished tabulations.

7. John Bartlett, *Familiar Quotations,* 16th ed., (Boston: Little, Brown and Company, 1992), p. 75.

8. Samuel L. Blumenfeld, *NEA: Trojan Horse in American Education,* (Boise, Idaho: The Paradigm Company, 1984), p. 102.

9. John B. Watson and William McDougall, *The Battle of Behaviorism,* (London: Kegan Paul, Trench, Trubner & Co., Ltd., 1928), p. 14.

10. Blumenfeld, *op. cit.,* p. 51.

11. Paolo Lionni, *The Leipzig Connection,* (Sheridan, Oregon: Delphian Press, 1988), pp. 31-32.

12. *Ibid.,* p. 36.

13. *Ibid.,* p. 35.

14. *Ibid.,* p. 33.

15. *Ibid.,* p. 19.

16. Edward L. Thorndike and Arthur I. Gates, *Elementary Principles of Education,* (New York: MacMillan, 1928), p. 147.

17. Lionni, *op. cit.,* p. 18.

18. Samuel L. Blumenfeld, "Who Killed Excellence," *Imprimis,* Vol. 14, No. 9, September 1985, Hillsdale, MI., pp. 3-4.

19. Lionni, *op. cit.,* p. 31.

20. *Ibid.,* pp. 55-6.

21. *Ibid.,* p. 63.

22. *Ibid.,* pp. 76-78.

23. *Ibid.,* p. 80.

24. *Ibid.,* p. 84.

25. *Ibid.,* p. 79.

26. *Ibid.,* p. 87.

27. Sol Cohen, "The Mental Hygiene Movement, The Development of Personality and the School: The Medicalization of American Education," *History of Education Quarterly,* Summer 1983, p. 124.

28. *Ibid.,* p. 124.

29. *Ibid.,* pp. 129-30.

30. *Ibid.,* pp. 127, 144.

31. *Ibid.,* p. 127.

32. *Ibid.,* p. 129.

33. *Ibid.,* p. 129.

34. *Ibid.,* p. 130.

35. *Ibid.,* pp. 130, 145.

36. *Ibid.,* p. 130.

37. *Ibid.,* pp. 130-31.

38. *Ibid.,* p. 135.

39. *Ibid.,* pp. 135-36.

40. *Ibid.,* p. 137.

41. *Ibid.,* pp. 137-38.

42. Edward A. Richards (general editor), "Proceedings of the Midcentury White House Conference on Children and Youth," (Raleich, N.C.: Health Publications Institute, Inc., December 3-7, 1950), p. 177.

43. *Ibid.,* p. 239.

44. Wesley Allinsmith and George W. Goethals, "The Role of Schools in Mental Health," Joint Commission on Mental Illness and Health, Monograph Series, No. 7, (New York: Basic Books, Inc., Publishers, 1962), p. 4.

45. *Ibid.,* p. 24.

46. *Ibid.,* p. 4.

47. "Mental Retardation Facilities and Community Mental Health Centers Construction Act of 1963," Public Law 88-164, Title II, Sec. 301(3).

48. Edited by W. David Stedman & LaVaughn G. Lewis, "Our Ageless

Constitution," published by W. David Stedman Associates, 1987, p. 137.

49. John Bartlett, *Familiar Quotations*, 16th ed., (Boston: Little, Brown and Company, Boston, 1992), p. 760.

50. Cohen, *op. cit.*, pp. 138, 147.

51. The National Commission on Excellence in Education, "A Nation At Risk," Washington, D.C.: U.S. Govt. Printing Office, 1983, p. 9.

52. "A Closer Look—Special Education," *Right to Read Report*, January 1994, Vol. 1, No. 8, pp. 1-3.

53. Dr. Fred A. Baughman, Jr., "Johnny can't read because phonics is all but ignored," *The Daily Californian*, February 16, 1994.

54. Allen Shanker, "FOCUS: Public Schools Need Drastic Change," *Education Reporter*, December 1989, p. 3.

55. *Ibid.*, p. 3

56. Blumenfeld, *op. cit.*, p. 5.

57. Rudolph Flesch, *Why Johnny Can't Read: And What You Can Do About It*, (New York: Harper & Brothers, 1955), p. 12.

58. *Right to Read Report*, 1991.

59. Samuel L. Blumenfeld, *The New Illiterates: And How to Keep Your Child From Becoming One*, (Boise: The Paradigm Company, 1988), p. 162.

60. *McGuffey's First Eclectic Reader*, revised edition, (New York: Van Nostrand Reinhold, 1920), pp. ii-iii, 22.

61. Franklin L. Smith, "Fighting Back," *The Executive Educator*, October 1994, p. 35.

62. William J. Bennett, "Why Johnny Can't Abstain," National Review, July 3, 1987, p. 36.

63. *Awake!*, August 8, 1993, p. 4.

64. John Lend, "Sorry Teaching of Teachers," *U.S. News & World Report*, April 27, 1992.

65. Interview with Alan Larson in December 1993 done by Dan Stradford.

66. Quote from C.M. Pierce, Harvard University, 1973 Childhood Education International Association seminar.

67. "California Mandates Abstinence In Sex Education," *Education Reporter*, October 1988, p. 1.

68. "A for effort. Or for showing up," *U.S. News & World Report*, October 18, 1993.

69. Interview with Alan Larson, *op. cit.*

70. "Separate and Unequal," *U.S. News & World Report*, December 13, 1993, p. 48.

71. *Ibid.*, p. 48.

72. Education for All Handicapped Children Act of 1975, Public Law 94-142, 20 USC 1401, November 29, 1975, Sec 620 (b)(4)(A).

73. U.S. Dept. of Education: Table: "Number and Change in Number of Children Age 6-21 Served under IDEA, Part B—SPECIFIC LEARNING DISABILITIES," October 1, 1992, p. A-32.

74. "Labeling away problem kids," *U.S. News & World Report*, March 13, 1989, pp. 59-61

75. "A Closer Look—Special Education," *Right to Read Report*, January 1994, Vol. 1, No. 8, p. 3.

76. *Right to Read Report*, April/May 1994.

77. *Right to Read Report*, January 1994, p. 3

78. Robert Castel, Francoise Castel and Anne Lovell, *The Psychiatric Society*, (New York: Columbia University Press, 1982), p. 205.

79. *Diagnostic and Statistical Manual of Mental Disorders* (Third edition—Revised) *DSM-III-R*, American Psychiatric Association, Washington, D.C., 1987, pp. 43-4.

80. *Right to Read Report*, June 1993.

81. *Ibid.*, p. 1.

82. Interview with Fred Baughman, July 1995.

83. Fred A. Baughman, Jr., M.D., "ADHD—DISEASE OR FOR-

PROFIT HOAX?"

84. *Diagnostic and Statistical Manual of Mental Disorders* Fourth Edition DSM-IV, American Psychiatric Association, Washington, D.C., 1994, pp. 83-85.

85. ADHD—DISEASE OR FOR-PROFIT HOAX, *op. cit.*

86. *Ibid.*

87. Dr. Peter Breggin, "The Scapegoating of American Children," *Wall Street Journal*, November 7, 1989, p. 1.

88. Gabrielle Weiss, M.D., et al., "Effect of long-term treatment of hyperactive children with methylphenidate," *The Canadian Medical Association Journal*, Vol. 112, No. 2, January 25, 1975, p. 164.

89. Package insert for Ritalin (methylphenidate), CIBA Pharmaceutical Company, Division of CIBA-GEIGY Corporation, Summit, New Jersey, revision 2/92.

90. Philip Bennett and Bob Hohler, "Boy, 15, held in killings of father, mother, sister...," *The Boston Globe*, October 12, 1993.

91. Televised interview with Dr. Alan Larson for educational close ups, Part 2, Oregon, January 1990.

92. Fred Baughman, *Journal of the American Medical Association*, 1993, quoted by Richard E. Vatz, "Attention Deficit Delirium," *The Wall Street Journal*, July 27, 1994.

93. Letter from Thomas Fagan, Professor and Coordinator of School Psychology Training Programs in the Department of Psychology at Memphis State University, dated May 21, 1993.

CHAPTER X
THE DEPRIVATION OF
HUMAN RIGHTS

1. Howard S. Levie, "Terrorism in War—The Law of War Crimes," by Oceana Publication, Inc., p. 322.

2. Lenny Lapon, "Mass Murderers in White Coats," Psychiatric Genocide Research Institute, Springfield, MA., (1986), p. 60 referencing: Douglas Goldman, M.D. and Maynard Murray, M.D., "Studies on the Use of Refrigeration Therapy in Mental Disease with Report of Sixteen Cases," *Journal of Nervous and Mental Diseases*, Vol. 97, February 1943, pp. 152-165.

3. David Foster, "A Mother's Day Denied for 48 Years," *Los Angeles Times*, May 14, 1995.

4. Lee Coleman, M.D., *Reign of Error*, (Boston: Beacon Press, 1984), pp. ix, 249.

5. Thomas Szasz, M.D., "The Therapeutic State," (Buffalo, N.Y.: Prometheus Books, 1984), p. 69.

6. Richard Van Duizend, J.D. et al., "An Overview of State Involuntary Civil Commitment Statutes," *Mental and Physical Disability Law Reporter*, Vol. 8, No. 3, May-June, 1984.

7. *Ibid*, p. 329.

8. Coleman, *op. cit.*, p. 158.

9. Leonard Frank interview, January 4, 1994.

10. Robert D. Miller et al., "The Right to Remain Silent During Psychiatric Examination in Civil and Criminal Cases—A National Survey and an Analysis," *International Journal of Law and Psychiatry*, Vol. 9, No. 1, pp. 77-94, 1986.

11. Coleman, *op. cit.*, p. 161.

12. *Ibid.*, p. 166.

13. Rael Jean Issac and Virginia C. Armat, "Madness in the Streets—How Psychiatry and the Law Abandoned the Mentally Ill," (New York: The Free Press, 1990), pp. 119-20.

14. Elizabeth Shogren, "Treatment Against Their Will," *Los Angeles Times*, August 18, 1994.

15. Szasz, *Psychiatric Slavery*.

16. Szasz, *The Therapeutic State, op. cit.*

17. Quote from Thomas Jefferson, Monticello, September 23, 1800.

18. "Barbara Noel's explosive accusation-that her psychiatrist sedated and sexually assaulted her during therapy-throws profession into turmoil-Waking To A Nightmare," *People Weekly*, December 7, 1992, Vol. 38, No. 23, p. 87.

19. *Ibid.*

20. Kenneth S. Pope and Jacqueline C. Bouhoutsos, "Sexual Intimacy Between Therapists and Patients," (New York: Praeger Publishers, 1986), p. 4.

21. *Ibid.*, ch. 1, p. 14.

22. *Ibid.*

23. Janet Fife Yeomans quoted by Gary Schoener, "Responding Therapeutically to Clients who have been Sexually Involved with their Psychotherapists," *Australian Magazine*, "The Abuse of Trust—When Playing Doctors Is No Game," August 1994.

24. American Psychiatric Association amicus brief filed with the United States Supreme Court, October 1979, No. 79, p. 1127.

25. Nanette Gartrell, M.D., et al., "Psychiatrist-Patient Sexual Contact: Results of a National Survey, I: Prevalence," *American Journal of Psychiatry*, September 1986 143:9.

26. Erica E. Goode, "The Ultimate Betrayal," *U.S. News & World Report*, March 12, 1990, Vol. 108, No. 10; p. 63.

27. "Sexual Contact With Patients," tape transcriptions, American Psychiatric Association, May 1986.

28. Lawrence Hartmann, M.D., "Presidential Address: Reflections on Humane Values and Biopsycholosocial Integration," *American Journal of Psychiatry,* September 1992, 149:9.

29. Nanette Gartrell, M.D., et. al., "Reporting Practices of Psychiatrists Who Knew Of Sexual Misconduct By Colleagues," *American Journal of Orthopsychiatry*, April 1987, Vol. 57, No. 2.

30. "Sexual Contact With Patients," tape transcriptions, American Psychiatric Association, May 1986, p. 26.

31. Nanette Gartrell, M.D., et. al., "Psychiatrist-Patient Sexual Contact: Results of a National Survey, I: Prevalence," *American Journal of Psychiatry*, September 1986, 143:9.

32. Erica E. Goode, "The Ultimate Betrayal," *U.S. News & World Report*, Vol. 108, No. 10, March 12, 1990, p. 63.

33. *Ibid.*, p. 64.

34. CCHR publication, *Betraying Women: Psychiatric Rape*, 1995, p. 5

35. Nanette Gartrell, M.D., et al., "Reporting Practices of Psychiatrists Who Knew Of Sexual Misconduct By Colleagues," *American Journal of Orthopsychiatry*, Vol. 57, No. 2, April 1987, p. 291.

36. Kenneth S. Pope and Valerie A. Vetter, "Prior Therapists-Patient Sexual Involvement Among Patients Seen by Psychologists," *Psychotherapy*, 1991, 28:429-437; Jacqueline Bouhoutsos and Jean Holroyd, "Sexual Intimacy Between Psychotherapists and Patients, Professional Psychology: Research and Practice," Vol. 14, No. 2, 1983, p. 190; Sheldon H. Kardener, M.D., "A Survey of Physicians' Attitudes and Practices Regarding Erotic and Nonerotic Contact with Patients," *American Journal of Psychiatry*, 130:10, October 1973, p. 1080; Nanette Gartrell, M.D., "Reporting Practices of Psychiatrists Who Knew Of Sexual Misconduct By Colleagues," *American Journal of Orthopsychiatry*, Vol. 57, No. 2, April 1987, p. 291; "Sexual Misconduct in the Practice of

Medicine," Council on Ethical and Judicial Affairs, American Medical Association, JAMA, Vol. 266, No. 19, November 20, 1991, p. 2741.

37. Thomas Szasz, quote from *Sex by Prescription*, (New York: Anchor Press/Doubleday, 1980), p. 51.

38. "Sex Doctor jailed for four years," *The Valley Sun*, June 25, 1991.

39. J. Delora and C. Warren, "Understanding Sexual Interaction," Boston: Houghton Mifflin, 1977.

40. David Corvette, "Anneewakee deal: $35 million: Total Pay-out Highest in Ga. Court History," *The Atlanta Journal and Constitution*, March 20, 1990.

41. Ann Woolner, "Feds Seeking 30-Year Term for Dr. Berry," *The Atlanta Journal*, July 17, 1986; "Berry Admits he Molested Six Children," by Gayle White, July 19, 1986.

42. Letter to the Office of the District Attorney, Santa Ana County, California, regarding James Harrington White, November 15, 1990.

43. Letter from the Office of the District Attorney, County of Orange, California, regarding James Harrington White, January 18, 1991.

44. *Orange County Register*, January 10, 1991, given six-year, eight-month sentence, psychiatrist gets jail term for molesting adopted son.

45. Samuel A. Cartwright, M.D., "Report on the Diseases and Physical Peculiarities of the Negro Race," *New Orleans and Surgical Journal*, (1851).

46. *Ibid.*

47. Thomas S. Szasz, M.D., "The Manufacture of Madness," (New York: Harper & Row, Publishers, 1970).

48. Lenny Lapon, "Mass Murderers in White Coats: Psychiatric Genocide in Nazi Germany and the United States," (Springfield, Mass.: Psychiatric Genocide Research

Institute, 1986), p. 78-79.

49. Allan Chase, *The Legacy of Malthus: The Social Costs of the New Scientific Racism*, (Chicago: University of Illinois Press, 1980), pp. 164, 172.

50. Chase, *op. cit.*, Lapon, *op. cit.*, pp. 78-79

51. David Hothersall, *History of Psychology*, (Philadelphia: Temple University Press, 1984), pp. 308-09, 314-15.

52. Chase, *op. cit.*, pp. 236-38.

53. Paul Popenoe, M.D., "Intelligence and Race—a Review of the Results of the Army Intelligence Tests—The Negro in 1981."

54. Harry Bailey, M.D., Lecture to nurses at Chelsmford Hospital, New South Wales, Australia, (1970s).

55. Lapon, *op. cit.*, p. 92.

56. Alan W. Scheflin and Edward M. Opton Jr., *The Mind Manipulators*, (New York & London: Paddington Press Ltd.,1978), pp. 314-315.

57. Martin A. Lee and Bruce Shlain, *Acid Dreams—The CIA, LSD, and the Sixties Rebellion*, (New York: Grove Press, Inc., 1985), p. 189.

58. Joseph P. Shapiro, et. al., "Separate and Unequal—America's special education system was intended to give disabled kids an edge. But it is cheating many—and costing the rest of us billions," *U.S. News & World Report*, December 13, 1993, pp. 46-60.

59. Allister Sparks, *The Mind of South Africa*, (New York: Alfred A. Knopf, 1990), p. 193.

60. Richard A. Lerner, *Final Solutions: Biology, Prejudice and Genocide*, (University Park, Pennsylvania: The Pennsylvania State University Press, 1992).

61. "Mental Health Industry Is Uncovered," *Peace and Freedom*, South Africa, January 1976.

62. *Ibid.*

63. *Ibid.*

64. "Apartheid and Mental Health Care," World Health Organization,

Objective: Justice, Published by the United Nations Office of Public Information, Vol. 9, No. 1, Spring 1977.

65. "Apartheid and Health," *World Health Organization Report*, 1983.

CHAPTER XI
THE ECONOMICS OF DECEPTION: PSYCHIATRIC FRAUD

1. Ralph Ranalli, "Fed judge's ruling in fraud case a precedent for insanity plea," *Boston Herald*, July 13, 1995.
2. "Mind Menageries," *Omni*, Vol. 8 No. 4, January 1986, p. 31.
3. David P. Blaine, Director of Federal Health Care Delivery Issues, Human Resources Division, Defense Health Care Benefits to CHAMPUS Beneficiaries, United States General Accounting Office, April 28, 1992, p. 11.
4. Donald Mancuso, Assistant Inspector General For Investigations, Department of Defense, Hearing-House Select Committee on Children, Youth and Families Regarding Fraudulent Practices In The Mental Health Industry, April 28, 1992, pp. 5-6.
5. Edward D. Martin, Rear Admiral, Director of Federal Health Care Delivery, Issues, Human Resources, Testimony—Before the Select Committee on Children, Youth and Families. House of Representatives: "Defense Health Care, Efforts to Manage Mental Health Care Benefits to Champus Beneficiaries," United States General Accounting Office, p. 3.
6. Louis Parisi, Director, Fraud Division of the New Jersey Department of Insurance: Testimony-Before the Select Committee on Children, Youth and Families; House of Representatives, Defense Health Care, "Efforts to Manage Mental Health Care Benefits

to Champus Beneficiaries," United States General Accounting Office, April 28, 1992, pp. 1-2.
7. Mike Moncrief, Texas State Senator: Testimony—U. S. House of Representatives; Select Committee on Children, Youth and Families, Texas Senate Interim Committee on Health and Human Services, April 28, 1992, p. 10.
8. Walter E. Afield, M.D., The Mental Health Programs Corporation: Testimony—U.S. House of Representatives, Select Committee on Children, Youth and Families, April 28, 1992, p. 7.
9. Joe Sharkey, "Bedlam," (New York: St. Martin's Press, 1994), p. 104.
10. *Ibid.*
11. *Ibid.*
12. *Ibid.*, p. 92.
13. *Ibid.*, p. 139.
14. Rhonda L. Rundle, "National Medical Facilities Raided By U. S. Agents," *The Wall Street Journal*, August 27, 1993, p. A3.
15. Sharkey, *op. cit.*, p. 273.
16. Mike Moncrief, Texas State Senator: Testimony-U.S. House of Representatives, Select Committee on Children, Youth and Families, Texas State Senate Interim Committee on Health and Human Services, April 28, 1992, pp. 2-3.
17. Sharkey, *op. cit.*, p. 42.
18. Olive Talley and Jacqueline Floyd, "Texas targets psychiatric hospitals," *The Dallas Morning News*, October 20, 1991.
19. *Ibid.*
20. *Ibid.*
21. Peter Kerr, "Chain of Mental Hospitals Faces Inquiry in 4 States," *The New York Times*, October 22, 1991.
22. William E. Clayton, Jr., "House sub-committee hears tales of horror," *Houston Chronicle*, July 20, 1994.
23. Kerr, *op. cit.*

24. *Ibid.*

25. *Ibid.*

26. *Ibid.*

27. Bill Lodge, "Former psychiatric hospital exec receives probation," *The Dallas Morning News*, January 11, 1995.

28. Sharkey, *op. cit.*, p. 273.

29. David R. Olmos, "NME Offices Raided in Major Fraud Probe," *Los Angeles Times*, August 27, 1993.

30. *Ibid.*

31. *Ibid.*

32. E. Scott Reckard, "NME to settle U.S. fraud charges," *L.A. Daily News*, April 15, 1994.

33. *Ibid.*

34. Sharky, *op. cit.*, pp. 276-77.

35. David J. Jefferson, "Community Psychiatric Is Fourth Firm To Agree to Changes at Texas Facilities," *The Wall Street Journal*, January 18, 1993.

36. Jane Freeman, M.S.W., "Nightmare on Healthcare Street," *The John Cooke Fraud Report*, Vol. 2 No. 2, July/August 1995, p. 3.

37. *Ibid.*

38. Jeff Testerman and Carol A. Morbin, "Hernando County Woman Called Industry 'Queen,' The Patient Pipeline," *St. Petersburg Times*, 1993.

39. Kathy Walt, "Citing 'grave' concerns, Texas freezes funds to 35 drug projects," *Houston Chronicle*, July 21, 1995, p. 33A.

40. "Fraud-fighting team being bolstered," *Port St. Lucie Tribune*, March 7, 1995.

41. United States District Court For The Central District of California, Aetna Life Insurance Company-plaintiff, March 11, 1994.

42. Donna Jean Frisbie, Affidavit, State of Ohio, County of Williams, May 10, 1994.

43. Alexander English, Affidavit, State of Pennsylvania, County of Lebanon, March 8, 1994.

44. Jan Eastgate, "I Just Remembered...'Repressed Memory' The Latest Psychiatric Fraud on the Courts," *Freedom* Magazine, Vol. 27, Iss. 6, p. 12.

45. *Ibid.*, pp. 12-13.

46. *Ibid.*, p. 13.

47. *Ibid.*, pp. 13, 15.

48. *Ibid.*, pp. 15-16.

49. *Ibid.*, p. 16-17.

50. *Ibid.*, p. 17.

51. Olive Talley, "Texas targets psychiatric hospitals," *The Dallas Morning News*, October 20, 1991.

CHAPTER XII
THE MANUFACTURE OF MADNESS

1. Peter D. Kramer, *Listening to Prozac*, (New York: Penguin Books U.S.A. Inc., 1993), p. xii-xiii

2. Paula J. Caplan, Ph.D., *They Say You're Crazy*, (New York: Addison-Wesley Publishing Company, 1995), pp. 165-167.

3. Thomas Szasz, *The Myth of Mental Illness*, (New York: Harper and Row, 1974).

4. Paula J. Caplan, *op. cit.*, p. 56.

5. Walter Afield, interview, January 11, 1994.

6. Paula J. Caplan, *op. cit.*, p. 222.

7. American Psychiatric Association: *Diagnostic and Statistical Manual of Mental Disorders*, Third Edition, Washington, D.C., 1980, p. 1.

8. *Ibid.*, p. 9.

9. "Lawyers Fear New Psychiatric Labels," *San Francisco Examiner*, August 15, 1986.

10. *Ibid.*

11. Paula J. Caplan, *op. cit.*, p. xv.

12. "Politics, women and mental disorders," *Los Angeles Herald Examiner*, August 15, 1986.

13. Paula J. Caplan, *op. cit.*, p. 90.

14. *Ibid.*, p. 91.

15. *Ibid.*, p. 108.

16. "Politics, women and mental disorders," *Los Angeles Herald Examiner*, August

15, 1986.

17. Paula J. Caplan, *op. cit.*, p. 227.

18. Mark Syverud, "Don't stop the insanity (my therapist needs the money)," *Daily Messenger*, August 13, 1995.

19. *Webster's New World Dictionary of the American Language*, The World Publishing Company, 1966, p. 539.

20. Stanley Jacobson, *The Atlantic Monthly*, April 1995.

21. Richard Hall and Michel Popkin, *American Journal of Psychiatry*, 1967, p. vi: 2.

22. B. I. Comroe, "Physical Illness Presenting As Psychiatric Disease," Journal of Nervous Mental Disorders, *Archives of General Psychiatry*, 1936, p. 1315.

23. *Ibid.*

24. *Ibid.*

25. Ivan Fras, M.D., Edward M. Litin, M.D., and John S. Pearson, Ph.D., "Comparison of Psychiatric Systems in Carcinoma of the Pancreas with Those in Some Other Intra-abdominal Neoplasm," *American Journal of Psychiatry*, June 12, 1967, p. 1553.

26. Erwin K. Koranyi, M.D., "Morbidity and Rate of Undiagnosed Physical Illnesses in a Psychiatric Clinic Population," *Archives of General Psychology*, Vol.36; April 1979, p. 414.

27. Douglas M. D. Hunt, "No More Fears: How to Free Yourself from Disabling Phobias and Unreasonable Panic With a Simple, New Program of Nutritional Suppliments," (New York: Warner Books, 1988), pp. 305-306.

28. *Ibid.*

29. H.L. Newbold, M.D., *Mega-Nutrients for Your Nerves*, (New York: Peter H. Wyden Publisher, 1975).

30. George Watson, "Nutrition and Your Mind: The Psychochemical Response," 1972.

31. Eric Braverman and Carl Pfeiffer, The Healing Nutrients Within: Facts, Findings, and New research in Amino Acids, 1987.

32. *Ibid.*

33. *Ibid.*

34. *Ibid.*

35. *Ibid.*

36. *Ibid.*, p. 166

37. *Ibid.*

38. *Ibid.*

39. *Ibid.*

40. Doris Rapp, M.D., The Impossible Child, (New York: Practical Allergy Research Foundation, 1986).

41. Bonnie Sigren Busick and Martha Gorman, "Ill Not Insane," New Idea Press, Inc., 1987, pp. 188-92.

42. *Ibid.*, p. 168.

CHAPTER XIII
...THE SINGLE MOST
DESTRUCTIVE FORCE...

1. Paula J. Caplan, Ph.D., *They Say You're Crazy*, (New York: Addison-Wesley, 1995, p. 90.

2. *Ibid.*, P. 16.

3. John Bartlett, *Familiar Quotations*, 16th Ed., (Brown: Little, Brown and Company, Boston, 1992), p. 760.

INDEX

MORE INFORMATION CARD

YES, I would like to receive more information (FREE OF CHARGE) on:

❑ PSYCHIATRIC VIOLATIONS OF HUMAN RIGHTS AND WHAT CAN BE DONE TO ELIMINATE THEM.

I am also interested in receiving more information on the specific subjects of:

❑ PSYCHIATRY'S ROLE IN THE CREATION OF CRIME

❑ PSYCHIATRIC HEALTH CARE FRAUD

❑ PSYCHIATRY'S DESTRUCTION OF EDUCATION

❑ PSYCHIATRIC ABUSE OF THE ELDERLY

❑ PSYCHIATRIC RAPE

Call 1-800-307-1211
or fill out and mail in the following form.

Please mail information on the items checked above to:

NAME: _____

ADDRESS: _____

CITY: _____STATE: _____ ZIP: _____

TELEPHONE NUMBER: _____FAX: _____

ORDER FORM

Who really stood behind Hitler, indoctrinating and inspiring him?
Is there still cause for concern?

FIND OUT.
ORDER THIS CHILLING NON-FICTION EXPOSÉ TODAY!
Psychiatrists—the Men Behind Hitler by Dr. Thomas Röder, Volker Kubillus & Anthony Burwell

Call 1-800-307-1211 or fill out and mail in the following form:

NAME: _____

ADDRESS: _____

CITY: _____STATE: _____ ZIP: _____

TELEPHONE NUMBER: _____FAX: _____

❑ Please send me ____ copies of *Psychiatrists—the Men Behind Hitler.*

PSYCHIATRISTS—THE MEN BEHIND HITLER: $24.95

I am enclosing $_____ (includes postage and handling costs*)

I am making my payment by: ❑ check** ❑ credit card

❑ Amex ❑ Visa ❑ M/C ❑ Discover

Card # _____ Expiration Date _____

* Add $1.75 per item for shipping and handling. California residents add 8.25% sales tax. ** Please use envelope.
ORDERS SHIPPED WITHIN 24 HOURS OF RECEIPT.

❑ I would like to order ____ additional copies of *Psychiatry—the Ultimate Betrayal*
at $24.95 each, plus shipping and handling.

BUSINESS REPLY MAIL

FIRST CLASS MAIL   PERMIT NO. 70527   LOS ANGELES, CA

POSTAGE WILL BE PAID BY ADDRESSEE

CITIZENS COMMISSION ON HUMAN RIGHTS
6362 HOLLYWOOD BOULEVARD, SUITE B
LOS ANGELES, CA 90028

BUSINESS REPLY MAIL

FIRST CLASS MAIL   PERMIT NO. 70527   LOS ANGELES, CA

POSTAGE WILL BE PAID BY ADDRESSEE

CITIZENS COMMISSION ON HUMAN RIGHTS
6362 HOLLYWOOD BOULEVARD, SUITE B
LOS ANGELES, CA 90028